Introduction

Mathematical Thinking at Grade 4

Grade 4

Also appropriate for Grade 5

Cornelia Tierney

Developed at TERC, Cambridge, Massachusetts

Editorial Offices: Glenview, Illinois • Parsippany, New Jersey • New York, New York
Sales Offices: Needham, Massachusetts • Duluth, Georgia • Glenview, Illinois
Coppell, Texas • Ontario, California • Mesa, Arizona

http://www.scottforesman.com

This project was supported, in part,
by the
National Science Foundation
Opinions expressed are those of the authors
and not necessarily those of the Foundation

TERC

The *Investigations* curriculum was developed at TERC (formerly Technical
Education Research Centers) in collaboration with Kent State University and
the State University of New York at Buffalo. The work was supported in part
by National Science Foundation Grant No. ESI-9050210. TERC is a nonprofit
company working to improve mathematics and science education. TERC is
located at 2067 Massachusetts Avenue, Cambridge, MA 02140.

Managing Editor: Catherine Anderson
Series Editor: Beverly Cory
Revision Team: Laura Marshall Alavosus, Ellen Harding, Patty Green Holubar,
Suzanne Knott, John Lanyi, Beverly Hersh Lozoff
ESL Consultant: Nancy Sokol Green
Production/Manufacturing Director: Janet Yearian
Production/Manufacturing Manager: Karen Edmonds
Production/Manufacturing Coordinator: Joe Conte
Design Manager: Jeff Kelly
Design: Don Taka
Illustrations: Susan Jaekel, Carl Yoshihara
Cover: Bay Graphics

ISBN 0-328-16725-8
This product may appear as part of package ISBN 0-328-17405-X.
2 3 4 5 6 7 8 9 10-V031-10 09 08 07 06 05

T E R C

INVESTIGATIONS IN NUMBER, DATA, AND SPACE®

Principal Investigator Susan Jo Russell

Co-Principal Investigator Cornelia Tierney

Director of Research and Evaluation Jan Mokros

Curriculum Development
Joan Akers
Michael T. Battista
Mary Berle-Carman
Douglas H. Clements
Karen Economopoulos
Ricardo Nemirovsky
Andee Rubin
Susan Jo Russell
Cornelia Tierney
Amy Shulman Weinberg

Evaluation and Assessment
Mary Berle-Carman
Abouali Farmanfarmaian
Jan Mokros
Mark Ogonowski
Amy Shulman Weinberg
Tracey Wright
Lisa Yaffee

Teacher Support
Rebecca B. Corwin
Karen Economopoulos
Tracey Wright
Lisa Yaffee

Technology Development
Michael T. Battista
Douglas H. Clements
Julie Sarama
Andee Rubin

Video Production
David A. Smith

Cooperating Classrooms for This Unit
Ruth Shea
Cambridge Public Schools
Cambridge, MA

Kathleen O'Connell
Arlington Public Schools
Arlington, MA

Nancy Buell
Brookline Public Schools
Brookline, MA

Consultants and Advisors
Elizabeth Badger
Deborah Lowenberg Ball
Marilyn Burns
Ann Grady
Joanne M. Gurry
James J. Kaput
Steven Leinwand
Mary M. Lindquist
David S. Moore
John Olive
Leslie P. Steffe
Peter Sullivan
Grayson Wheatley
Virginia Woolley
Anne Zarinnia

Administration and Production
Amy Catlin
Amy Taber

Graduate Assistants
Joanne Caniglia
Pam DeLong
Carol King
Kent State University

Rosa Gonzalez
Sue McMillen
Julie Sarama
Sudha Swaminathan
State University of New York at Buffalo

Revisions and Home Materials
Cathy Miles Grant
Marlene Kliman
Margaret McGaffigan
Megan Murray
Kim O'Neil
Andee Rubin
Susan Jo Russell
Lisa Seyferth
Myriam Steinback
Judy Storeygard
Anna Suarez
Cornelia Tierney
Carol Walker
Tracey Wright

CONTENTS

TEACHER NOTES

Investigations in Number, Data, and Space® is a K–5 mathematics curriculum with four major goals:

- to offer students meaningful mathematical problems
- to emphasize depth in mathematical thinking rather than superficial exposure to a series of fragmented topics
- to communicate mathematics content and pedagogy to teachers
- to substantially expand the pool of mathematically literate students

The *Investigations* curriculum embodies a new approach based on years of research about how children learn mathematics. Each grade level consists of a set of separate units, each offering 2–8 weeks of work. These units of study are presented through investigations that involve students in the exploration of major mathematical ideas.

Approaching the mathematics content through investigations helps students develop flexibility and confidence in approaching problems, fluency in using mathematical skills and tools to solve problems, and proficiency in evaluating their solutions. Students also build a repertoire of ways to communicate about their mathematical thinking, while their enjoyment and appreciation of mathematics grows.

The investigations are carefully designed to invite all students into mathematics—girls and boys, members of diverse cultural, ethnic, and language groups, and students with different strengths and interests. Problem contexts often call on students to share experiences from their family, culture, or community. The curriculum eliminates barriers—such as work in isolation from peers, or emphasis on speed and memorization—that exclude some students from participating successfully in mathematics. The following aspects of the curriculum ensure that all students are included in significant mathematics learning:

- Students spend time exploring problems in depth.
- They find more than one solution to many of the problems they work on.
- They invent their own strategies and approaches, rather than rely on memorized procedures.
- They choose from a variety of concrete materials and appropriate technology, including calculators, as a natural part of their everyday mathematical work.
- They express their mathematical thinking through drawing, writing, and talking.
- They work in a variety of groupings—as a whole class, individually, in pairs, and in small groups.
- They move around the classroom as they explore the mathematics in their environment and talk with their peers.

While reading and other language activities are typically given a great deal of time and emphasis in elementary classrooms, mathematics often does not get the time it needs. If students are to experience mathematics in depth, they must have enough time to become engaged in real mathematical problems. We believe that a minimum of 5 hours of mathematics classroom time a week—about an hour a day—is critical at the elementary level. The scope and pacing of the *Investigations* curriculum are based on that belief.

We explain more about the pedagogy and principles that underlie these investigations in Teacher Notes throughout the units. For correlations of the curriculum to the NCTM Standards and further help in using this research-based program for teaching mathematics, see the following books:

- *Implementing the* Investigations in Number, Data, and Space® *Curriculum*
- *Beyond Arithmetic: Changing Mathematics in the Elementary Classroom* by Jan Mokros, Susan Jo Russell, and Karen Economopoulos

This book is one of the curriculum units for *Investigations in Number, Data, and Space*. In addition to providing part of a complete mathematics curriculum for your students, this unit offers information to support your own professional development. You, the teacher, are the person who will make this curriculum come alive in the classroom; the book for each unit is your main support system.

Although the curriculum does not include student textbooks, reproducible sheets for student work are provided in the unit and are also available as Student Activity Booklets. Students work actively with objects and experiences in their own environment and with a variety of manipulative materials and technology, rather than with a book of instruction and problems. We strongly recommend use of the overhead projector as a way to present problems, to focus group discussion, and to help students share ideas and strategies.

Ultimately, every teacher will use these investigations in ways that make sense for his or her particular style, the particular group of students, and the constraints and supports of a particular school environment. Each unit offers information and guidance for a wide variety of situations, drawn from our collaborations with many teachers and students over many years. Our goal in this book is to help you, a professional educator, implement this curriculum in a way that will give all your students access to mathematical power.

Investigation Format

The opening two pages of each investigation help you get ready for the work that follows.

What Happens This gives a synopsis of each session or block of sessions.

Mathematical Emphasis This lists the most important ideas and processes students will encounter in this investigation.

What to Plan Ahead of Time These lists alert you to materials to gather, sheets to duplicate, transparencies to make, and anything else you need to do before starting.

INVESTIGATION 1

How Many Hundreds?

What Happens

Session 1: Getting Started with Interlocking Cubes Each student or pair builds an object with interlocking cubes. In small groups, students estimate how many cubes were used to make each object. Students count the cubes in their objects and then write about the activity.

Sessions 2 and 3: How Many Hundreds? Pairs count out 100 interlocking cubes and group them to show clearly that the total is 100. Groups of students then estimate how many hundreds there are in the box of cubes their group received. The teacher records the estimates from all of the groups, and students figure out how many hundreds there are in the total of all the estimates. After counting their cubes, groups estimate how many hundreds of cubes there are in the class total. Finally, individuals figure out exactly how many cubes there are altogether.

Session 4: Close to 100 Students play a game that involves arranging digits to make numbers that have a sum as near as possible to 100.

Mathematical Emphasis

- Grouping things for more efficient counting
- Reordering numbers for more efficient mental arithmetic
- Finding how many more are needed
- Exploring materials that will be used throughout this curriculum as problem-solving tools
- Estimating how many hundreds are in the total of a group of three-digit numbers
- Communicating about mathematical thinking through written and spoken language

---

INVESTIGATION 1

What to Plan Ahead of Time

Materials

- Interlocking cubes: at least 100 per pair (Sessions 1–3)
- Containers for cubes: 6–8 (Sessions 1–3)
- Stick-on notes (Session 1)
- Chart paper (Sessions 1–3, optional)
- Overhead projector, transparency pen (Sessions 1–3)
- Calculators: at least 1 per pair (Sessions 2–3)
- Scissors (Session 4)

Other Preparation

- Duplicate student sheets and teaching resources (located at the end of this unit) in the following quantities. If you have Student Activity Booklets, copy only the items marked with an asterisk.

  For Session 1
  Student Sheet 1, How Many Cubes in Each Object? (p. 99): 1 per student, 1 transparency*

  For Sessions 2–3
  Family letter* (p. 98): 1 per student. Remember to sign the letter before copying.
  Student Sheet 2, Making Hundreds (p. 100): 1 per student
  Student Sheet 3, How Many Cubes in the Class? (p. 101): 1 per student
  Student Sheet 4, A Design with 100 Squares (p. 102): 1 per student (homework)

  Student Sheet 5, How Many Hundreds? How Many Altogether? (p. 103): 1 per student (homework)
  Chart for How Many Cubes?* (p. 105): 1 transparency
  One-centimeter graph paper (p. 107): 1–2 per student (homework)

  For Session 4
  Student Sheet 6, Problems for Close to 100 (p. 104): 1 per student
  How to Play Close to 100 (p. 106): 1 per student (homework)
  Close to 100 Score Sheet (p. 135): 1 per student (class), 2 per student (homework)
  Numeral Cards (p. 136): 1 set per group for class use, ideally copied on tagboard (if you don't have the manufactured decks), plus 1 set per student to take home

- Divide your supply of interlocking cubes into buckets or shoe boxes for each small group. Put a different number of cubes in each box for an estimation activity. The cubes should be loose for this activity, rather than in stacks of 10. (Session 1)
- Make a simple object, such as a chair, from 30 to 60 interlocking cubes. (Session 1)
- If you are making your own class sets of Numeral Cards, see p. 24. (Session 4)
- If you plan to provide folders, notebooks, or journals in which students will save their work for the entire unit, prepare these for distribution during Session 1.

Sessions Within an investigation, the activities are organized by class session, a session being at least a one-hour math class. Sessions are numbered consecutively through an investigation. Often several sessions are grouped together, presenting a block of activities with a single major focus.

When you find a block of sessions presented together—for example, Sessions 1, 2, and 3—read through the entire block first to understand the overall flow and sequence of the activities. Make some preliminary decisions about how you will divide the activities into three sessions for your class, based on what you know about your students. You may need to modify your initial plans as you progress through the activities, and you may want to make notes in the margins of the pages as reminders for the next time you use the unit.

Be sure to read the Session Follow-Up section at the end of the session block to see what homework assignments and extensions are suggested as you make your initial plans.

While you may be used to a curriculum that tells you exactly what each class session should cover, we have found that the teacher is in a better position to make these decisions. Each unit is flexible and may be handled somewhat differently by every teacher. Although we provide guidance for how many sessions a particular group of activities is likely to need, we want you to be active in determining an appropriate pace and the best transition points for your class. It is not unusual for a teacher to spend more or less time than is proposed for the activities.

Ten-Minute Math At the beginning of some sessions, you will find Ten-Minute Math activities. These are designed to be used in tandem with the investigations, but not during the math hour. Rather, we hope you will do them whenever you have a spare 10 minutes—maybe before lunch or recess, or at the end of the day.

Ten-Minute Math offers practice in key concepts, but not always those being covered in the unit. For example, in a unit on using data, Ten-Minute Math must revisit geometric activities done earlier in the year. Complete directions for the suggested activities are included at the end of each unit.

Session 1

Getting Started with Interlocking Cubes

Materials

- Sample object made of interlocking cubes
- Interlocking cubes (at least 100 per pair)
- Containers for cubes: 6–8
- Stick-on notes
- Student Sheet 1 (1 per student)
- Transparency of Student Sheet 1
- Chart paper (optional)
- Overhead projector, transparency pen

What Happens

Each student or pair builds an object with interlocking cubes. In small groups, students estimate how many cubes were used to make each object. Students count the cubes in their objects and then write about the activity. Their work focuses on:

- building with interlocking cubes
- estimating numbers of cubes
- counting cubes
- writing about math

Activity

Introducing the Mathematical Environment

Begin this session with a brief discussion about some of the tools you'll be using and the kind of work students will be doing in this unit. See the Teacher Note, Introducing Materials (p. 9), for hints about establishing routines for using and caring for manipulatives.

In our mathematics class this year, you will be using many different tools to help you solve problems and to show people how you are thinking about a problem. During the next few weeks, we will be using tools like calculators, pattern blocks, 100 charts, and interlocking cubes as we play math games and solve math problems.

❖ **Tip for the Linguistically Diverse Classroom** Ensure that this introduction is comprehensible to all students by showing the different mathematical tools as you mention them.

Activities The activities include pair and small-group work, individual tasks, and whole-class discussions. In any case, students are seated together, talking and sharing ideas during all work times. Students most often work cooperatively, although each student may record work individually.

Choice Time In most units, some sessions are structured with activity choices. In these cases, students may work simultaneously on different activities focused on the same mathematical ideas. Students choose which activities they want to do, and they cycle through them.

You will need to decide how to set up and introduce these activities and how to let students make their choices. Some teachers present them as station activities, in different parts of the room. Some list the choices on the board as reminders or have students keep their own lists.

Tips for the Linguistically Diverse Classroom At strategic points in each unit, you will find concrete suggestions for simple modifications of the teaching strategies to encourage the participation of all students. Many of these tips offer alternative ways to elicit critical thinking from students at varying levels of English proficiency, as well as from other students who find it difficult to verbalize their thinking.

The tips are supported by suggestions for specific vocabulary work to help ensure that all students can participate fully in the investigations. The Preview for the Linguistically Diverse Classroom lists important words that are assumed as part of the working vocabulary of the unit. Second-language learners will need to become familiar with these words in order to understand the problems and activities they will be doing. These terms can be incorporated into students' second-language work before or during the unit. Activities that can be used to present the words are found in the appendix, Vocabulary Support for Second-Language Learners. In addition, ideas for making connections to students' languages and cultures, included on the Preview page, help the class explore the unit's concepts from a multicultural perspective.

Session Follow-Up: Homework In *Investigations,* homework is an extension of classroom work. Sometimes it offers review and practice of work done in class, sometimes preparation for upcoming activities, and sometimes numerical practice that revisits work in earlier units. Homework plays a role both in supporting students' learning and in helping inform families about the ways in which students in this curriculum work with mathematical ideas.

Depending on your school's homework policies and your own judgment, you may want to assign more homework than is suggested in the units. For this purpose you might use the practice pages, included as blackline masters at the end of this unit, to give students additional work with numbers.

For some homework assignments, you will want to adapt the activity to meet the needs of a variety of students in your class: those with special needs, those ready for more challenge, and second-language learners. You might change the numbers in a problem, make the activity more or less complex, or go through a sample activity with

those who need extra help. You can modify any student sheet for either homework or class use. In particular, making numbers in a problem smaller or larger can make the same basic activity appropriate for a wider range of students.

Another issue to consider is how to handle the homework that students bring back to class—how to recognize the work they have done at home without spending too much time on it. Some teachers hold a short group discussion of different approaches to the assignment; others ask students to share and discuss their work with a neighbor; still others post the homework around the room and give students time to tour it briefly. If you want to keep track of homework students bring in, be sure it ends up in a designated place.

Session Follow-Up: Extensions Sometimes in Session Follow-Up, you will find suggested extension activities. These are opportunities for some or all students to explore a topic in greater depth or in a different context. They are not designed for "fast" students; mathematics is a multifaceted discipline, and different students will want to go further in different investigations. Look for and encourage the sparks of interest and enthusiasm you see in your students, and use the extensions to help them pursue these interests.

Excursions Some of the *Investigations* units include excursions—blocks of activities that could be omitted without harming the integrity of the unit. This is one way of dealing with the great depth and variety of elementary mathematics— much more than a class has time to explore in any one year. Excursions give you the flexibility to make different choices from year to year, doing the excursion in one unit this time, and next year trying another excursion.

Materials

A complete list of the materials needed for teaching this unit follows the unit overview. Some of these materials are available in kits for the *Investigations* curriculum. Individual items can also be purchased from school supply dealers.

Classroom Materials In an active mathematics classroom, certain basic materials should be available at all times: interlocking cubes, pencils, unlined paper, graph paper, calculators, things to count with, and measuring tools. Some activities in this curriculum require scissors and glue sticks or tape. Stick-on notes and large paper are also useful materials throughout.

So that students can independently get what they need at any time, they should know where these materials are kept, how they are stored, and how they are to be returned to the storage area. For example, interlocking cubes are best stored in towers of ten; then, whatever the activity, they should be returned to storage in groups of ten at the end of the hour. You'll find that establishing such routines at the beginning of the year is well worth the time and effort.

Student Sheets and Teaching Resources Student recording sheets and other teaching tools needed for both class and homework are provided as reproducible blackline masters at the end of each unit. We think it's important that students find their own ways of organizing and recording their work. They need to learn how to explain their thinking with both drawings and written words, and how to organize their results so someone else can understand them. For this reason, we deliberately do not provide student sheets for every activity. Regardless of the form in which students do

their work, we recommend that they keep their work in a mathematics folder, notebook, or journal so that it is always available to them for reference.

Student Activity Booklets These booklets contain all the sheets each student will need for individual work, freeing you from extensive copying (although you may need or want to copy the occasional teaching resource on transparency film or card stock, or make extra copies of a student sheet).

Assessment Sourcebook The *Assessment Sourcebook* provides sets of End-of-Unit Assessment Tasks and Assessment Masters designed to assess students' understanding of the most important mathematical ideas of the unit. The *Sourcebook* also provides information about the mathematical significance of each assessment task; suggestions on how to observe students and evaluate their work; and unit checklists of mathematical emphases. Each checklist provides space to make short notes about individual students.

Calculators and Computers Calculators are used throughout Investigations. Many of the unity recommend that you have at least one calculator for each pair. You will find calculator activities, plus Teacher Notes discussing this important mathematical tool, in an early unit at each grade level. It is assumed that calculators will be readily available for student use.

Computer activities are offered at all grade levels. How you use the computer activities depends on the number of computers you have available. Technology in the Curriculum discusses ways to incorporate the use of calculators and computers into classroom activities.

Children's Literature Each unit offers a list of related children's literature that can be used to support the mathematical ideas in the unit. Sometimes an activity is based on a specific children's book, with suggestions for substitutions where practical. While such activities can be adapted and taught without the book, the literature offers a rich introduction and should be used whenever possible.

Investigations **at Home** It is a good idea to make your policy on homework explicit to both students and their families when you begin teaching with *Investigations*. How frequently will you be assigning homework? When do you expect homework to be completed and brought back to school? What are your goals in assigning homework? How independent should families expect their children to be? What should the parent's or guardian's role be? The more explicit you can be about your expectations, the better the homework experience will be for everyone.

Investigations at Home (a booklet available separately for each unit, to send home with students) gives you a way to communicate with families about the work students are doing in class. This booklet includes a brief description of every session, a list of the mathematics content emphasized in each investigation, and a discussion of each homework assignment to help families more effectively support their children. Whether or not you are using the *Investigations* at Home booklets, we expect you to make your own choices about homework assignments. Feel free to omit any and to add extra ones you think are appropriate.

Schools and Families: Creating a Math Partnership This book suggests ways schools and districts can encourage family participation in students' mathematics education.

Family Letter A letter that you can send home to students' families is included with the blackline masters for each unit. Families need to be informed about the mathematics work in your classroom; they should be encouraged to participate in and support their children's work. A reminder to send home the letter for each unit appears in one of the early investigations. These letters are also available separately in Spanish, Vietnamese, Cantonese, Hmong, and Cambodian.

Help for You, the Teacher

Because we believe strongly that a new curriculum must help teachers think in new ways about mathematics and about their students' mathematical thinking processes, we have included a great deal of material to help you learn more about both.

About the Mathematics in This Unit This introductory section (p. I-18) summarizes the critical information about the mathematics you will be teaching. It describes the unit's central mathema-

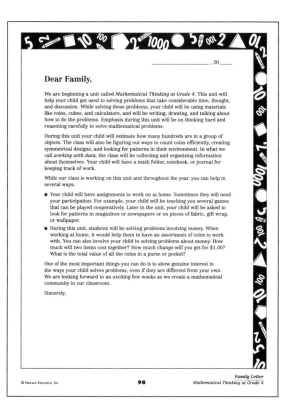

tical ideas and the ways students will encounter them through the unit's activities.

About the Assessment in This Unit This introductory section (p. I-20) highlights Teacher Checkpoints and assessment activities contained in the unit. It offers questions to stimulate your assessment as you observe the development of students' mathematical thinking and learning.

Teacher Notes These reference notes provide practical information about the mathematics you are teaching and about our experience with how students learn. Many of the notes were written in response to actual questions from teachers or to discuss important things we saw happening in the field-test classrooms. Some teachers like to read them all before starting the unit, then review them as they come up in particular investigations.

Dialogue Boxes Sample dialogues demonstrate how students typically express their mathematical ideas, what issues and confusions arise in their thinking, and how some teachers have guided class discussions.

These dialogues are based on the extensive classroom testing of this curriculum; many are word-for-word transcriptions of recorded class discussions. They are not always easy reading; sometimes it may take some effort to unravel what the students are trying to say. But this is the value of these dialogues; they offer good clues to how your students may develop and express their approaches and strategies, helping you prepare for your own class discussions.

Where to Start You may not have time to read everything the first time you use this unit. As a first-time user, you will likely focus on understanding the activities and working them out with your students. For a quick way to become familiar with the unit, see the **Where to Start** suggestions on the inside front cover.

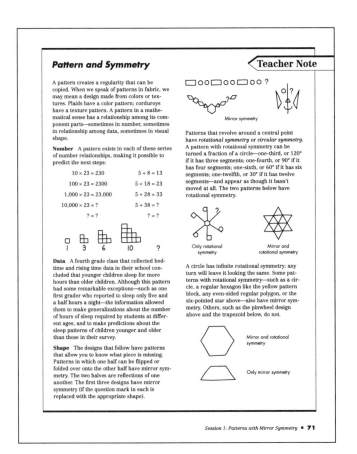

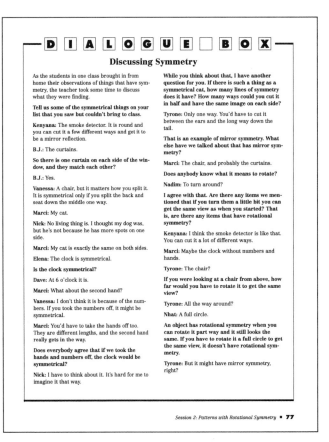

The *Investigations* curriculum incorporates the use of two forms of technology in the classroom: calculators and computers. Calculators are assumed to be standard classroom materials, available for student use in any unit. Computers are explicitly linked to one or more units at each grade level; they are used with the unit on 2-D geometry at each grade, as well as with some of the units on measuring, data, and changes.

Using Calculators

In this curriculum, calculators are considered tools for doing mathematics, similar to pattern blocks or interlocking cubes. Just as with other tools, students must learn both *how* to use calculators correctly and *when* they are appropriate to use. This knowledge is crucial for daily life, as calculators are now a standard way of handling numerical operations, both at work and at home.

Using a calculator correctly is not a simple task; it depends on a good knowledge of the four operations and of the number system, so that students can select suitable calculations and also determine what a reasonable result would be. These skills are the basis of any work with numbers, whether or not a calculator is involved.

Unfortunately, calculators are often seen as tools to check computations with, as if other methods are somehow more fallible. Students need to understand that any computational method can be used to check any other; it's just as easy to make a mistake on the calculator as it is to make a mistake on paper or with mental arithmetic. Throughout this curriculum, we encourage students to solve computation problems in more than one way in order to double-check their accuracy. We present mental arithmetic, paper-and-pencil computation, and calculators as three possible approaches.

In this curriculum we also recognize that, despite their importance, calculators are not always appropriate in mathematics instruction. Like any tools, calculators are useful for some tasks but not for others. You will need to make decisions about when to allow students access to calculators and when to ask that they solve problems without them so that they can concentrate on other tools and skills. At times when calculators are or are not appropriate for a particular activity, we make specific recommendations. Help your students develop their own sense of which problems they can tackle with their own reasoning and which ones might be better solved with a combination of their own reasoning and the calculator.

Managing calculators in your classroom so that they are a tool, and not a distraction, requires some planning. When calculators are first introduced, students often want to use them for everything, even problems that can be solved quite simply by other methods. However, once the novelty wears off, students are just as interested in developing their own strategies, especially when these strategies are emphasized and valued in the classroom. Over time, students will come to recognize the ease and value of solving problems mentally, with paper and pencil, or with manipulatives, while also understanding the power of the calculator to facilitate work with larger numbers.

Experience shows that if calculators are available only occasionally, students become excited and distracted when they are permitted to use them. They focus on the tool rather than on the mathematics. In order to learn when calculators are appropriate and when they are not, students must have easy access to them and use them routinely in their work.

If you have a calculator for each student, and if you think your students can accept the responsibility, you might allow them to keep their calculators with the rest of their individual materials, at least for the first few weeks of school. Alternatively, you might store them in boxes on a shelf, number each calculator, and assign a corresponding number to each student. This system can give students a sense of ownership while also helping you keep track of the calculators.

Using Computers

Students can use computers to approach and visualize mathematical situations in new ways. The computer allows students to construct and manipulate geometric shapes, see objects move according to rules they specify, and turn, flip, and repeat a pattern.

This curriculum calls for computers in units where they are a particularly effective tool for learning mathematics content. One unit on 2-D geometry at each of the grades 3–5 includes a core of activities that rely on access to computers, either in the classroom or in a lab. Other units on geometry, measuring, data, and changes include computer activities, but can be taught without them. In these units, however, students' experience is greatly enhanced by computer use.

The following list outlines the recommended use of computers in this curriculum. The software is available for download at http://investigations. scottforesman.com.

Kindergarten
Unit: *Making Shapes and Building Blocks* (Exploring Geometry)
Software: *MS_Shapes*

Grade 1
Unit: *Quilt Squares and Block Towns* (2-D and 3-D Geometry)
Software: *QS_Shapes*

Grade 2
Unit: *Mathematical Thinking at Grade 2* (Introduction)
Software: *MT_Shapes*

Unit: *Shapes, Halves, and Symmetry* (Geometry and Fractions)
Software: *SH_Shapes*

Unit: *How Long? How Far?* (Measuring)
Software: *HL_Geo-Logo*

Grade 3
Unit: *Flips, Turns, and Area* (2-D Geometry)
Software: *Tumbling Tetrominoes*

Unit: *Turtle Paths* (2-D Geometry)
Software: *TP_Geo-Logo*

Grade 4
Unit: *Sunken Ships and Grid Patterns* (2-D Geometry)
Software: *SS_Geo-Logo*

Grade 5
Unit: *Picturing Polygons* (2-D Geometry)
Software: *PP_Geo-Logo*

Unit: *Patterns of Change* (Tables and Graphs)
Software: *Trips*

The software for the *Investigations* units uses the power of the computer to help students explore mathematical ideas and relationships that cannot be explored in the same way with physical materials. With the *Shapes* (grades K–2) and *Tumbling Tetrominoes* (grade 3) software, students explore symmetry, pattern, rotation and reflection, area, and characteristics of 2-D shapes. With the *Geo-Logo* software (grades 2–5), students investigate rotation and reflection, coordinate geometry, the properties of 2-D shapes, and angles. The *Trips* software (grade 5) is a mathematical exploration of motion in which students run experiments and interpret data presented in graphs and tables.

We suggest that students work in pairs on the computer; this not only maximizes computer resources but also encourages students to consult, monitor, and teach each other. Generally, more than two students at one computer find it difficult to share. Managing access to computers is an issue for every classroom. The curriculum gives you explicit support for setting up a system. The units are structured on the assumption that you have enough computers for half your students to work on the machines in pairs at one time. If you do not have access to that many computers, suggestions are made for structuring class time to use the unit with fewer than five.

Assessment plays a critical role in teaching and learning, and it is an integral part of the *Investigations* curriculum. For a teacher using these units, assessment is an ongoing process. You observe students' discussions and explanations of their strategies on a daily basis and examine their work as it evolves. While students are busy recording and representing their work, working on projects, sharing with partners, and playing mathematical games, you have many opportunities to observe their mathematical thinking. What you learn through observation guides your decisions about how to proceed. In any of the units, you will repeatedly consider questions like these:

■ Do students come up with their own strategies for solving problems, or do they expect others to tell them what to do? What do their strategies reveal about their mathematical understanding?

■ Do students understand that there are different strategies for solving problems? Do they articulate their strategies and try to understand other students' strategies?

■ How effectively do students use materials as tools to help with their mathematical work?

■ Do students have effective ideas for keeping track of and recording their work? Do keeping track of and recording their work seem difficult for them?

You will need to develop a comfortable and efficient system for recording and keeping track of your observations. Some teachers keep a clipboard handy and jot notes on a class list or on adhesive labels that are later transferred to student files. Others keep loose-leaf notebooks with a page for each student and make weekly notes about what they have observed in class.

Assessment Tools in the Unit

With the activities in each unit, you will find questions to guide your thinking while observing the students at work. You will also find two built-in assessment tools: Teacher Checkpoints and embedded Assessment activities.

Teacher Checkpoints The designated Teacher Checkpoints in each unit offer a time to "check in" with individual students, watch them at work, and ask questions that illuminate how they are

thinking.

At first it may be hard to know what to look for, hard to know what kinds of questions to ask. Students may be reluctant to talk; they may not be accustomed to having the teacher ask them about their work, or they may not know how to explain their thinking. Two important ingredients of this process are asking students open-ended questions about their work and showing genuine interest in how they are approaching the task. When students see that you are interested in their thinking and are counting on them to come up with their own ways of solving problems, they may surprise you with the depth of their understanding.

Teacher Checkpoints also give you the chance to pause in the teaching sequence and reflect on how your class is doing overall. Think about whether you need to adjust your pacing: Are most students fluent with strategies for solving a particular kind of problem? Are they just starting to formulate good strategies? Or are they still struggling with how to start? Depending on what you see as the students work, you may want to spend more time on similar problems, change some of the problems to use smaller numbers, move quickly to more challenging material, modify subsequent activities for some students, work on particular ideas with a small group, or pair students who have good strategies with those who are having more difficulty.

Embedded Assessment Activities Assessment activities embedded in each unit will help you examine specific pieces of student work, figure out what they mean, and provide feedback. From the students' point of view, these assessment activities are no different from any others. Each is a learning experience in and of itself, as well as an opportunity for you to gather evidence about students' mathematical understanding.

The embedded Assessment activities sometimes involve writing and reflecting; at other times, a discussion or brief interaction between student and teacher; and in still other instances, the creation and explanation of a product. In most cases, the assessments require that students *show* what they did, *write* or *talk* about it, or do both. Having to explain how they worked through a problem helps students be more focused and clear in their mathematical thinking. It also helps them realize that doing mathematics is a process that may involve tentative starts, revising one's approach, taking different paths, and working through ideas.

Teachers often find the hardest part of assessment to be interpreting their students' work. We provide guidelines to help with that interpretation. If you have used a process approach to teaching writing, the assessment in *Investigations* will seem familiar. For many of the assessment activities, a Teacher Note provides examples of student work and a commentary on what it indicates about student thinking.

Documentation of Student Growth

To form an overall picture of mathematical progress, it is important to document each student's work. Many teachers have students keep their work in folders, notebooks, or journals, and some like to have students summarize their learning in journals at the end of each unit. It's important to document students' progress, and we recommend that you keep a portfolio of selected work for each student, unit by unit, for the entire year. The final activity in each *Investigations* unit, called Choosing Student Work to Save, helps you and the students select representative samples for a record of their work.

This kind of regular documentation helps you synthesize information about each student as a mathematical learner. From different pieces of evidence, you can put together the big picture. This synthesis will be invaluable in thinking about where to go next with a particular child, deciding where more work is needed, or explaining to parents (or other teachers) how a child is doing.

If you use portfolios, you need to collect a good balance of work, yet avoid being swamped with an overwhelming amount of paper. Following are some tips for effective portfolios:

- Collect a representative sample of work, including some pieces that students themselves select for inclusion in the portfolio. There should be just a few pieces for each unit, showing different kinds of work—some assignments that involve writing as well as some that do not.

- If students do not date their work, do so yourself so that you can reconstruct the order in which pieces were done.

- Include your reflections on the work. When you are looking back over the whole year, such comments are reminders of what seemed especially interesting about a particular piece; they can also be helpful to other teachers and to parents. Older students should be encouraged to write their own reflections about their work.

Assessment Overview

There are two places to turn for a preview of the assessment opportunities in each *Investigations* unit. The Assessment Resources column in the unit Overview Chart identifies the Teacher Checkpoints and Assessment activities embedded in each investigation, guidelines for observing the students that appear within classroom activities, and any Teacher Notes and Dialogue Boxes that explain what to look for and what types of student responses you might expect to see in your classroom. Additionally, the section About the Assessment in This Unit gives you a detailed list of questions for each investigation, keyed to the mathematical emphases, to help you observe student growth.

Assessment Sourcebook   The *Assessment Sourcebook* complements and supports the embedded assessments of *Investigations* by offering further opportunities to gather information about students' growing mathematical understanding.

The *Assessment Sourcebook* provides you with sets of Assessment Tasks and Masters designed to assess your students' understanding of the most important mathematical ideas of the unit. The *Sourcebook* also provides information about the mathematical significance of each assessment task; suggestions on how to observe students and evaluate their work; and unit checklists of mathematical emphases. Each checklist provides space to make short notes about individual students.

The assessments in the *Sourcebook* should be used in addition to other assessments that are presented in each unit. The combination of these assessments, along with samples of student work, will offer a picture of a student's understanding of the mathematical concepts and skills presented in the unit.

Mathematical Thinking at Grade 4

Content of This Unit   This unit is meant to familiarize you and your students with the mathematics content and approaches of *Investigations* and to help you assess the strengths and needs of your new class of students. It is not designed to provide a final encounter with important mathematical ideas. Students will revisit key ideas in this unit in greater depth as the year goes on. Even if some of your students have only a partial understanding of some of the topics, we recommend that you not spend more time on this unit than is suggested in the Unit Overview.

The emphases in this unit, and throughout the year, are on mathematical thinking and reasoning, using a variety of tools and models to explore mathematics, and being able to communicate about mathematical ideas through drawing, writing, and talking. Students become familiar with using and caring for materials: interlocking cubes, calculators, play money, geoboards, pattern blocks. They have experiences working cooperatively, recording their work in a systematic way, reporting what they have learned, and writing about their thinking. Tasks are provided for assessing students in number work and geometric thinking.

Connections with Other Units   If you are doing the full-year *Investigations* curriculum in the suggested sequence for grade 4, this is the first of eleven units. It has connections with every other unit in the fourth grade sequence, both in its content and in its emphasis on ways of thinking and doing mathematics. The number work in this unit is specifically continued and extended in *Landmarks in the Thousands,* and in the Addition and Subtraction unit, *Money, Miles, and Large Numbers.*

This unit can be used successfully at either grade 4 or grade 5 at any time of the year, depending on the previous experience and needs of your students. It offers a way to help students focus on thinking, working, and talking mathematically, and helps you assess student understanding of some key mathematical content.

Investigations Curriculum ■ Suggested Grade 4 Sequence

▶ *Mathematical Thinking at Grade 4* (Introduction)

Arrays and Shares (Multiplication and Division)

Seeing Solids and Silhouettes (3-D Geometry)

Landmarks in the Thousands (The Number System)

Different Shapes, Equal Pieces (Fractions and Area)

The Shape of the Data (Statistics)

Money, Miles, and Large Numbers (Addition and Subtraction)

Changes Over Time (Graphs)

Packages and Groups (Multiplication and Division)

Sunken Ships and Grid Patterns (2-D Geometry)

Three out of Four Like Spaghetti (Data and Fractions)

Investigation 1 ■ How Many Hundreds?

Class Sessions	Activities	Pacing
Session 1 (p. 4) GETTING STARTED WITH INTERLOCKING CUBES	Introducing the Mathematical Environment Building with Cubes How Many in Each Object? Writing About the First Session	minimum 1 hr
Sessions 2 and 3 (p. 11) HOW MANY HUNDREDS?	Counting Out 100 Cubes Estimating How Many Cubes Altogether Counting How Many Altogether How Many Hundreds? Finding How Many in All Homework: A Design with 100 Squares Homework: How Many?	minimum 2 hr
Session 4 (p. 23) CLOSE TO 100	Introducing Close to 100 Playing Close to 100 Teacher Checkpoint: Thinking About Close to 100 Homework: Playing Close to 100	minimum 1 hr

◔ **Ten-Minute Math ■ Estimation and Number Sense**

Mathematical Emphasis	Assessment Resources	Materials
■ Grouping things for more efficient counting ■ Recording numbers for more efficient mental arithmetic ■ Finding how many more are needed ■ Estimating how many hundreds are in the total of a group of three-digit numbers ■ Communicating about mathematical thinking through written and spoken language ■ Exploring materials that will be used throughout this curriculum as problem-solving tools	Finding How Many in All: Observing the Students (p. 18) Introducing Calculators (Teacher Note, p. 20) Teacher Checkpoint: Thinking About Close to 100 (p. 27) Strategies for Close to 100 (Dialogue Box, p. 31)	Snap™ Cubes and containers Stick-on notes Chart paper Overhead projector, transparency pen Calculators Scissors Student Sheets 1–6 Teaching resource sheets Family letter

Investigation 2 ■ How Many Dollars?

Class Sessions	Activities	Pacing
Sessions 1 and 2 (p. 34) HOW MUCH MONEY?	Counting Money Adding Coin Values Teacher Checkpoint: The Collecting Dollars Game Homework: Playing Collecting Dollars	minimum 2 hr
Sessions 3 and 4 (p. 40) NUMBER SENSE AND COINS	The Hidden Coins Game Choice Time: Playing Math Games Homework: Playing Hidden Coins	minimum 2 hr

◐ **Ten-Minute Math** ■ **Estimation and Number Sense**

Mathematical Emphasis

- Grouping coins for more efficient counting

- Recognizing values of U.S. coins

- Recognizing the decimal point on the calculator

Assessment Resources

Teacher Checkpoint: The Collecting Dollars Game (p. 38)

Choice Time: Observing the Students (p. 43)

Materials

Play money

Resealable plastic bags for play money

Scissors

Opaque paper bags of real coins, holding 2 quarters, 3 dimes, 3 nickels, and 5 pennies to make exactly $1

Calculators

Student Sheet 7

Teaching resource sheets

Investigation 3 ■ Using Number Patterns

Class Sessions	Activities	Pacing
Sessions 1 and 2 (p. 48) THE 300 CHART	Filling in the 300 Chart How Many Steps? Counting by 10's Playing 101 to 200 Bingo Homework: Playing 101 to 200 Bingo	minimum 2 hr
Session 3 (p. 54) RELATED PROBLEM SETS	Solving Sets of Related Problems Teacher Checkpoint: Writing About Strategies Comparing Solutions in Groups Homework: Related Problem Sets	minimum 1 hr
Sessions 4 and 5 (p. 58) ADDITION AND SUBTRACTION STRATEGIES	Choice Time: Learning Together Assessment: Numbers and Money Homework: Complete the Booklet Extension: Invent a New Game	minimum 2 hr

Ten-Minute Math ■ Exploring Data

Mathematical Emphasis

■ Using known answers to find others

■ Subtracting on a 300 chart and with a calculator

■ Adding and subtracting multiples of ten

Assessment Resources

Filling in the 300 Chart (p. 49)

Teacher Checkpoint: Writing About Strategies (p. 55)

Choice Time: Observing the Students (p. 60)

Assessment: Numbers and Money (Teacher Note, p. 62)

Materials

Calculator

Scissors, tape

Game markers (such as cubes, square tiles, counting chips)

Colored pencils, crayons, or markers

Snap™ Cubes

Alexander, Who Used to Be Rich Last Sunday, by Judith Viorst (opt.)

Overhead projector

Student Sheets 8–10

Teaching resource sheets

Coin cards and plastic coins from previous investigations

Investigation 4 ■ Making Geometric Patterns

Class Sessions	Activities	Pacing
Session 1 (p. 66) PATTERNS WITH MIRROR SYMMETRY	Symmetry with Pattern Blocks Symmetry in the Environment Homework: Finding Examples of Symmetry Homework: Making a New Design Extension: Making Symmetrical Linear and 3-D Designs	minimum 1 hr
Session 2 (p. 72) PATTERNS WITH ROTATIONAL SYMMETRY	Two Symmetries: Which Is Which? Patterns Around Hexagons What Is a Pattern? Homework: Collecting Designs for Display Extension: Pattern Puzzles	minimum 1 hr
Sessions 3 and 4 (p. 78) PATTERNS AND NONPATTERNS	Teacher Checkpoint: A Display of Patterns Writing About Our Designs Draw the Hidden Design Guessing from Descriptions	minimum 2 hr
Sessions 5 and 6 (p. 83) SYMMETRICAL GEOBOARD PATTERNS	Teacher Checkpoint: Symmetry on the Geoboard Counting Lines of Symmetry Assessment: Mirror and Rotational Symmetry Choosing Student Work to Save Homework: Multiple Lines of Symmetry Extension: Displaying More Patterns	minimum 2 hr

◔ Ten-Minute Math ■ Exploring Data

Mathematical Emphasis	Assessment Resources	Materials
■ Distinguishing between geometric patterns and random designs ■ Distinguishing between mirror symmetry and rotational symmetry ■ Writing about designs	Discussing Symmetry (Dialogue Box, p. 77) Teacher Checkpoint: A Display of Patterns (p. 78) Teacher Checkpoint: Symmetry on the Geoboard (p. 83) Assessment: Mirror and Rotational Symmetry (p. 87) Choosing Student Work to Save (p. 88)	Pattern blocks Ruler or straightedge Pencils, crayons, or markers in red, green, yellow, and blue Scraps of patterned fabric, wrapping paper, or wall-paper (opt.) Scissors Stick-on notes Geoboards with rubber bands in assorted colors Overhead projector Overhead pattern blocks (opt.) Student Sheets 11–12 Teaching resource sheets Resealable plastic bags Small mirror

Following are the basic materials needed for the activities in this unit.

- Snap™ Cubes (interlocking cubes): 1 container per 4–6 students (60 per student)

- Pattern blocks: 1 bucket per 4–6 students

- Overhead pattern blocks (optional)

- Play money: at least 2 one-dollar bills, 1 five-dollar bill, 2 fifty-cent pieces, 6 quarters, 8 dimes, 8 nickels, and 10 pennies per pair of students

- Real coins: several collections of $1 in 2 quarters, 3 dimes, 3 nickels, and 5 pennies, each in a small paper bag

- Numeral Cards (manufactured; or use blackline masters to make your own sets)

- Geoboards with rubber bands: 1 per pair

- *Alexander, Who Used to Be Rich Last Sunday,* by Judith Viorst (optional)

- Scissors: 1 per student

- Calculators: 1 per student

- Resealable plastic bags or envelopes for storage of card sets and play money: 3 per student

- Old magazines, linoleum brochures, scraps of wrapping paper, scraps of wallpaper, and other sources of patterned pictures and designs (optional)

- Overhead projector, pens, and blank transparencies

- Stick-on notes

- Chart paper

- Game markers, such as cubes, square tiles, counting chips: 2 per student

- Colored pencils, crayons, or markers

- Ruler or straightedge: 1 per pair

- Tape

- Small mirror

The following materials are provided at the end of this unit as blackline masters. A Student Activity Booklet containing all student sheets and teacher resources needed for individual work is available.

Family Letter (p. 98)

Student Sheets 1–12 (p. 99)

Teaching Resources:

   Chart for How Many Cubes? (p. 105)

   How to Play Close to 100 (p. 106)

   One-Centimeter Graph Paper (p. 107)

   Coin Cards (p. 109)

   How to Play Collecting Dollars (p. 113)

   How to Play Hidden Coins (p. 114)

   How to Play 101 to 200 Bingo (p. 126)

   101 to 200 Bingo Board (p. 127)

   Tens Cards (p. 128)

   Shaded Geoboard Design (p. 132)

   Geoboard Dot Paper (p. 133)

   Triangle Paper (p. 134)

   Close to 100 Score Sheet (p. 135)

   Numeral Cards (p. 136)

   Coin Value Strips (p. 139)

   Choice List (p. 140)

Practice Pages (p. 141)

Related Children's Literature

Dahl, Roald. *Matilda.* New York: Puffin Books, 1988.

Kipling, Rudyard. *The Elephant's Child.* New York: Prentice-Hall, 1987.

Tompert, Ann. *Grandfather Tan's Story.* New York: Crown, 1990.

Viorst, Judith. *Alexander, Who Used to Be Rich Last Sunday.* New York: Macmillan, 1989.

Zimelman, Nathan. *How the Second Grade Got $8205.50 to Visit the Statue of Liberty.* Morton Grove, IL: Albert Whitman, 1992.

Mathematical Thinking at Grade 4, as the title indicates, is designed to be an introduction to mathematical thinking—to some of the content, materials, processes, and ways of working that mathematics entails. Through the work in this unit, we provide experiences to engage students in:

■ solving mathematical problems in ways that make sense to them

■ talking, writing, and drawing about their work

■ working with peers

■ building models of mathematical situations

■ relying on their own thinking and learning from the thinking of others

Students work with problems in the areas of number, data, and space (geometry). In number they explore what happens when ten or multiples of ten are added or subtracted, work on estimating hundreds in number and whole dollars in sums of money, and begin to develop strategies for combining and comparing large quantities. Their work with geometry includes exploring mirror symmetry and rotational symmetry as they build designs with pattern blocks and on geoboards. In Ten-Minute Math activities related to working with data, students collect information about themselves as a group and begin to find ways of organizing, representing, and discussing the data they have collected. Throughout the unit they are introduced to basic mathematical tools and materials such as interlocking cubes, 100 charts, calculators, money, pattern blocks, and geoboards.

Much of the work in this unit involves patterns. Students work with patterns in a variety of contexts: building with pattern blocks and interlocking cubes, using money, and counting on by 10's and 20's. They look at patterns on the 300 chart and discuss what they know about 100. They develop strategies for picking two-digit numbers with a sum of 100. They distinguish between visual displays that have patterns and those that are pictures or abstract designs without any repeating design.

A major focus of these activities is the development and use of good number sense to combine and compare two-digit and three-digit numbers. We

expect that fourth graders know the one-digit addition combinations. Just as common sense grows from experience with the world and how it works, number sense grows from experience with how numbers work. Throughout these activities, students are encouraged to solve addition and subtraction problems by thinking about how the numbers are structured and how they are related to other numbers.

For example, in solving an addition combination they don't know, such as 28 + 38, students are encouraged to use what they do know—perhaps 30 + 40 – 2 – 2 or 20 + 30 and 8 + 8—to reason about the sum. In solving two- and three-digit addition or subtraction problems, we urge students not to apply rote procedures, but to look at the whole problem first and then apply what they know about the numbers to solve the problem.

Investigation 4 focuses on geometry as a central part of mathematics. Students' investigation of symmetry provides a foundation for their exploration of visual pattern in their environment. Students create designs and color them to highlight symmetry, and find ways to complete designs to create a pattern.

Mathematical Thinking at Grade 4 is designed not only to involve students with some central mathematical concepts but also to introduce them to a particular way of approaching mathematics. Throughout the unit students are encouraged to share their strategies, work cooperatively, use materials, and communicate both verbally and in writing about how they are solving problems. These approaches may be quite difficult for some students. Even taking out, using, and putting away materials may be unfamiliar. Certainly writing and drawing pictures to describe mathematical thinking will be quite difficult for some students.

This unit is a time to focus on the development of these processes; to spend time establishing routines and expectations; to communicate to students your own interest in and respect for their mathematical ideas; to assure students that you want to know about their *thinking,* not just their answers; and to insist that students work hard to solve problems in ways that make sense to them. As the unit unfolds, a mathematical community begins to take shape—a community that you and your students are together responsible for creating and maintaining.

At the beginning of each investigation, the Mathematical Emphasis section tells you what is most important for students to learn during that investigation. Many of these mathematical understandings and processes are difficult and complex. Students gradually learn more and more about each idea over many years of schooling. Individual students will begin and end the unit with different levels of knowledge and skill, but all will gain greater knowledge about recognizing spatial patterns and solving mathematical problems with number and money in ways that make sense to them.

Throughout the *Investigations* curriculum, there are many opportunities for ongoing daily assessment as you observe, listen to, and interact with students at work. In this unit, you will find five Teacher Checkpoints:

Investigation 1, Session 4:
Thinking About Close to 100 (p. 27)

Investigation 2, Sessions 1–2:
The Collecting Dollars Game (p. 38)

Investigation 3, Session 3:
Writing About Strategies (p. 55)

Investigation 4, Sessions 3–4:
A Display of Patterns (p. 78)

Investigation 4, Sessions 5–6:
Symmetry on the Geoboard (p. 83)

This unit also has two embedded Assessment activities:

Investigation 3, Sessions 4–5:
Numbers and Money (p. 61)

Investigation 4, Sessions 5–6:
Mirror and Rotational Symmetry (p. 87)

In addition, you can use almost any activity in this unit to assess your students' needs and strengths. Listed below are questions to help you focus your observations in each investigation. You may want to keep track of your observations for each student to help you plan your curriculum and monitor students' growth. Suggestions for documenting student growth can be found in the section About Assessment.

Investigation 1: How Many Hundreds?

- How do students count out 100 objects? Can they count by grouping in more than one way? Can students read and write two-digit and three-digit numbers?

- How do students use landmarks to guide addition and subtraction? For example, do they recognize that 27 + 27 is too small to have a sum close to 100, but that 72 + 26 is close to 100?

- What do students know about the structure of the numbers? For example, do they know that the 80's are closer to 100 than the 40's are; that a number in the 70's requires less than 30 to reach 100; that 723 has 7 hundreds in it, whereas 792 is almost 8 hundreds?

- Do students have a good strategy for solving addition problems involving two-digit and three-digit numbers? Can they break apart and reorder numbers to work on a problem more efficiently?

- How do students use materials and mental strategies to find the difference between two numbers? What strategies do they use to find "how many more"? Are they tied to counting by 1's? Are they frequently off by 1 when comparing two quantities?

Investigation 2: How Many Dollars?

- What strategies do students use to combine coins? Can they count easily by 5's, 10's, 25's? When they add coins, do they need to count on by 1's, or do they recognize how to add 5's and 10's to a number?

- Are students familiar with coins and their values?

- Can students add amounts of money on a calculator, using the decimal point appropriately?

Investigation 3: Using Number Patterns

- How do students use known answers to solve related problems? Do they use their knowledge of place value to see relations among problems?

- How do students work with a 300 chart? Can they add and subtract by tens and hundreds? Do they understand how to use a calculator for subtraction? What strategies do they use for checking the reasonableness of an answer on the calculator?

- Do students know what happens when 10 (or a multiple of 10) is added to or subtracted from a two-digit number and use this to compute efficiently?

Investigation 4: Making Geometric Patterns

- Can students distinguish between a design with a pattern and a design without a pattern?

- Can students make a pattern with mirror symmetry? Can they make a pattern with rotational symmetry? Can students recognize patterns with mirror symmetry? with rotational symmetry? Are students clear about the differences between mirror and rotational symmetry?

- What vocabulary do students use when describing designs? Do students use both words and pictures effectively?

Thinking and Working in Mathematics

Mathematical Thinking at Grade 4 provides the chance for you to observe students' work habits and communication skills. Think about these questions to help you decide which of these routines, processes, and materials will require the most ongoing support, guidance, and opportunities for practice.

- Are students comfortable and focused working together in pairs? in small groups?

- Do students expect to devise their own strategies for solving problems, or do they expect you to tell them what to do or expect to copy from another student? Do they understand that different people may solve problems in different ways?

- Are students familiar with the basic mathematics materials used in this unit? Do they know how to use them? Do they have strategies to use these materials as tools when solving problems?

- Can students work well with materials? Do they take them out and put them away efficiently?

- Can students express their ideas orally? Who participates in discussions? Are they always the same students? Are there students who never participate?

- Do students have ideas about how to record their work, or does writing and drawing about mathematics seem new to them?

- Can students choose an activity from among several that are offered, then move smoothly to a second activity when finished with the first?

Assessment Sourcebook

In the *Assessment Sourcebook* you will find End-of-Unit Assessment Tasks and Assessment Masters available in English and Spanish. You will also find suggestions to help you observe and evaluate student work and checklists of mathematical emphases with space for you to record individual student information.

In the *Investigations* curriculum, mathematical vocabulary is introduced naturally during the activities. We don't ask students to learn definitions of new terms; rather, they come to understand such words as *factor* or *area* or *symmetry* by hearing them used frequently in discussion as they investigate new concepts. This approach is compatible with current theories of second-language acquisition, which emphasize the use of new vocabulary in meaningful contexts while students are actively involved with objects, pictures, and physical movement.

Listed below are some key words used in this unit that will not be new to most English speakers at this age level, but may be unfamiliar to students with limited English proficiency. You will want to spend additional time working on these words with your students who are learning English. If your students are working with a second-language teacher, you might enlist your colleague's aid in familiarizing students with these words before and during this unit. In the classroom, look for opportunities for students to hear and use these words. Activities you can use to present the words are given in the appendix, Vocabulary Support for Second-Language Learners (p. 95).

the numbers 1 to 300 Students add and subtract numbers in the hundreds and use the 300 chart. They should be able to write the numerals and identify each by name.

same, different, compare Students compare many things—two numbers, two patterns, two amounts of money—and determine whether they are the *same* or *different*. These terms are also an important part of checking and double-checking answers to problems.

add, plus, subtract, minus, difference Students perform addition and subtraction throughout the unit, in games and activities, with and without the calculator, and use these terms to describe their work.

lowest, close to In a game they play many times, Close to 100, students need to recognize numbers that are *close to* 100 and need to know what it means to try for the *lowest* score.

money: coins, cents, penny, nickel, dime, quarter, dollar Students need to recognize U.S. coins and know the value of each as they practice counting coins mentally to find the total value.

pattern Students look for patterns on the 300 chart; they find number patterns that can help them solve related computation problems; and they also work with patterns of shape and color as they explore symmetrical designs with pattern blocks.

shape, triangle, square, hexagon, trapezoid, diamond Students use pattern block shapes to build and explore symmetrical patterns.

Multicultural Extensions for All Students

Whenever possible, encourage students to share words, objects, customs, or any aspects of daily life from their own cultures and backgrounds that are relevant to the activities in this unit.

For example, during their exploration of symmetry in Investigation 4, you might help students locate pictures of national flags from around the world (found in almanacs or the encyclopedia) and determine which designs have either mirror or rotational symmetry. Students who have actual flags from their countries of origin might bring them in to share for this discussion. Additionally, students might bring in for display and discussion other emblems, fabrics, or objects with repeated patterns or symmetrical designs.

Investigations

How Many Hundreds?

What Happens

Session 1: Getting Started with Interlocking Cubes   Each student or pair builds an object with interlocking cubes. In small groups, students estimate how many cubes were used to make each object. Students count the cubes in their objects and then write about the activity.

Sessions 2 and 3: How Many Hundreds?   Pairs count out 100 interlocking cubes and group them to show clearly that the total is 100. Groups of students then estimate how many hundreds there are in the box of cubes their group received. The teacher records the estimates from all of the groups, and students figure out how many hundreds there are in the total of all the estimates. After counting their cubes, groups estimate how many hundreds of cubes there are in the class total. Finally, individuals figure out exactly how many cubes there are altogether.

Session 4: Close to 100   Students play a game that involves arranging digits to make numbers that have a sum as near as possible to 100.

Mathematical Emphasis

- Grouping things for more efficient counting
- Reordering numbers for more efficient mental arithmetic
- Finding how many more are needed
- Exploring materials that will be used throughout this curriculum as problem-solving tools
- Estimating how many hundreds are in the total of a group of three-digit numbers
- Communicating about mathematical thinking through written and spoken language

INVESTIGATION 1

What to Plan Ahead of Time

Materials

- Interlocking cubes: at least 100 per pair (Sessions 1–3)
- Containers for cubes: 6–8 (Sessions 1–3)
- Stick-on notes (Session 1)
- Chart paper (Sessions 1–3, optional)
- Overhead projector, transparency pen (Sessions 1–3)
- Calculators: at least 1 per pair (Sessions 2–3)
- Scissors (Session 4)

Other Preparation

- Duplicate student sheets and teaching resources (located at the end of this unit) in the following quantities. If you have Student Activity Booklets, copy only the items marked with an asterisk.

For Session 1

Student Sheet 1, How Many Cubes in Each Object? (p. 99): 1 per student, 1 transparency*

For Sessions 2–3

Family letter* (p. 98): 1 per student. Remember to sign the letter before copying.

Student Sheet 2, Making Hundreds (p. 100): 1 per student

Student Sheet 3, How Many Cubes in the Class? (p. 101): 1 per student

Student Sheet 4, A Design with 100 Squares (p. 102): 1 per student (homework)

Student Sheet 5, How Many Hundreds? How Many Altogether? (p. 103): 1 per student (homework)

Chart for How Many Cubes?* (p. 105): 1 transparency

One-centimeter graph paper (p. 107): 1–2 per student (homework)

For Session 4

Student Sheet 6, Problems for Close to 100 (p. 104): 1 per student

How to Play Close to 100 (p. 106): 1 per student (homework)

Close to 100 Score Sheet (p. 135): 1 per student (class), 2 per student (homework)

Numeral Cards (p. 136): 1 set per group for class use, ideally copied on tagboard (if you don't have the manufactured decks), plus 1 set per student to take home

- Divide your supply of interlocking cubes into buckets or shoe boxes for each small group. Put a different number of cubes in each box for an estimation activity. The cubes should be loose for this activity, rather than in stacks of 10. (Session 1)
- Make a simple object, such as a chair, from 30 to 60 interlocking cubes. (Session 1)
- If you are making your own class sets of Numeral Cards, see p. 24. (Session 4)
- If you plan to provide folders, notebooks, or journals in which students will save their work for the entire unit, prepare these for distribution during Session 1.

Investigation 1: How Many Hundreds? ■ **3**

Getting Started with Interlocking Cubes

Materials

- Sample object made of interlocking cubes
- Interlocking cubes (at least 100 per pair)
- Containers for cubes: 6–8
- Stick-on notes
- Student Sheet 1 (1 per student)
- Transparency of Student Sheet 1
- Chart paper (optional)
- Overhead projector, transparency pen

What Happens

Each student or pair builds an object with interlocking cubes. In small groups, students estimate how many cubes were used to make each object. Students count the cubes in their objects and then write about the activity. Their work focuses on:

- building with interlocking cubes
- estimating numbers of cubes
- counting cubes
- writing about math

Activity

Introducing the Mathematical Environment

Begin this session with a brief discussion about some of the tools you'll be using and the kind of work students will be doing in this unit. See the **Teacher Note**, Introducing Materials (p. 9), for hints about establishing routines for using and caring for manipulatives.

In our mathematics class this year, you will be using many different tools to help you solve problems and to show people how you are thinking about a problem. During the next few weeks, we will be using tools like calculators, pattern blocks, 100 charts, and interlocking cubes as we play math games and solve math problems.

❖ **Tip for the Linguistically Diverse Classroom** Ensure that this introduction is comprehensible to all students by showing the different mathematical tools as you mention them.

Ask students if they are familiar with any of these materials and how they have used them in the past.

Mathematicians use lots of different tools when they solve problems. Mathematicians also show us how they think about and solve problems. They talk about their work, draw pictures, build models, and write about their work so they can share their ideas with other people.

When you are working on a math problem, I will often ask you to use words, pictures, or numbers to explain how you solved it. Lots of times I will ask you to talk about how you solved a problem—either with a partner, in a small group, or with the whole class. This is one of the ways we can share good ideas and strategies for thinking about the math problems we are working on.

Many of you will invent ways of solving problems on your own, and I look forward to hearing all your ideas.

Building with Cubes

Pass out containers of interlocking cubes to groups of four to six students who will work together. Give students time to experiment with how to put the cubes together to make objects. Then tell them they are to build an object, on their own or with a partner, that will be used in the next activity.

Have the class brainstorm objects they can make (for example, chair, table, car, and so on). Allow 10 to 15 minutes for this, and give a 3-minute warning for students to complete their object and put away extra cubes. Students can label their objects with stick-on notes or small pieces of paper:

When your object is ready, put it in front of you so others can see it. Write the name of your object on a small label [*demonstrate*], and put the label in front of your object.

Give students a chance to look at each other's objects. You might allow them to walk around and view the objects, talking quietly, as if they were in a museum.

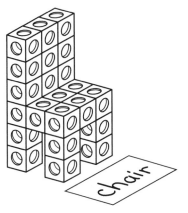

How Many in Each Object?

Display the transparency of Student Sheet 1, How Many Cubes in Each Object? on the overhead or draw the chart on the board. Fill in your name in the first row. Show students your sample object, and write its name on the chart. For example:

Name of maker	Name of object	Estimate	Count
Ms. Brown	Chair	15-30	26

Carry your object around to show to students. Ask them to estimate how many cubes you used.

Talk quietly in your groups and see if you can agree on an estimate of about how many cubes I used in my object. For example, you might say something like "around 30" or "about 15." If your group can't decide on one number, give a range as your estimate—maybe "between 35 and 40." Decide on an estimate that seems right to all the people in your group.

As groups are ready to share their estimates, list their ideas on the board. Ask a few students how they came up with their estimates. Support any use of systematic grouping, such as: "There are 4 legs and they each have 3 cubes, so that is 3, 6, 9, 12. Then the top part looked like about 10." On your chart, write the range of estimates for the number of cubes in your object, as shown above.

Making Estimates for Student Objects   Hand out Student Sheet 1, How Many Cubes in Each Object? In the first row, each student writes your name, the name of your object, and his or her estimate as to how many cubes it took. Explain that their individual estimate may be different from their group's estimate. Whatever number they write down, they are not to change it after you count.

When everyone has written an estimate, disassemble your object into countable pieces (some single cubes, some in groups) and count the cubes. Count by groups when appropriate, rather than all by ones. Students write this actual count on their charts in the last column. They can compare the last two columns to see how good their estimates were.

Now you will estimate the number of cubes in each of the objects that the other people in your group made. Work with one object at a time. In your chart, write who made the object, the name of the object, and an estimate of the number of cubes in it.

❖ **Tip for the Linguistically Diverse Classroom** Students who have difficulty writing in English may draw simple pictures in the "Name of object" column.

Advise students not to pick up the objects as they make their estimates, as the objects might break apart.

Look closely, but don't count all the cubes. You are only trying to guess *about* how many. You may talk about your estimates with classmates, but you do not need to agree on them. Write down the number that *you* think is right.

When everyone in your group has written an estimate, the maker of the object will take it apart and count the cubes. Everyone in the group writes down that actual count.

Don't hurry. Work together. By estimating one object at a time and learning the actual number of cubes, you may make a more accurate estimate of the *next* object.

It's important not to change your estimates after you have written them down. Don't worry if they are not as close to the actual count as you wish. You will become better estimators with practice.

Get around to groups quickly to make sure they understand the task and to clear up any confusion. You might appoint one student in each group to help the others fill in their charts and to be sure everyone has written an estimate before counting. Ask some students to show or tell both you and their group how they are estimating.

Writing About the First Session

For the remainder of the session, students write in responses to the questions on Student Sheet 1, How Many Cubes in Each Object?

■ Tell about what you enjoyed in math class today.
■ Suppose someone was trying to estimate how many cubes were in an object. What advice would you give that person?

❖ **Tip for the Linguistically Diverse Classroom** Give students the option of responding to these questions in their native language. If they are not yet writing, they may communicate their answers orally to a family member, as homework. Ask for an adult signature at the bottom of Student Sheet 1, signifying that the child answered the questions.

Students may need some ideas about how to respond to these questions. Some fourth graders have said they enjoyed building, cooperating, estimating, and doing other things that weren't like real math.

To show that you value students' ideas about math, you might copy all their answers to the second question onto chart paper for display. Some answers that one fourth grade teacher recorded are given in the **Dialogue Box**, Advice About Estimating Numbers of Cubes (p. 10).

If you have prepared math folders or notebooks for students to keep their work in, this is a good time to pass them out. Students can put their names on the folders and put Student Sheet 1 inside.

Name **Saloni**   Date **Sept 10**

How Many Cubes in Each Object?

Name of maker	Name of object	Estimate	Count
Rebecca	dragon	33	35
Joey	zap	50	49
Rafael	Gate	45-50	47
Shoshana	wink	25-30	23
Jesse	pencil holder	40	40

Tell about what you enjoyed in math class today.

I enjoyed estamating the Objects. and I lerned to estamate better.

Suppose someone was trying to estimate how many cubes were in an object. What advice would you give that person?

To look at them and then brake them apart and then estamate the peces and add them all together.

99   *Investigation 1 • Session 1*
Mathematical Thinking at Grade 4

Investigations in Number, Data, and Space®

GRADE

4

Curriculum Units Package

Package Contents

Quantity	Description of Item
1	Implementing the *Investigations in Number, Data, and Space®* Curriculum, Gr. 3–5
1	**Mathematical Thinking at Grade 4** (Introduction)
1	**Arrays and Shares** (Multiplication and Division)
1	**Seeing Solids and Silhouettes** (3-D Geometry)
1	**Landmarks in the Thousands** (The Number System)
1	**Different Shapes, Equal Pieces** (Fractions and Area)
1	**The Shape of the Data (Statistics)**
1	**Money, Miles, and Large Numbers** (Addition and Subtraction)
1	**Changes Over Time (Graphs)**
1	**Packages and Groups** (Multiplication and Division)
1	**Sunken Ships and Grid Patterns*** (2-D Geometry)
1	**Three out of Four Like Spaghetti** (Data and Fractions)

* Incorporates Investigations Software

Pearson Education, Inc.

800-552-2259 ■ Visit our Web site: www.scottforesman.com/investigations

0-7690-0633-7

How Many Hundreds?

What Happens

Pairs count out 100 interlocking cubes and group them to show clearly that the total is 100. Groups of students then estimate how many hundreds there are in the box of cubes their group received. The teacher records the estimates from all of the groups and students figure out how many hundreds there are in the total of all the estimates. After counting their cubes, groups estimate how many hundreds of cubes there are in the class total. Finally, individuals figure out exactly how many cubes there are altogether.

- arranging cubes to show how many
- estimating how many hundreds of objects
- estimating hundreds in a sum of numbers
- keeping track while counting
- adding three-digit numbers
- using calculators

 Ten-Minute Math: Estimation and Number Sense Two or three times during the next week, try the Ten-Minute Math activity Estimation and Number Sense. These activities are designed to be done in any 10 minutes outside of math class, perhaps before lunch or at the end of the day.

In this activity, students estimate an answer to a problem that you show for a brief time. Then they see the problem again and find a more precise solution. Begin with problems like those students are doing in the main activity in these sessions, How Many Hundreds? Present a problem on the chalkboard or overhead. For example:

$$53 + 404 + 248 + 99$$

How many hundreds are in all these numbers together?

Allow students to think about the problem for a short time. Cover up the problem, and ask for students' estimates. Then uncover the problem and continue the discussion.

You might write the four numbers on four cards and ask students how they could rearrange the cards to make it easier to find how many hundreds (for example, $53 + 248$ is approximately 300).

For a full description and variations on this activity, see p. 91.

Materials

- Containers of interlocking cubes
- Student Sheet 2 (1 per student)
- Chart for How Many Cubes? transparency
- Student Sheet 3 (1 per student)
- Student Sheet 4 (1 per student, homework)
- Student Sheet 5 (1 per student, homework)
- One-centimeter graph paper (1–2 per student, homework)
- Calculators (at least 1 per pair)
- Family letter (1 per student)
- Chart paper (optional)
- Overhead projector, transparency pen

Counting Out 100 Cubes

Tell students that today they will be arranging cubes in hundreds so they can find out how many cubes the class has altogether.

Work with a partner to arrange exactly 100 cubes in a way that makes it easy for me to count them. I don't want to have to count the cubes by 1's; I want to be able to count them quickly. What would be a good number to count by—one that would help me count to 100 easily? (5's, 10's, 20's)

Distribute the interlocking cubes so that each group has a box or bucket. Pairs (or individuals, if there are enough cubes) each take 100 cubes and group them in some way to show that they have 100. Some pairs may decide they will each take 50 to arrange, and then put their 50's together.

You may need to help some students get started. Suggest they look around at what their classmates are doing and see if they can find an easier way to count the cubes. As students are working, observe each pair. Move quickly to students who appear not to understand the task. When it is unclear how they are making their 100, ask them questions like these:

How can I tell by counting just *part* of your arrangement how many cubes you have?

What will your 100 (or 50) cubes look like when you finish?

How many cubes have you arranged already?

Students who finish making their 100 early can help others in their group finish. Or, if there are enough cubes, they might count out another 100 and arrange it in a different way from their first 100.

Draw on the board or on chart paper some of the ways students arranged 100 cubes. Label any rectangular arrays with dimensions, as in this 5-by-20 array:

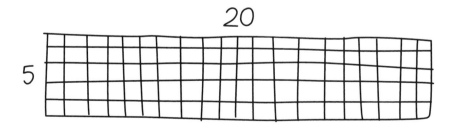

Call attention to the drawings you have made. Ask which students made each of these arrangements, and whether there are any arrangements you missed. Some students may make three-dimensional shapes. Add these to your drawings. Do not try to draw all shapes; those that are difficult to draw may also be difficult to count, and thus don't fit the task you posed. If students would like you to draw their irregular shape, enlist their help in explaining how you should make the drawing.

Writing About 100   Hand out Student Sheet 2, Making Hundreds, to each student. This sheet asks students to draw and write about their work with the cubes:

1. Make a drawing to show how you grouped 100 cubes.

2. How do you know you have exactly 100 cubes?

3. What other ways could you have arranged 100 cubes?

As they finish this writing and drawing task, students leave their hundreds grouping out near them, and group any extra cubes together on the table.

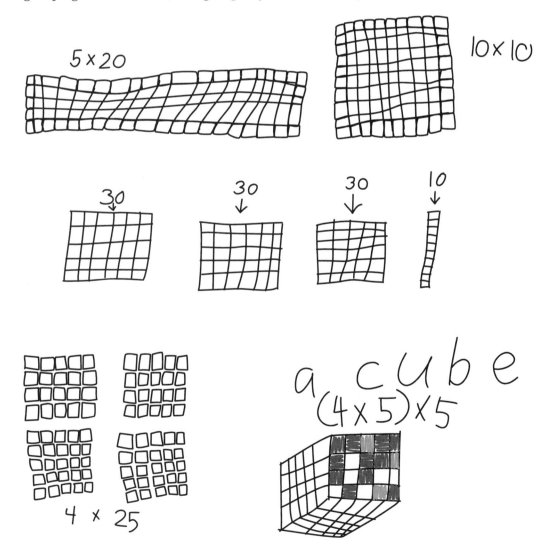

Estimating How Many Cubes Altogether

When students have finished writing about their hundreds, ask them to turn over their sheets. Pose this problem:

We're going to make an estimate of all the cubes we have in the whole class. But to start with, each group must come up with one number as an estimate of how many cubes *they* have.

How many cubes do you think were in your box [bucket] when I handed them out? Think about the hundreds that people in your group have made, and think about the extras. Group the extras into piles that look to be about 100. Don't count them; just estimate groups of 100.

Everyone in your group must agree to one estimate of the number of cubes in your box [bucket].

As students are working, set up the Chart for How Many Cubes? transparency, or set up a chart like the following on the board or chart paper. After 3 or 4 minutes, write the groups' estimates on your chart. (The "counts" will be added in the next activity.)

How Many Cubes?		
Group	*Estimates*	*Counts*
Rebecca's group	350	
Qi Sun's group	315	
Kenyana's group	450	
B.J.'s group	300	
Marci's group	400	

Finding the total of all the estimates will be more challenging if you can get at least two estimates that have partial hundreds in them. If all of the groups give answers in exact hundreds, ask about the extras that didn't group into hundreds.

You said about 400—but would 350 or maybe 450 be a closer estimate than 400?

When your chart includes estimates for every group, ask students to figure out how many hundreds of cubes there are in the total of all the estimates *without writing anything.*

Talk quietly with your partner to figure out the number of hundreds in the total of all the groups' estimates. Figure this out in your head, without writing down the numbers.

Take a poll of the different answers, and tally how many pairs found each answer.

Fourth graders will often count only the hundreds in the hundreds column. They would, for example, get 1700 for the numbers 350, 315, 450, 300, and 400, adding $3 + 3 + 4 + 3 + 4$. Ask one of these students to explain his or her thinking. Then ask a student who gets a higher answer (1800 in this case) to explain that answer. See the **Teacher Note**, Estimating Is Not Rounding (p. 19), for information on ways students may confuse rounding with good estimation strategies.

Note: At this level, some students, when hearing an answer like "seventeen hundred," will think that their answer of "one thousand, seven hundred" is different. Discuss these two ways of saying numbers that are larger than 1000. Students can count by hundreds to 1000 and find how many hundreds are in 1000.

Counting How Many Altogether

As in earlier activities, students now check their estimates by making actual counts. Each group counts all their cubes once, writes down the total, then counts again to check. They can split up the work in any way that makes sense to them and involves everyone in either counting or checking. For discussion later, notice the ways that groups organize the counting. Encourage them to keep the arrangements of hundreds they have and to make more arrangements of exactly 100 so they can easily check their counting.

Students record the total of each count on the back of Student Sheet 2. Collect the totals from the groups as they finish checking, and display them in the Counts column on the How Many Cubes? chart you started in the preceding activity.

Ask representatives of groups to tell the class all the different ways they organized their counting. You might make a list, *Easy Ways to Count Many Things,* and post it for future reference.

Many teachers find this is a good place to end Session 2; students can go on to find the number of hundreds in the whole class in Session 3.

Note: Refer to the suggestions on p. 19 for suitable homework to follow Session 2.

How Many Hundreds?

Display again the How Many Cubes? chart you have been keeping on a transparency, chart paper, or the board. Pose the same question you asked earlier about the group estimates:

About how many hundreds are in all the numbers you counted? How many hundreds of cubes do you think are in all the boxes? Take your time to answer this question. Try to think of an easy way to do it—a way that you could teach someone else.

After you have an answer, talk with your neighbors about it. Change your answer only if they really convince you. If you do change your answer, explain how you got the new answer.

Write all the answers on the board. As before, some students are likely to count only the hundreds in the hundreds place. Others will combine the parts smaller than 100 to make more hundreds.

Ask two or three volunteers to explain how they got their answer. Many students are not accustomed to listening to other students. Use this as a chance for students to practice explaining their thinking and listening to each other.

Here is another chance for you to decide which is the best answer. Listen to how other people in class thought about this. Be ready to change your original answer or to defend your answer more firmly.

Hand out Student Sheet 3, How Many Cubes in the Class? Explain what they are to write in each column.

In the first column of this chart, copy down all the counts from the different groups.

In the second column, write how many hundreds you think are in all the counts. Then write how you figured it out in your head.

We'll do the third column later today.

Circulate to help students with this task. When students have trouble explaining how they got their answer, ask, "How do you know the number of hundreds?" If they can explain how they know, tell them to write that explanation down.

Name *Sean*		Date 9/15
		Student Sheet 3

How Many Cubes in the Class?

Number of cubes in each group	About how many hundreds altogether? Estimate.	Add the numbers to find the exact total.
509 470 417 538	1800 Show or explain how you got your answer. Each group has 400 and some extra. 4 groups is 400 × 4 = 1600 and I gessed 200 extra.	

Once students have completed the first two columns of Student Sheet 3, they work alone to fill in the third column, finding the exact total of the cubes in the class.

What is the total number of the cubes we counted in our class? You can figure this out in any way you want. Write the answer in the third column, where it asks for the exact total. Be sure your work shows how you figured it out.

Finding How Many in All

As students are finishing, suggest that they compare their two answers.

Check to see how close your exact answer is to the answer you estimated. If your answers are very different, estimate again. See if you can find out what went wrong. Ask your partner to help you.

Observing the Students   While students are working, you can learn a lot about their familiarity with numbers and addition by observing what they do. This entire unit is designed to help you assess your students' understanding of mathematical ideas, as illustrated by the sample assessment questions on p. I-20. Do not expect that all beginning fourth graders will be able to add so many large numbers, but use this chance to see what they *can* do. See the **Teacher Note,** Two Powerful Addition Strategies (p. 21), before evaluating their work. As you watch them, consider the following:

■ Do students recognize the numbers they are adding? Does their method of addition take into account the values of the numbers?

■ Do they work from right to left as in a traditional algorithm, or from left to right, adding larger values first? If they work from right to left, can they explain what they are doing? What they are "carrying"?

■ Do they group numbers in a way that makes them easier to add?

■ Can they interpret their answer and compare it to their estimate of the number of hundreds?

■ Do they attempt repairs if their estimate and answer are very different?

Students who finish writing early might put away their group's cubes in stacks of ten. Let students know that from now on, they will store the cubes in stacks of ten to make counting and computing easier.

Adding with the Calculator   When students are ready, distribute calculators for them to check the total number of cubes. If students have written the numbers under one another, they have probably written only one plus sign. Write the problem on the board horizontally (for example, 345 + 267 + 411 + 318 + 429 =), and remind students to put a plus sign in front of each number when adding on the calculator.

You can help students by dictating the numbers and pluses to them, or suggest that students do this for each other. Students can check their answers with their partners and with other students nearby.

If your students are not familiar with using calculators, allow some time for exploring. The **Teacher Note,** Introducing Calculators (p. 20), offers some ideas about how you might do this. At the end of class, put calculators in a place accessible to students, and explain that they are there for anyone to use when they need to. If you have enough calculators for each student to have one, you might let students keep them in their math folders.

A Design with 100 Squares   Send home the family letter or the *Investigations* at Home booklet. After Session 2, give each student a copy of Student Sheet 4, A Design with 100 Squares, and one or two sheets of one-centimeter graph paper. At home, they make a design using exactly 100 squares. On Student Sheet 4, they write, "I know my design is 100 squares because . . ."

How Many?   After Session 3, send home Student Sheet 5, How Many Hundreds? How Many Altogether? The two problems are similar to the one on Student Sheet 3. Students estimate the answers to the nearest 100, then add the numbers to get an exact total.

Estimating Is Not Rounding

Teacher Note

Ways to round numbers, often taught as arbitrary rules out of context, have frequently confused students. One fourth grader demonstrated this use of badly remembered rules in estimating the price of four items at $3.49 each. By the rule of rounding down if less than half a dollar, he rounded the $3.49 down to $3.00, and then he rounded the $3.00 down to $2.00 "because 3 dollars is less than 5 dollars." He then multiplied $4 \times \$2.00$, and concluded that $4 \times \$3.49$ is about $8.00—nowhere near the $14.00 that he would have arrived at by doubling and redoubling three dollars and fifty cents (4×3.50), a result that is only 4 cents away from the exact answer.

Done sensibly, rounding is a useful skill. Consider these numbers of cubes:

423, 352, 475, 360

If we simply round each number to the nearest hundred and add them, we get 1700 cubes. However, if we look at the *value* of the numbers while rounding, we can pair up numbers to get a more accurate estimation. Adding the hundreds, we get 1400; then putting the 52 with the 60, we get just over another 100, making a little more than 1500. Finally, putting the 75 with the 23,

we get just under another hundred, for a total of about 1600. (Actual total: 1610.)

Many times, the sum of rounded numbers makes a good estimate, and rounding is an efficient estimation strategy. However, teaching routine rounding rules discourages students from paying attention to the values of the numbers. Practicing sensible estimating, on the other hand, develops good number sense. Routine rounding rules focus students' attention on the digits furthest to the right, which make up the least part of the numbers. Good estimation strategies teach us to look first at the digits with highest value—those furthest to the left.

If students have not used calculators during mathematics class before, they will at first be distracted by having them. As with any new material, students need time to explore the calculator and find out what it can do. As you circulate, make sure students know how to clear the calculator between problems and how to use the +, −, and = keys. If they are comfortable with the + and − keys, ask them if they can make up a problem using the × or ÷ keys to see if they get the answer they expect. Get a sense of how comfortable students are with the calculator:

- Can they do straightforward computation easily?
- Do they know how to recover if they make a mistake?
- Are they familiar with the symbols on the keyboard?
- Can they read the screen?

When students seem reasonably comfortable, you might talk about using the equals key as a repeat key:

Clear your calculator. Then press the plus key, the number 2, and the equals key. Watch your calculator display while you slowly press the equals key again, and then again. What is happening? [*The calculator is counting by 2's.*] **Stop for a moment. Guess what number the calculator is going to display next.**

Write on the board:

| + | 2 | = | = | = |

You might also write answers below the equal signs as students say them:

| + | 2 | = | = | = |

2   4   6

(Don't write the answers *after* the equal signs, as the statement would be untrue.)

Once students have tried the repeating equals, suggest that they try it with a different number.

Choose another number you would like the calculator to count by. Press the plus key, the number you want the calculator to count by, and then the equals key. Guess what the next number will be before you press the equals key. Then guess the next number and press equals again; guess and press again. Do this until you get over 100.

Two students sharing a calculator can present puzzles to each other. While one student looks away, the other presses +, a number, =, and then presses = a few more times. The other student must guess by pressing only = what number the calculator is counting by (that is, the number the first student chose).

If you use this puzzle to challenge students, choose an appropriate level of difficulty for each student. As puzzle numbers, start with 5, 10, 3, or 4; then, for students who figure these out easily, use 12 or 15.

This task is a good informal diagnostic. Ask yourself:

- Do they understand the task?
- Do they understand that to find out what the calculator is counting by, they must find the difference between two consecutive numbers? Do they see that to decide what number will appear next, they must add on the number being counted by?
- Can they add easily, or can they count on?
- Do they recognize that the sums of ones digits repeat? (For example, 9 + 3 is 1<u>2</u>, so 9 + 63 is 7<u>2</u>.)

If any students have difficulty with the calculator, you may need to work with individuals or schedule other sessions like this one. Rather than teaching the use of the calculator to the entire class at once, work with small groups. You might ask students who know how to use the calculator to work with those who don't.

Two Powerful Addition Strategies

By fourth grade, many students know the traditional algorithms for addition and subtraction ("carrying" and "borrowing"), and some can apply them with ease when they encounter a clear-cut addition or subtraction problem. But many real mathematical problems do not shout out "I am *this* kind of problem! Use *this* operation to solve me!" Students have learned that when they have two numbers, they need to do an operation to get the right result. What they often don't understand is that a major piece of mathematics is figuring out what operation to use and why it works.

Even when students have done the hard work of determining whether their problems involve addition or subtraction, we want to discourage them from automatically applying a correct algorithm. Why? Again and again in classrooms, we have seen students incorrectly apply or incorrectly remember memorized algorithms. As soon as the "correct" algorithm is introduced, students seem to forget their own valuable strategies and understanding of number relationships in favor of a procedure they believe they are expected to use. For example, we have often seen students make the following type of error:

$$\begin{array}{r} {}^{1}17 \\ 17 \\ + \ 17 \\ \hline 42 \end{array}$$

These students are saying to themselves the familiar chant, "put down the 2 and carry the 1." In their focus on the mechanics of this rule, they fail to see that they should instead "put down the 1 and carry the 2."

Most of us who are teaching today learned to add in the manner these students are attempting, starting with the ones, then the tens, then the hundreds, and so forth, moving from right to left and "carrying" from one column to another. While this algorithm is efficient once it is mastered, there are many other ways of adding that are just as efficient, are closer to the ways we naturally think about quantities, connect better

with good estimation strategies, and generally result in fewer errors.

When students rely only on memorized rules and procedures they do not understand, they usually do not estimate or double-check. They make mistakes by rote that make no sense if they think about the numbers. We want students to use strategies that encourage, rather than discourage, them to think about the quantities they are using and what a result is likely to be. We want them to use their knowledge of the number system and important landmarks in that system. We want them to easily break apart and recombine numbers in ways that help them make computation more straightforward and, therefore, less prone to error. Writing addition and subtraction problems horizontally rather than vertically is one way to help students focus on the whole quantities. Varying the way you write problems will help students become more flexible in their addition and subtraction strategies.

The two powerful addition strategies discussed here are familiar to many competent users of mathematics. If you encourage students to come up with their own strategies, some of them will probably invent others. It is critical that every student have more than one way of adding so that an answer obtained using one method can be checked by using another. Anyone can make a mistake while doing routine computation—even with a calculator. What is critical, when accuracy matters, is that you have spent enough time estimating and double-checking to be able to rely on your result.

Left-to-Right Addition: Biggest Quantities First When students develop their own strategies for addition from an early age, they usually move from left to right, starting with the bigger parts of the quantities. For example, when adding 27 + 27, a student might say "20 and 20 is 40, then 7 and 7 is 14, so 40 plus 10 more is 50 and then 4 more makes 54." This strategy is both efficient and accurate. Some people who are extremely good at computation use this strategy as their basic approach to addition, even with large numbers.

One advantage of this approach for students is that when they work with the largest quantities first, it's easier to maintain a good sense of what the final sum should be. Another advantage is that students tend to continue seeing the two 27's as whole quantities, rather than breaking them up into their digits and losing track of the whole. Using the traditional algorithm ("7 and 7 is 14, put down the 4, carry the 1"), students too often see the two 7's, the 4, the 1, and the two 2's as individual digits. They lose their sense of the quantities involved, and if they end up with a nonsensical answer, they do not see it because they believe they "did it the right way."

Rounding to Nearby Landmarks Changing a number to a more familiar one that is easier to compute with is another strategy that students should develop. Multiples of 10 and multiples of 100 are especially useful landmarks for students at this age. For example, in order to add 199 and 149, you might think of the problem as 200 plus 150, find the total of 350, then subtract 2 to compensate for the 2 you added on at the beginning.

To add 27 and 27, as in the previous example, some students might think of the problem as 30 + 30, then subtract 3 and 3 to give them the final result. Of course there are other useful landmarks, too. Another student might think of this problem more easily as 25 + 25 + 2 + 2. There are no rules about which landmarks in the number system are best. It simply depends on whether using nearby landmarks helps you solve the problem.

If you have students who have already memorized the traditional right-to-left algorithm and believe that this is how they are "supposed" to do addition, you will have to work hard to instill some new values—that looking at the whole problem first and estimating the result is critical, that having more than one strategy is a necessary part of doing computation, and that using what you know about the numbers to simplify the problem leads to fewer errors. Students must develop procedures that make sense to them and will therefore be used with greater confidence and accuracy.

Hand out Student Sheet 6, Problems for Close to 100, for students to do individually. Students may want to use Numeral Cards so they can move the numbers around to try different combinations. They can share the sets they have been playing with.

Circulate around the class to be sure students understand what is expected and have a way to begin. Observe their strategies. You may need to ask questions of individuals to understand their thinking.

■ Are they able to add or estimate mentally, or do they need to write down each problem?

■ Do they use a strategy, or do they try combinations almost randomly?

■ If they begin randomly, do they narrow down the choices to reasonable numbers, or do they try combinations indiscriminately, adding pairs of two-digit numbers until they find a sum close to 100?

■ Do students consider the sum of the tens digits when picking two numbers? For example, do they recognize that if they have a number in the twenties, they will need another number in the seventies or the eighties to be close to 100?

Be sure to save the class decks of Numeral Cards you used in this investigation for use in games throughout this unit.

Session 4 Follow-Up

Homework

Playing Close to 100   Send home copies of How to Play Close to 100 and a couple of new Close to 100 Score Sheets with each student. Students also take home the Numeral Cards they have prepared (or a set of Numeral Card sheets to cut out). Students play the game with family members and report the next day on their experiences playing at home.

Advise students to find a safe spot at home to keep their Numeral Cards, because they'll be learning more games in the next couple of weeks to play at home with their cards.

Close to 100 can be played as a solitaire game, but in class, two or three students will play together. Each group will need one deck of Numeral Cards and a Close to 100 Score Sheet for each player.

How to Play

1. For the first round, deal out six cards to each player.

2. Each player uses any four of these cards to make two numbers that, when added, come as close as possible to a total of 100. (See the sample round below.) Wild Cards can be used for any numeral.

3. The player records these two numbers and the total on the Close to 100 Score Sheet. The player's score for each round is the difference between the sum of the two numbers and 100. The four cards used are then placed in a discard pile.

4. For each successive round, four new cards are dealt to each player, so that all players again have six cards.

The game ends after five rounds. If the deck runs out of cards before the game is over, shuffle the discard pile and continue to deal. At the end of five rounds, players total their scores. The lowest score wins.

Sample Game

Round 1
Joey is dealt these cards:

| 5 | 8 | 6 | 9 | 2 | 7 |

Luisa is dealt these cards:

| 9 | 1 | 5 | 5 | 4 | 7 |

Joey makes 58 + 29, and Luisa makes 45 + 57.

Round 2

Joey has 6 and 7 left from round 1, and is dealt

| 3 | 6 | 9 | 2 |

Luisa has 9 and 1 left from round 1, and is dealt

| 8 | 2 | 5 | 0 |

Joey makes 36 + 62, and Luisa makes 98 + 02.

Note: Both Joey and Luisa could have gotten closer to 100 in round 1, and Joey could have gotten closer to 100 in round 2. Can you see how?

The game proceeds, and their final scores look like this:

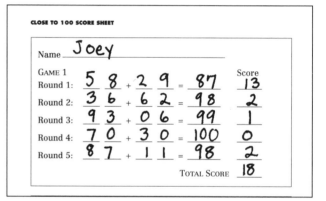

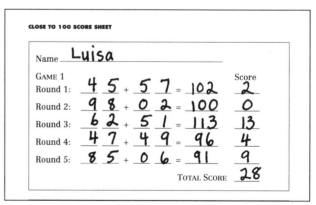

Joey has the lowest score, so he wins.

Scoring Variation:
Negative and Positive Integers

Students should be very comfortable with the basic game before trying this variation. Its use is specifically suggested during Choice Time in Investigation 3.

In this variation, the game is scored with negative and positive integers. If a player's total is above 100, the score is recorded as positive. If the total is below 100, the score is negative. For example, a total of 103 is scored as +3 (3 above 100) while a total of 98 is scored as –2 (2 below 100). If using this variation, Joey's and Luisa's score sheets from the sample game would look like this:

CLOSE TO 100 SCORE SHEET

Name **Joey**

GAME 1

				Score
Round 1:	5 8	+ 2 9	= 87	⁻13
Round 2:	3 6	+ 6 2	= 98	-2
Round 3:	9 3	+ 0 6	= 99	⁻1
Round 4:	7 0	+ 3 0	= 100	0
Round 5:	8 7	+ 1 1	= 98	-2

TOTAL SCORE ⁻18

CLOSE TO 100 SCORE SHEET

Name **Luisa**

GAME 1

				Score
Round 1:	4 5	+ 5 7	= 102	+2
Round 2:	9 8	+ 0 2	= 100	0
Round 3:	6 2	+ 5 1	= 113	+13
Round 4:	4 7	+ 4 9	= 96	-4
Round 5:	8 5	+ 0 6	= 91	-9

TOTAL SCORE +2

The player with the total score closest to zero wins. So, in this case, Luisa wins (her +2 is 2 away from 0, and Joey's –18 is 18 away from zero).

Scoring this way changes the strategy for the game. Even though Joey got many scores very close to 100, he did not compensate for his negative values with some positive ones. Luisa had totals further away from 100, but she balanced off her negative and positive scores more evenly to come out with a total score closer to zero.

Close to 100 is the first of several games students will be playing in this unit. We include games for several reasons. Students enjoy them, so they play them again and again and get lots of practice. Because numbers are generated randomly, responsibility shifts from the teacher to the students. Whether playing collaboratively or as opponents in a game, students are likely to correct each other, which takes from the teacher the onerous task of telling students they have made a mistake. Students will also learn strategies from one another.

Because you are freed from teaching and checking work, you have an opportunity to observe. You can spend time with students whose mathematical thinking you would like to know more about. Ask questions about students' strategies. Play collaboratively with a student if that feels comfortable. Stop a group, or possibly the whole class, to share an interesting hand that you observed students grappling with. Collect ideas and strategies to share with the class. Your students have much to teach you about difficulties and strategies.

Strategies that work in mathematical games involve thinking about the mathematics involved. In Close to 100, one good strategy is to try to make 9 (90) with the tens digits and 10 with the ones digits. Students who think this way are making use of the concept of place value. For some examples of students' strategies, see the **Dialogue Box,** Strategies for Close to 100 (p. 31).

Some students may not be accustomed to thinking about strategies. Instead, they might pick digits randomly to make numbers and add them with paper and pencil as they have been taught. When you talk with these students, encourage them to estimate mentally before they do written addition.

To: Classroom, Special Education & Title 1 teachers
From: Heather Dropps, Math Coach
Date: September 14, 2005
Re In-Service Workshop.

On September 21st, 12:00 – 2:30 there will be a Math Investigations Workshop.
Staff should please bring the following Curriculum Unit Teachers Guide:

Grade K – "Patterns Trains & Hopscotch
Grade 1 – "Building Number Sense"
Grade 2 – "Coins, Coupons & Combinations"
Grade 3 – "Things that Come in Groups"
Grade 4 – "Arrays & Shares"
Grade 5 – "Picturing Polygons"

Strategies for Close to 100

During this discussion of the strategies that students were using for making numbers in the Close to 100 game, only a few students spoke up. The teacher posted the students' ideas on chart paper, planning to add to them another day.

Think about how you chose numbers to try. Do you have any advice for your friends on how to get close to 100? Tell me something that *you* look for when you try to get close to 100.

Rikki: I first try to find two numbers that equal 10, like 7 and 3, or 6 and 4.

For the tens digits?

Rikki: Yes.

Alex: I'd look for 9, and put another number with it, and it might come close to 100.

When you started with 9, was it on the tens side or the ones side?

Alex: On the tens side.

So you started with 90? What else did you look at?

Alex: I tried to get 10 on the ones side.

Emilio: I tried to find a high number and then a little one, like ninety-something, and then if I had a zero I made something like zero five (05).

So you tried to make something in the nineties and a single-digit number.

Teresa: I tried to find a way to get 9, and then I tried to find a way to get 10.

So you looked for two numbers that would make 90 and two that would make 10?

Teresa: Yeah, I make 9 with the first two numbers [meaning the tens digits; for example, 70 + 20, or 80 + 10], and 10 with the second two. I don't want to make 10 with the first numbers [70 + 30], because then I'd need two zeros for the last ones—and you hardly ever have two zeros. So I try to get numbers that make 9 instead of 10, and then I try to make 10 in the ones place.

Most of you had a strategy, a plan for how to put the numbers down. You weren't just trying things. Do you have any other thoughts? Think about what you were doing.

Alex: My way that I said is like Teresa's. Or if I couldn't make a 9, I tried for an 8 with the first numbers so I worked with 80 and 20.

Teresa: You can't get 100 that way 'cause you can't make 10 and 10.

Alex: But I can get almost there with 9's or 8's.

How Many Dollars?

What Happens

Sessions 1 and 2: How Much Money?   Each pair sorts a package of play money and counts how much money they have, keeping track on paper as they count. Then pairs report to the whole class on how they organized their counting, before exchanging bags of money to count again. They explore different ways to count coins—mentally, with a calculator, or with paper and pencil—to discover a "best" way. Finally, students play a game that involves finding two groups of coins that total one dollar.

Sessions 3 and 4: Number Sense and Coins
Students learn a new game, picking out amounts of money in real coins by feel—without looking. Then they are introduced to Choice Time, in which they choose from among three games—the new one, and games introduced in the previous sessions—while keeping track of how they spend their time.

Mathematical Emphasis

■ Grouping coins for more efficient counting
■ Recognizing values of U.S. coins
■ Recognizing the decimal point on the calculator

What to Plan Ahead of Time

Materials

- Play money—paper $1 and $5 bills, and plastic pennies, nickels, dimes, quarters, and a few half dollars (Sessions 1–4)
- Resealable plastic bags for play money: 1 per pair (Sessions 1–4)
- Scissors (Sessions 1–2)
- Calculators (Sessions 1–4)
- Paper bags (bags must be opaque) of real coins, holding 2 quarters, 3 dimes, 3 nickels, and 5 pennies to make exactly $1: several for Choice Time (Sessions 3–4)
- Numeral Cards: all available decks for Choice Time (Sessions 3–4)

Other Preparation

- Duplicate student sheets and teaching resources (located at the end of this unit) in the following quantities. If you have Student Activity Booklets, copy only the item marked with an asterisk.

For Sessions 1–2

Student Sheet 7, Ways to Count Money (p. 108): 1 per student

Coin Cards (p. 109): 1 set per 2–3 students (class), 1 set per student (homework)

How to Play Collecting Dollars (p. 113): 1 per student (homework)

Coin Value Strips* (p. 139): copy and cut apart to provide each student with a desktop strip

For Sessions 3–4

How to Play Hidden Coins (p. 114): 1 per student (homework)

Close to 100 Score Sheet (p. 135): 1 per student

Choice List (p. 140): 1 per student (optional)

- Divide your play money to make a bag for every pair. Rather than counting out, distribute the money by random handfuls so there are similar, but not equal, amounts in each bag. Ideally, there would be at least $5 per bag, but less will work if you don't have enough coins. Label bags with numbers or letters to identify them. (Sessions 1–2)
- Decide on your rules for Choice Time and how students will record what activities they have done. See the **Teacher Note,** About Choice Time (p. 44), for guidance. (Sessions 3–4)

How Much Money?

Materials

- Bags of play money (1 per pair)
- Coin Value Strips (1 per student)
- Student Sheet 7 (1 per student)
- Coin Cards sheets (1 set per 2–3 students, class; 1 set per student, homework)
- Scissors
- How to Play Collecting Dollars (1 per student, homework)
- Calculators

What Happens

Each pair sorts a package of play money and counts how much money they have, keeping track on paper as they count. Then pairs report to the whole class on how they organized their counting, before exchanging bags of money to count again. They explore different ways to count coins—mentally, with a calculator, or with paper and pencil—to discover a "best" way. Finally, students play a game that involves finding two groups of coins that total one dollar. Their work focuses on:

- recognizing the value of U.S. coins
- organizing and keeping track of counting money
- finding amounts in coins with a total of one or more dollars

 Ten-Minute Math: Estimation and Number Sense As you proceed through Investigation 2, continue to do the Estimation and Number Sense activity in any 10 minutes outside of math class. Present problems related to estimating amounts of money. For example:

$$25¢ + 52¢ + 79¢ \qquad 8 \times 39¢ \qquad \$10.00 - \$5.75$$

Some classes have enjoyed estimating totals on cash register receipts.

Milk	2.39
Carrots	.79
Chicken	4.43
Rice	2.69

Suppose I'm in the grocery store and I have only ten dollars. Do I have enough money to pay for these items? How many dollars do I need?

Students may bring in short receipts to challenge the class to find how many dollars are needed.

Students do not write or use a calculator while estimating the answers to problems that you display for 15 to 20 seconds. Encourage all kinds of estimation statements and strategies.

For a full description and variations on this activity, see p. 91.

Counting Money

Hand out a bag of play money to each pair. Distribute the Coin Value Strips for students to tape to their desks for reference. Students work together in pairs, counting the play money in their bag. They will need paper to keep track of their counting. Point out that you are not providing a special sheet for recording their work, but that they will need to keep track carefully enough so they can explain their counting to themselves and to others.

As you observe them working, pick two or three pairs to report how they are organizing their counting. Stop the class briefly for these reports. Caution students not to say their total, because another group will be counting the same bag.

When students are finished, they write the total value on their paper, with the letter or number that identifies the bag they counted. Pairs then trade bags of money with another pair who is finished.

Students may be tempted to hurry to count one bag after another; discourage this. If they have extra time while waiting for another pair to trade with, ask them to record their counting in more detail or to check their total by counting in a different way.

To conclude this activity, pairs who exchanged bags get together to compare results. Whether they agree or differ about the amounts, they should show each other how they kept track of their counting. They may work together to count the money again if they want.

Adding Coin Values

Student Sheet 7, Ways to Count Money, lists the contents of three handfuls of coins. Students are asked to find the total value of each. Many fourth grade students, when they see such problems on paper, don't realize that they can add coin values mentally. Instead, they write the values and add them with paper and pencil. This activity is designed to encourage them to use the more efficient and practical method of adding mentally to count coins.

Demonstrate to the whole class the process of adding coins mentally. List several coins on the board:

> 1 quarter
> 2 dimes
> 1 nickel
> 2 pennies

How much money do you think this is altogether? We're going to count it mentally. [*Point to "1 quarter."*] **How much is the quarter worth? Whisper the value.** [*Pause for the answer. Write $ .25 on the chalkboard. Then point to "2 dimes."*] **Add the dimes to the quarter. How much is 25 cents plus 10 cents?** [*Pause.*] **Plus another 10 cents?** [*Pause. When students agree, put a line through the $ .25 and write $ .45.*]

Continue adding one kind of coin at a time, with students giving the accumulated total and you writing it in decimal form (this is to prepare for calculator work). Then do it again, this time counting the same coins in a different order: the nickel, quarter, pennies, and then the dimes. Doing the nickel first will raise the issue of how to write 5 cents as a decimal.

How can I write 5 cents using a decimal point?

If students suggest "point 5," explain that cents are always written with two numbers, and write $ .50 on the board.

But that is the way to write 50 cents. How could we write 5 cents?

Establish that amounts below 10 cents, written with a decimal point, have a zero between the point and the number.

After you have counted the coins on the board in a different order, ask students which order seemed easiest. Tell them that many people always start with the coins with the highest values, and add each lower amount in order. Other people group coins to make easy numbers to work with—such as 50 cents or 1 dollar. So, for this group of coins, they might group the two dimes and a nickel to make 25 cents, which combines with the other quarter to make 50 cents. Then all they have to add is the two pennies.

Counting Money in Other Ways   Invite students to try the same problem in another way. Have play money and calculators available.

How could we find the total value of these coins in another way? What tools might we use? I'd like you to work in pairs to do this problem another way. You may use the plastic coins, or a calculator, or paper and pencil.

As students work, move quickly to any pairs you think might have difficulty.

Fourth graders who choose the calculator are likely to find this problem difficult if they use decimal points. The problem requires pressing 24 individual keys: .25 + .10 + .10 + .05 + .01 + .01 = . If students want to try this, suggest that one student call out what keys to press while the other does the entering. Some will discover that it's much easier to treat all the values as whole numbers of cents, and easier yet to group values, perhaps entering only 25 + 20 + 7 = . Let students struggle a bit to discover that using a calculator efficiently takes some planning.

As you circulate, you might stop from time to time to have pairs share with the class the way they are computing the total. Look, for example, for pairs who write the coin values in a vertical column and add them; for students who use play coins and add mentally as they touch each coin; and for pairs who are using the calculator in an efficient way.

Deciding on the "Best" Way   When pairs have all completed the problem in another way, hand out Student Sheet 7, Ways to Count Money, one to each student. Emphasize that they are to find the total value of each group of coins *in more than one way*. Explain the reason for this:

When you've done these three problems, I want you to decide which is the best way to count coins. And to make a good decision, you need to try several different ways.

Pairs of students may consult with one another to compare answers and methods, but strongly discourage erasing and writing the answer another student got. Insist that students who have differing answers take time to show each other, step by step, how they did the problem. Together they can agree on an answer.

As you observe students working, ask them to explain what they are doing. Encourage those who write out every problem first to try some mental addition, perhaps writing only partial totals to help them keep track.

❖ **Tip for the Linguistically Diverse Classroom** Refer students to their desktop Coin Value Strips for help in identifying the coins listed on Student Sheet 7. Students may answer the advice question orally.

Follow up with a brief discussion of students' "advice to a friend" on what they feel is the best way to count coins. Ask them to give reasons for their choice.

Activity

**Teacher
Checkpoint**

The Collecting
Dollars Game

Becoming Familiar with the Coin Cards In preparation for playing the Collecting Dollars game, distribute scissors and a set of Coin Card sheets to each pair or group of three who will play together.

First cut apart the 32 Coin Cards. When this is done, work with your partners to make pairs of cards that add to one dollar.

This pairing task may be quite challenging at first. Make available the play coins for students to use as they need to.

Once students have made 16 pairs, they may shuffle the cards and try again. As there are two cards with each quantity, there is more than one way to make each pair.

If students have difficulty recognizing the coins, suggest that they write lightly (so it can be erased later) the value of each coin near its picture— 25¢ near the quarters, 10¢ near the dimes, and so forth.

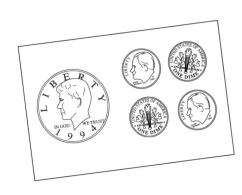

While students are sorting the Coin Cards into pairs that make one dollar, and later when they are playing the game, observe and ask questions:

- Can students recognize the coins and their values?
- Can students count by 5's, 10's, and 25's to determine the totals?
- Can students determine how much more money is needed to make one dollar?
- Can students recognize groupings of three, four, and five coins without counting (for example, do they know that five pennies is 5 cents without counting each penny)?

Introducing the Game   As students seem ready, teach them how to play Collecting Dollars.

Players deal out eight Coin Cards, face up in the center, and place the remaining pack face down. They then take turns making pairs that equal one dollar. At the end of a turn, the player turns up new cards from the face down pack to replace any pairs made, so there are always eight cards available at the beginning of the next player's turn.

If a player finds that no pair among the eight cards makes one dollar, and all players agree, the player may shuffle all eight back into the pack, deal out eight new cards, and take another turn. The game ends when all the cards have been paired.

Students can continue playing until the end of the class session. They may prefer to play cooperatively, finding pairs but not keeping track of turns or of who found each pair.

Making Coin Card Decks for Use at Home   If there is a possibility that your students may not have scissors at home, make time for them to cut out their own sets of Coin Cards. Don't let them take home the Coin Cards they made for class use, as students will need them again for the Choice Time activities in Sessions 3 and 4.

Sessions 1 and 2 Follow-Up

Playing Collecting Dollars   Hand out copies of How to Play Collecting Dollars along with sets of Coin Card sheets (or cards prepared at school). Students can play the game at home, by themselves or with a family member. Tell them to practice so they will be better at finding pairs when they play again in school.

 **Homework**

Number Sense and Coins

Materials

- Choice List (1 per student, optional)
- $1 of real coins in opaque paper bags (several)
- Numeral Cards (all class sets)
- Close to 100 Score Sheet (1 per student)
- Coin Cards (from previous session)
- Bags of play money
- How to Play Hidden Coins (1 per student, homework)
- Calculators (optional)

What Happens

Students learn a new game, picking out amounts of money in real coins by feel—without looking. Then they are introduced to Choice Time, in which they choose from among three games—the new one, and games introduced in the previous sessions—while keeping track of how they spend their time. Their work focuses on:

- organizing themselves to play games
- making numbers whose sum is close to 100
- adding coins to make dollars

Activity

The Hidden Coins Game

Spend some class time introducing the Hidden Coins game that will be one of the options during Choice Time throughout Sessions 3 and 4. Explain and demonstrate the game as follows:

Empty the real coins from one of the prepared bags onto a table or the overhead, and count the money with the students ($1.00). Use the mental counting strategies they worked with earlier.

Return the coins to the bag. Ask a volunteer to name any amount of money less than one dollar. Suggest that you'd like to start with an easy task, perhaps an amount that can be made with only two coins. Then, talking about what you are doing but not looking into the bag, take the coins for that amount from the bag. Ask students after each choice whether the coin will help you reach the target. If you select a coin that you cannot use (for example, one that makes your total exceed the target), put it back in the bag. Ask students to double-check that your selected coins total the amount named.

Suggest that when students play together, they might begin by trying to remove just one particular coin at a time. When they are able to do this easily, they can start naming amounts that require two, three, or more coins.

Since this is real money, set up a structure with the students to be sure a full dollar is returned to each bag after each turn, and that all of the bags are returned to you at the end of class.

Choice Time: Playing Math Games

Introducing Choice Time The remainder of this session and the next will be Choice Time, and students choose from the new game and two estimation and addition games they have played in earlier sessions. These activities are designed to give students more experience with number sense and coins.

Choice Time is a format that recurs throughout the *Investigations* units, so this is a good time for students to become familiar with its structure. The **Teacher Note**, About Choice Time (p. 44), will give you ideas about how to set up and organize the choices, and how students might use a Choice List to keep track of their work.

Introduce your rules and students' responsibilities for Choice Time. Students should try each choice sometime during the two sessions. You might encourage them to play the games with several different classmates.

How to Set Up the Choices If you set up the choices at centers, show students what they will find at each center. If students will be playing the games at their desks, make sure they know where they will find the materials they need.

> Choice 1: Hidden Coins—paper bags, each holding $1 in real coins (2 quarters, 3 dimes, 3 nickels, 5 pennies)
>
> Choice 2: Close to 100—Numeral Cards, Close to 100 Score Sheets, pencils, calculators (optional)
>
> Choice 3: Collecting Dollars—Coin Cards, plastic coins (for those who need them)

Introduce the Three Choices Briefly remind students how to play the games they learned earlier. Close to 100 and Collecting Dollars have variations you can suggest to add interest. Rather than presenting these to the whole group, teach the variations to small groups as you observe they are ready for a different challenge.

Once students have decided on their first choice, they may begin. Some may need your help in finding a partner or in deciding where to start.

Choice 1: Hidden Coins

Students play this game in pairs, and take turns trying to pick coins out of the bag by feel, without looking. If you have a limited number of bags, be sure students take turns so that everyone gets a chance to play the game. Players begin by picking one coin at a time. When they are comfortable identifying single coins, they move on to amounts of money made with two or more coins.

Choice 2: Close to 100

Students play this game in pairs or threes. Players are dealt six cards each and work simultaneously, each with their own six cards, to make two two-digit numbers (or a one-digit number with a zero, such as 07) that have a sum as close as possible to 100. Their score for that round is the distance of the sum from 100. Scores from five rounds are added, and the player with the lowest total is the winner.

Scoring Variation: Negative and Positive Integers   As appropriate, introduce the scoring variation described in the **Teacher Note,** Directions for Close to 100 (p. 28). In this version, a player's score is positive if the sum is over 100, negative if the sum is under 100. Thus, 103 scores +3; 97 scores –3. The new object is to get a score as close to zero as possible. These scoring rules change players' strategy—now they must try to balance scores over 100 with scores under 100. Don't expect students to understand right away how the scoring affects strategy. Tell them to play a practice game so they can see how the scoring works.

Introduce the new scoring to six or eight students at a time. Students who understand the idea of positive and negative changes can use the calculator to help them total their score. Once you have introduced the variation, students can split into pairs or groups of three to play it. Students who have learned the new version can teach other students as they are ready.

Choice 3: Collecting Dollars

The object of Collecting Dollars is to find pairs of Coin Cards showing coins with a total value of one dollar. Students may simply work independently or with a partner to find all the pairs in the deck, or they may play a game; see p. 39 to review the rules. If students have marked the coins on the cards with amounts, they can challenge themselves now by erasing the amounts and determining values from the coin images alone.

Variation: Whole Dollars   If students become so accustomed to the 32 Coin Cards that they memorize the pairs, you can introduce an alternative form of the game: Players make combinations of two or more cards that equal *other* whole numbers of dollars. For example, a player could take three cards with 50¢, 70¢, and 80¢ for a total of $2.00. Players may decide to score either by number of dollars collected or by number of cards collected.

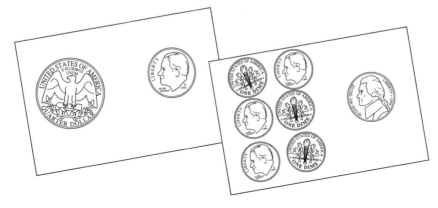

Observing the Students

As students work, plan to meet with pairs or small groups who need help on the activities, or with those you have not had much chance to observe. Encourage students to get help from other groups while you are busy. As needed, enlist the help of students who understand specific games to act as resources for their peers who have questions.

Once you are settled into playing, I will be visiting with different groups to learn about your thinking. I might teach some new ways to play the games. If you have a question or need some help, ask another group who knows that game for help or for permission to quietly watch them play.

As you circulate among the groups and observe students, you might look for the following:

- How are students making decisions about how to organize their time and activity?
- Are there too many (or not enough) activities going on at once?
- Are students keeping track of the choices they have completed?
- Are students able to handle the mathematics well enough to develop strategies in games?
- What strategies are students using?
- Which game gives students the most difficulty? What mathematics in that game needs more discussion and practice?

Save 5 or 10 minutes at the end of Session 3 to have a discussion about the games. Ask students to share what they have particularly enjoyed, and what has challenged them.

As a whole class, do some planning for the Session 4 Choice Time. Would students like help in learning how to play certain games better? Who will volunteer to teach or to play with students who are less familiar with a game or with a variation? See the **Teacher Note,** Collaborating with the Authors (p. 45), for more about your role and your students' roles in finding the right level of challenge for each of them.

You may decide to make adjustments in the number of choices offered in Session 4, to pair students who you think will benefit from working together, or to spend some time on work you feel is needed, perhaps sharing strategies for doing some of the mathematics in the games.

Organizing Folders The end of Session 4 marks the end of Investigation 2. This would be a good time for students to bring their mathematics folders or notebooks up to date, checking that they have completed and saved appropriate samples of their work to this point.

Sessions 3 and 4 Follow-Up

 **Homework**

Playing Hidden Coins   Send home the game directions, How to Play Hidden Coins. Students enjoy challenging family members—especially adults—to try their skill at picking out coins without looking. Ask them to report back to class on how successful these new players were, and if there are some coins that seem to confuse people more than others.

Teacher Note

About Choice Time

Choice Time is an opportunity for students to work on a variety of activities that focus on similar content. The activities are not sequential; as students move among them, they continually revisit important concepts and ideas, such as grouping in tens and hundreds to estimate or add. Some activities require that students work in pairs, while others can be done alone or with a partner. Many involve some type of recording or writing; these records will help you assess students' growth.

Students can use the Choice List (p. 140) to keep track of their work. As students finish a choice, they write it on their list and attach any written work they have done. Some teachers list the choices for each day on the board or overhead and have students copy the list at the beginning of class. Students are then responsible for checking off completed activities. You may also want to make the choices available at other times during the day.

In any classroom, there will be a range of how much work students can complete. Each choice may also provide extensions and additional problems for students to do once they have completed their required work. Choice Time encourages students to return to choices they have

done before, doing another page of problems or playing a game again. Students benefit from such repeated experiences.

If you and your students have not used a structure like Choice Time before, establish clear guidelines when you introduce it. Discuss what students' responsibilities are during Choice Time. The following are examples:

- Try every choice at some time.
- Be productively engaged during Choice Time.
- Work with a partner or alone.
- Keep track, on paper, of the choices you have worked on.
- Keep all your work in your math folder or notebook.
- Ask questions of other students when you don't understand or feel stuck.

Some teachers establish the rule "Ask two other students before me," requiring students to check with two peers before coming to the teacher for help. You may need to try organizing Choice Times in a couple of different ways and decide from experience which approach best matches the needs of your students.

Collaborating with the Authors

Every unit in this curriculum is a guide, not a prescription or recipe. We tested these activities in many different classrooms, representing a range of students and teachers, and revised our ideas constantly as we learned from students and teachers. Each time we tried a curriculum unit in a classroom, no matter how many times it had been tried and revised before, we discovered new ideas we wanted to add and changes we wanted to make. This process could be endless, but at some point we had to decide that the curriculum worked well enough with a wide range of students.

We cannot anticipate the needs and strengths of your particular students this particular year. We believe that the only way for good curriculum to be used well is for teachers to participate in continually modifying it. Your role is to observe and listen carefully to your students, to try to understand how they are thinking, and to make decisions, based on your observations, about what they need next. Modifications to the curriculum that you will need to consider throughout the year include:

- changing the numbers in a problem to make the problem more accessible or more challenging for particular students

- repeating activities with which students need more experience

- engaging students in extensions and further questions

- rearranging pairs or small groups so that students learn from a variety of their peers

Your students can help you set the right pace and level of challenge. We have found that, when given choices of activities and problems, students often do choose the right level of difficulty for themselves. You can encourage students to do this by urging them to find problems that are "not too easy, not too hard, but just right." Help students understand that doing mathematics does not mean knowing the answer right away. Tell students often, "A good problem for you is a problem that makes you think hard and work hard—and you might have to try more than one way of doing it before you figure it out."

The *Investigations* curriculum provides more than enough material for any student. Suggestions are included for extending activities, and some curriculum units contain optional sessions (called Excursions) to provide more opportunities to explore the big mathematical ideas of that unit. Many teachers also have favorite activities that they integrate into this curriculum. We encourage you to be an active partner with us in creating the way this curriculum can work best for your students.

Using Number Patterns

What Happens

Sessions 1 and 2: The 300 Chart   Students enter numbers on a partially filled 300 chart, looking for patterns. They use their completed charts to compute differences. They then play a bingo game that involves adding and subtracting multiples of ten on a 101 to 200 chart.

Session 3: Related Problem Sets   Students work on closely linked groups of problems, called Related Problem Sets, involving addition, subtraction, and money. They meet in groups to assess their own work, and students individually write down something they learned from the group.

Sessions 4 and 5: Addition and Subtraction Strategies   During two sessions of Choice Time, students choose from Related Problem Sets, 101 to 200 Bingo, and other games learned earlier in this unit. As an assessment task, they do number and money problems based on the games.

Mathematical Emphasis

■ Using known answers to find others
■ Subtracting on a 300 chart and with a calculator
■ Adding and subtracting multiples of ten

What to Plan Ahead of Time

Materials

- Calculators: at least 1 per pair (Sessions 1–2)
- Scissors, tape (Sessions 1–2)
- Numeral Cards from previous investigations: 1 deck per pair (Sessions 1–2, 4–5)
- Game markers (such as cubes, square tiles, counting chips): 2 per student (Sessions 1–2)
- Colored pencils, crayons, or markers (Sessions 1–2, 4–5)
- Buckets or boxes of interlocking cubes (Session 3)
- *Alexander, Who Used to Be Rich Last Sunday,* by Judith Viorst (Macmillan, 1989) (Sessions 4–5, optional)
- Overhead projector (Sessions 1–2)
- Coin cards and plastic coins from previous investigation

Other Preparation

- Duplicate student sheets and teaching resources (located at the end of this unit) in the following quantities. If you have Student Activity Booklets, copy only the items marked with an asterisk.

  For Sessions 1–2

  Student Sheet 8, 300 Chart (p. 115): 1 per student

  How to Play 101 to 200 Bingo (p. 126): 1 per student, homework

101 to 200 Bingo Board (p. 127): 4 per pair (class), 2 per student (homework)

Tens Cards (p. 128): 1 set per pair (class), 1 transparency* of each (cut apart), 1 set per student (homework)

Numeral Cards* (p. 136): 1 transparency of each (cut apart)

For Session 3

Student Sheet 9, Related Problem Sets (p. 118): 1 packet per student. Staple together the pages to make a six-page Related Problems Sets booklet for each student. For second-language learners, use coin stamps or refer them to their Coin Value Strips to identify the coins on pages 4–6 of these booklets.

For Sessions 4–5

Student Sheet 10, Numbers and Money (p. 124): 1 per student

101 to 200 Bingo Board (p. 127): 1–2 per student

Close to 100 Score Sheets (p. 135): 1–2 per student (optional)

Choice List (p. 140): 1 per student (optional)

The 300 Chart

Materials

- Student Sheet 8 (1 per student)
- Scissors, tape
- Game markers (2 per student)
- Calculators (at least 1 per pair)
- 101 to 200 Bingo Board (4 per pair, class; 2 per student, homework)
- Numeral Cards (class sets from earlier sessions)
- Tens Cards (1 set per pair, class; 1 set per student, homework)
- Colored pencils, crayons, or markers
- Transparencies of Numeral Cards and Tens Cards (cut apart)
- Overhead projector
- How to Play 101 to 200 Bingo (1 per student, homework)

What Happens

Students enter numbers on a partially filled 300 chart, looking for patterns. They use their completed charts to compute differences. They then play a bingo game that involves adding and subtracting multiples of 10 on a 101 to 200 chart. Their work focuses on:

- writing numbers from 1 to 300
- counting by 10's and multiples of 10
- finding differences between numbers
- using a calculator to subtract

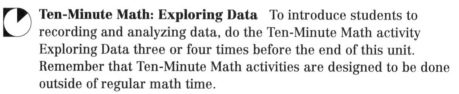 **Ten-Minute Math: Exploring Data**   To introduce students to recording and analyzing data, do the Ten-Minute Math activity Exploring Data three or four times before the end of this unit. Remember that Ten-Minute Math activities are designed to be done outside of regular math time.

To start the activity, you or the students choose a question about themselves. Because this is a 10-minute activity, the data they collect must be something they already know or can observe easily in the class. For example:

How did you get to school?

How many hours of TV did you watch yesterday?

How are your shoes fastened: laces, Velcro, buckle, no fastener?

Are you wearing red in any of your clothing? purple? yellow?

❖ **Tip for the Linguistically Diverse Classroom**   Selecting data questions that can be demonstrated by modeling or can be easily drawn with rebuses will help ensure that all students understand the activity.

As students supply their individual pieces of data, quickly graph the data using a line plot, list, table, or bar graph. Ask students to describe what they see in the data, generate new questions, and, if appropriate, make predictions about how the data might be different if they were to ask the same question another time.

Students will be doing more extended investigations of data in other grade 4 units *(The Shape of the Data,* and *Three out of Four Like Spaghetti)*, but will benefit from the quick, repeated practice that this Ten-Minute Math activity offers.

For a full description of this activity, see p. 93.

Filling in the 300 Chart

Distribute the three pages of Student Sheet 8 to each student (unstapled). Students trim off the bottom of the first two sheets and tape all three sheets together to make a long, continuous 300 chart. (Help them find a way to fold the three parts together so the chart can be put away neatly.)

Once students have their charts put together, write on the board two or three missing numbers from each page of the chart—for example, 34, 129, 67, 222, 185, 291, 281, 12, 102. Students write in these numbers where they belong. Then each student in turn suggests another number for everyone to write in. After everyone has called for one number, students continue filling their charts, using any patterns they see to complete rows and columns.

Observing the Students   While students are working, watch how they handle the 300 chart:

■ Are students using patterns to fill in the numbers?

■ Do they recognize counting by 10's on the columns?

■ Are they able to move across 100 and 200 without difficulty?

How Many Steps?

Introduce this activity to pairs as they finish filling in their charts. Pairs will need their completed 300 charts, two game markers each, and calculators to find differences between numbers.

To start, each student names a number. (As you are introducing the task, pick two numbers reasonably near each other, such as 132 and 146.) Both students place markers on both numbers on their 300 charts and figure out the distance from one number to the other.

Watch for students who include both numbers in the count ("132, 133, 134, 135, 136—that's five") instead of counting steps ("132 to 133, that's 1, 134, 135, 136—that's four").

When they have both decided on the difference between the numbers, one student uses the calculator to compute the difference by subtracting one number from the other. If students subtract the larger number from the smaller, the calculator will show a negative answer. If this occurs, suggest that they subtract the smaller number from the larger and compare that result with the first.

How are the two answers different? How are they the same? Why is that?

Observe to see how students compute differences. Encourage them to count by 10's or to figure out multiples of 10. Look for efficient ways students compute using the 300 chart; for example, to find the distance from 134 to 182, they might "add 50 to get 184, subtract 2, that's 48."

Once or twice, stop the class to do a problem together and share ways of figuring it out. As students explain their approaches, write down the steps they follow. You might use this idea to start a classroom list of ways to find differences on the 300 chart.

Activity

Counting by 10's

In preparation for the game 101 to 200 Bingo, give students practice, through unison counting, adding on 10's to numbers that are not multiples of ten.

We're going to do some counting together by 10's. We'll begin with a way that I _know_ you can count. I want you to count together in a whisper. Start with 10, and count by 10's: 10, 20 ...

Count with students, but don't get ahead of them. All will likely do fine until after 100, when some may say 200. Stop there, and ask students to take a moment to think and to talk quietly with each other about what number follows 100 when counting by 10's, and what number comes after that. Write 80, 90, 100 on the board. When students agree, write 110, then continue to count on in unison to over 200.

Then pose a harder problem:

This time, we'll start with 3 and count on by 10's. Take a moment to decide what the next number is, and the number after that. [_Pause._] OK, let's start with 3 and add on 10's. Whisper the numbers: 3, 13 ...

This time, write the numbers on the board as students say them. When you have your back turned to the class, stop saying the numbers yourself, and listen to the students. When you hear several different numbers for the same step, write them all on the board, and ask students to think again about which one comes next. Continue your count beyond 100.

If students are doing well, pose more difficult problems like these:

Start at 84, and count on by 10's.

Start at 394, and count on by 10's.

Start at 83, and count backward by 10's.

Start at 127, and count backward by 10's.

Start at 20 (or 23 or 30), and count on by 20's.

Playing 101 to 200 Bingo

Before you begin this activity, students will need to prepare the sets of Tens Cards, which provide positive and negative multiples of ten from 10 to 70. Hand out the sheets of Tens Cards and scissors. Each pair cuts apart one set for their use in the game, making a deck of 40 cards (including 6 Wild Cards). If you think students will not have scissors at home, they could also cut apart sets for home use at this time.

Everytime they play the game, each pair will need a single copy of the 101 to 200 Bingo Board; a set of Numeral Cards (from earlier sessions); a deck of Tens Cards; and colored pencils, crayons, or markers.

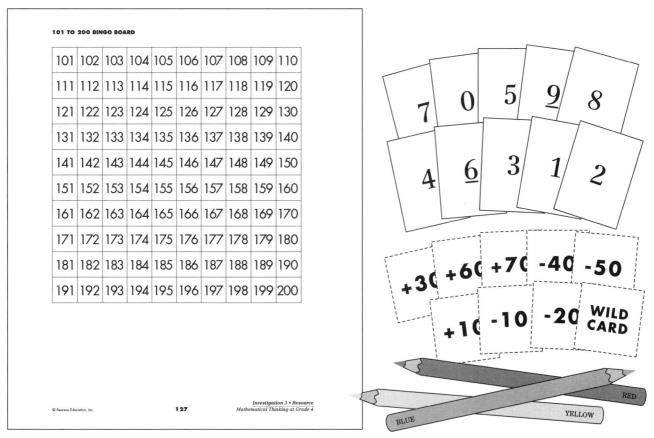

101 TO 200 BINGO BOARD

101	102	103	104	105	106	107	108	109	110
111	112	113	114	115	116	117	118	119	120
121	122	123	124	125	126	127	128	129	130
131	132	133	134	135	136	137	138	139	140
141	142	143	144	145	146	147	148	149	150
151	152	153	154	155	156	157	158	159	160
161	162	163	164	165	166	167	168	169	170
171	172	173	174	175	176	177	178	179	180
181	182	183	184	185	186	187	188	189	190
191	192	193	194	195	196	197	198	199	200

© Pearson Education, Inc.   **127**   *Investigation 3 • Resource*
Mathematical Thinking at Grade 4

Introduce this game to the whole class by modeling it on the overhead projector with transparent Numeral Cards and Tens Cards, or introduce it to a few pairs at a time with students using their own Numeral Cards and Tens Cards. If you introduce it to small groups, enlist those who have learned the game to help you teach other students.

Before the game, each player starts by taking a 1 from the Numeral Card deck. (Two more 1's are left in the deck.) Players keep this card to use throughout the game. They then shuffle both the Numeral Cards and Tens Cards and place each pack face down on the table.

Players work together on a single 101 to 200 Bingo Board, taking turns and helping each other with their turns. To determine a play, one player draws two Numeral Cards (these will be used as digits) and one Tens Card. The player arranges the 1 and the two other numerals to make a number between 100 and 199, then adds (or subtracts) the number on the Tens Card, and circles the resulting number on the board.

The goal is for the players, working together, to circle five adjacent numbers in a row, column, or diagonal. As necessary, demonstrate the meaning of *adjacent*—with sides or corners touching.

Note: Some combinations will yield only numbers that are not on the 101 to 200 Bingo Board. When this happens, students should make up their own rules about what to do. For example, one class let the player take another turn. Another class decided that the Tens Cards could be *either* added or subtracted in that instance. Another class allowed the player to use the 1 card anywhere in the number—a rule that is useful in some specific cases.

Students may want to play the game again. They will also have chances to play the game for homework and in later sessions in this investigation.

Sessions 1 and 2 Follow-Up

Playing 101 to 200 Bingo Students teach the game 101 to 200 Bingo to family members or friends. Each student will need How to Play 101 to 200 Bingo, copies of the 101 to 200 Bingo Board, and a set of Tens Cards. They should still have the Numeral Cards that they took home during Investigation 2.

 **Homework**

Related Problem Sets

Materials

■ Related Problem Sets booklets (1 per student)
■ Interlocking cubes

What Happens

Students work on closely linked groups of problems, called Related Problem Sets, involving addition, subtraction, and money. They meet in groups to assess their own work, and students individually write down something they learned from the group. Their work focuses on:

■ comparing addition or subtraction problems to see similarities and differences
■ doing addition and subtraction mentally
■ consulting with other students

Solving Sets of Related Problems

Before you hand out the Related Problem Sets booklets, introduce the idea of Related Problem Sets at the board.

For the next few days, we'll be thinking about good strategies for figuring out harder addition and subtraction problems. We'll be looking at Related Problem Sets. Each problem set is a group of four, five, or six problems that are related to each other in some way. You can work on the problems in a problem set in any order. You can use cubes to help solve them, but not the calculator.

There's one important thing about these Related Problem Sets: You are to find the answers to them without writing anything down. Then, after you find the answers, you will write down how you thought about the problems.

Present the following two problem sets on the board, the first subtraction, the second addition:

$$13 - 5 =$$
$$23 - 5 =$$
$$43 - 5 =$$
$$103 - 5 =$$
$$203 - 5 =$$

$$4 + 8 =$$
$$24 + 8 =$$
$$54 + 8 =$$
$$94 + 8 =$$
$$194 + 8 =$$
$$254 + 8 =$$

Students complete the two problem sets, working on the problems within a set in any order. They may copy the problems as necessary to keep track of their answers, but otherwise should be working in their heads (or with cubes) rather than on paper. As they finish, small groups of two or three students get together to compare strategies and answers. As the students are working and comparing solutions, circulate and take note of the strategies they are using and any errors they make.

When everyone has answers to both problem sets, ask students to share with the whole class strategies they have figured out or have learned from each other. You might focus their thinking with questions like these:

Did you learn something useful from someone else? Tell us about it.

In what order did you solve the problems?

Did anyone solve them in a different way?

Did you learn anything from one problem that helped you solve another problem? How are the problems similar?

Teacher Checkpoint

Writing About Strategies

Following the discussion, hand out the prepared booklets of Related Problem Sets. Explain that students will be doing these problem sets over the next few days. Today, they are to start on the first few pages.

Looking at one problem set at a time, students solve any problems that they can mentally and write only the answers on the page, then use those answers to solve the other problems in that problem set. Students choose one problem set on each page to write about. In the space next to that problem set, they write any patterns they noticed or how they used answers to some problems to solve others. Students who are interested may write about both problem sets.

❖ **Tip for the Linguistically Diverse Classroom** Students who are not writing comfortably in English may show their thinking with numbers and with symbols (circles and arrows), showing the patterns they followed.

Observe to see how students are writing about their solutions. If they don't know what to write, ask them to tell you how they thought about a specific problem or two. If they can express their ideas orally, tell them to write down just what they told you.

Students are just learning to write about their thinking, so their writing will be less rich than their thinking and their oral descriptions. In observing and talking with them, notice:

■ Are students able to work out problems mentally?

■ Do students use what they learn from one problem to help them solve another? Are they using patterns to do the problems? Do they reflect on their own learning?

■ Can students subtract across 100 (105 – 7, 205 – 7)?

■ Can they see a similarity between 105 – 7 and 15 – 7?

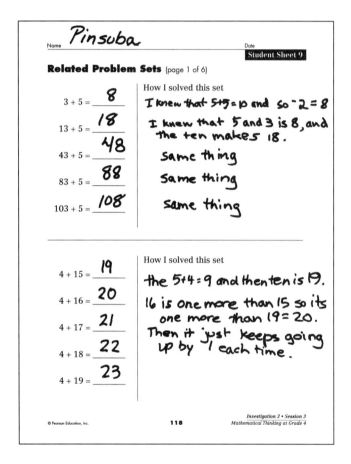

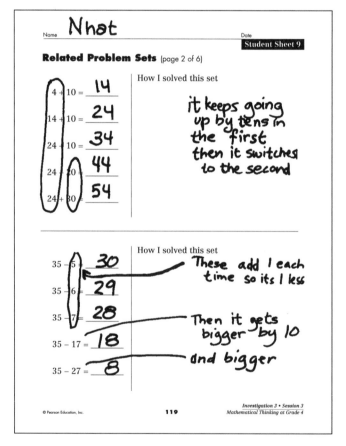

Comparing Solutions in Groups

After all students have completed a few pages of Related Problem Sets, group them in twos and threes to discuss their strategies.

This is a time for learning from one another. Talk among yourselves about how you worked out the answers for each set. Do not change your answers unless you are absolutely convinced the other answer is correct.

After you compare your ways of doing the problems, I will ask you what you learned from talking with the people in your group. Did you learn a different way to think about a problem? Did you find that you made the same kind of mistake more than once?

While students are talking, observe whether everyone is participating. In each small group, ask the students whether they have learned anything that will help them do the rest of the Related Problem Sets. Suggest that they use the back of the student sheet or a separate piece of paper to write about something they learned from doing the problems, or from correcting their mistakes, or from comparing their work to that of other students.

❖ **Tip for the Linguistically Diverse Classroom** Pair second-language learners with English-proficient students to check problems. Allow students to explain orally what they learned from doing the problems. Encourage them to refer to their problems by pointing or underlining key parts as they communicate their thoughts to you.

Working at their own speed, students continue to work on the Related Problem Sets booklets and write about their strategies. Some may finish all the problems in this session; most will not complete them until Choice Time in Sessions 4 and 5. If students finish quickly, check that they have written clear explanations.

Session 3 Follow-Up

Related Problem Sets Depending on the pace of student work in class, you might ask students to do one page of Related Problem Sets as homework. Remind them to write about how they did each set. If they take home their Related Problem Sets booklets, they must remember to bring them back the next day for continued work on them during Choice Time.

 **Homework**

Addition and Subtraction Strategies

Materials

- Choice List (1 per student, optional)
- Students' Related Problem Sets booklets
- 101 to 200 Bingo Boards (1–2 per student)
- Numeral Cards (class decks)
- Tens Cards (decks from earlier sessions)
- Colored pencils, crayons, or markers
- *Alexander, Who Used to Be Rich Last Sunday* by Judith Viorst (optional)
- Close to 100 Score Sheets (1–2 per student, optional)
- Coin Cards, plastic coins (optional)
- Student Sheet 10 (1 per student)

What Happens

During two sessions of Choice Time, students choose from Related Problem Sets, 101 to 200 Bingo, and other games learned earlier in this unit. As an assessment task, they do number and money problems based on the games. Their work focuses on:

- mental addition and subtraction
- adding and subtracting multiples of 10
- managing their time
- working with other students

Choice Time: Learning Together

Planning for Choice Time For the next two sessions, you may set up from two to five activity choices to be going on simultaneously in the classroom. Students work independently and in pairs and threes for all of Session 4. At the beginning of Session 5, you will present the assessment task on Student Sheet 10, Numbers and Money. As students finish work on the assessment, they return to the Choice Time activities for the rest of the session. The **Teacher Note** About Choice Time (p. 44) discusses how to organize the choices and how students can use the Choice List.

You may want to open Session 4 with just the first two or three of these choices, and add additional choices in Session 5 if students are finishing their Related Problem Sets booklets and have each played a few rounds of 101 to 200 Bingo.

How to Set Up the Choices If you set up your choices at centers, show students what they will find at each center. Otherwise, make sure they know where they will find the materials they need.

> Choice 1: Related Problem Sets—students' own booklets of Related Problem Sets, pencils
>
> Choice 2: 101 to 200 Bingo—Numeral Cards, Tens Cards; 101 to 200 Bingo Boards; colored pencil, crayon, or marker for each player
>
> Choice 3: How Much Alexander Spent (optional)—copy of the Judith Viorst book *Alexander, Who Used to Be Rich Last Sunday,* pencils, notebook paper
>
> Choice 4: Close to 100 (optional)—Numeral Cards, Close to 100 Score Sheets, pencils
>
> Choice 5: Collecting Dollars (optional)—Coin Cards, plastic coins (for those who need them)

Choice 3 is dependent on having a copy of the Judith Viorst book. This is the only new activity that will need introduction; see the description (following) for details. Review the other choices with the class as necessary.

Choice 1: Related Problem Sets

Students may continue to work on their Related Problem Sets booklets. As before, they should complete a whole set at a time and write about how they used one or more problems to help solve the others. When they finish two sets, they compare their work with that of a classmate. Then, on the back of the page or on a separate sheet of paper, they write something they learned from this comparison.

Ask students *not* to use calculators on these problems, because they should be using strategies based on their number sense.

Choice 2: 101 to 200 Bingo

Students may play 101 to 200 Bingo in pairs. Remember that this is a cooperative game played on a single Bingo Board; players take turns and help each other with their turns. The object is to circle five adjacent numbers vertically, horizontally, or diagonally. Review the rules (p. 51) as necessary.

Choice 3: How Much Alexander Spent

If you have a copy of the book *Alexander, Who Used to Be Rich Last Sunday,* read it aloud to the class, perhaps outside of math time. Explain that the prices of things may seem surprisingly low because the story took place a long time ago, when everything cost a lot less.

As a Choice Time activity, students work in pairs or groups of three. They look through the book to add up all the money that Alexander spent. They may want to keep track on paper as they figure the total.

Choice 4: Close to 100

Review the rules to this game (p. 28) as necessary. Encourage students to try the negative and positive scoring variation, or to invent a new game or a variation of the game using the Numeral Cards or calculators.

Choice 5: Collecting Dollars

Review the rules for Collecting Dollars (p. 39) as necessary. Remind students of the variation—making combinations of Coin Cards that equal *any* whole number of dollars. Challenge students to invent other variations, or to create other Coin Cards with differing totals.

Observing the Students

While students are working together, observe and talk with them to see whether they are learning from one another.

- In 101 to 200 Bingo, are they learning new strategies from their partner, or do they just accept help to get the turn played well?
- While doing Related Problem Sets, are they learning by checking with another student, or are they just erasing and putting in the other student's answers?

You might take some whole-group time toward the end of Session 4 to ask students to tell about some of the things they have learned from working with a partner. List these with the names of both students. You could begin this list with instances you learned of in your conversations with students.

Assessment

Numbers and Money

At the beginning of Session 5, hand out Student Sheet 10, Numbers and Money, to assess the work students have done up to this point in the unit.

❖ **Tip for the Linguistically Diverse Classroom** You may need to do this assessment orally with individual students who have limited English proficiency. Read aloud each problem, modeling actions whenever necessary to ensure comprehension.

Observe students while they are working. See the **Teacher Note, Assessment: Numbers and Money (p. 62),** for suggestions on what to be looking for, both while students are working and when you are evaluating their papers later.

Some students may need most of Session 5 to complete this assessment task. Those who finish early may quietly continue to do Choice Time activities.

Sessions 4 and 5 Follow-Up

Complete the Booklet Students who have not yet completed their Related Problem Sets booklets finish them as homework. If they have already finished the Related Problem Sets booklet, they continue to play one of this unit's math games at home.

 **Homework**

Invent a New Game You could challenge students to invent a new game that involves numbers or money. They may want to incorporate some of the cards or gameboards used for other games in this unit, or they might create new ones. Encourage them to bring their games in to share with the class. Plan to review any new games with the creator first to help work out any difficulties in the game rules.

 **Extension**

The work of Irena, Vanessa, and Kyle represents the range of answers you might see on the assessment tasks on Student Sheet 10, Numbers and Money.

1. Here are 6 Numeral Cards:

| 0 | 2 | 3 | 6 | 7 | 8 |

Use four of the numbers. Make two 2-digit numbers that you can add to make a number close to 100. Can you get 100 exactly? How close can you get?

Irena made 100 exactly by combining the cards into 68 + 32. Other students will make 100 with 62 + 38. Most students will get either 100 or very close to 100 (78 + 23 = 101; 23 + 67 = 90; 62 + 37 = 99).

Vanessa added incorrectly (86 + 20 = 100); she may have been concentrating on making 100 with the tens digits and forgot the ones digits. Other students sometimes use two of a certain digit when only one is available (78 + 22 = 100; 63 + 37 = 100).

Irena wrote the problem horizontally and added in her head, showing strong mental computation skills.

$$\boxed{6}\,\boxed{8} + \boxed{3}\,\boxed{2} = 100$$

Both Vanessa and Kyle, on the other hand, wrote their two-digit numbers one under the other and added traditionally, with carrying.

$$\begin{array}{r} 86 \\ +20 \\ \hline 106 \end{array} \qquad \begin{array}{r} \overset{1}{8}7 \\ +23 \\ \hline 110 \end{array}$$

As you observe students working, when you find them writing the numbers in columns, ask them to show you how they can add in their heads.

A few students may not estimate in order to plan a combination. They will pick numbers randomly and test them by doing the traditional algorithm. When you see this happening, encourage estimation by asking them first to make *any* number with two of the digits, and then tell you about how large a number they need to make 100.

2. Write the answers to these counting problems in the blanks:

  a. Start with 58. Count up by 10's by adding 10 each time.

    58 __ __ __ __ __ __ (+ 10 each time)

  b. Start with 4. Count up by 20's.

    4 __ __ __ __ __ __ (+ 20 each time)

  c. Start with 137. Count *backward* by 10's.

    137 __ __ __ __ __ __ (– 10 each time)

  d. What advice would you give to someone who was trying to count by 10's and 20's?

Most students will be successful at adding tens. Some, however, may have difficulty with adding by twenties and subtracting tens.

Irena's three counts were all perfect, and her advice for counting by 10's and 20's showed a corresponding grasp of the task: "Add 1 or 2 to the tens. Or take away 1."

Vanessa counted by 20's this way:

4 24 44 64 84 104 114

She has the overall pattern, but runs into difficulty working above 100.

Kyle recognized correctly that the changes for counting by 20's are only in the tens digits, but after the first answer, he reverted to the easier counting by 10's.

4 24 34 44 54 64 74

Kyle also counted up by 10's, instead of backwards, for the last problem.

A few students will make several mistakes in a series, apparently from counting by ones without looking for a pattern in either the tens or the ones digits: 4, 24, 33, 54, 64, 75, 84. These students need lots of practice adding or subtracting multiples of 10. They might benefit from playing a simpler version of bingo, using the 100 chart instead of the 101 to 200 Bingo Board. Limit the Tens Cards at first to +10, –10, +20, and –20; they need to see these relationships in two-digit numbers.

3. Count and make groups of coins.

a. What is the total value of these coins?

b. What is the total value of 3 quarters, 2 dimes, 2 nickels, and 2 pennies?

On problems 3a and 3b, Irena worked mentally and just wrote down a total. She shows the ability to count money and use coins in a practical way.

Vanessa wrote number amounts next to each coin picture (3a) and drew in coins next to the number values (3b) before adding. Kyle listed the values in columns to add:

$$
\begin{array}{r} 75 \\ +20 \\ \hline 95 \end{array}
\qquad
\begin{array}{r} 95 \\ +10 \\ \hline 1.05 \end{array}
\qquad
\begin{array}{r} 1.05 \\ .02 \\ \hline 1.07 \end{array}
$$

Even though students like Vanessa and Kyle may find the correct total, they are not yet working with coins in a useful way.

A few students may still not recognize the coins shown. Let them compare the pictures with real coins, if possible.

c. Show what coins you could use to make 63¢.

d. Show a different way to make 63¢.

Irena's answer starts with larger denominations and adds smaller ones as needed, in the most efficient use of different coins:

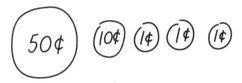

She uses her answer in 3c for 3d, exchanging two quarters for the half dollar and two nickels for the dime.

Vanessa started out on the right foot, with a half dollar, but then depended on 13 pennies to take her to 63¢.

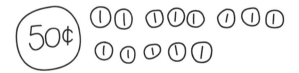

For 3d, she also replaced the half dollar with two quarters, and substituted a nickel for five of the pennies, but still used 8 pennies to reach the total.

Kyle seemed lost in problems 3c and 3d, and worked out his answers with plastic coins and the teacher's help.

When students are not yet comfortable with finding the total values of coins, suggest that they practice this frequently, maybe at home, or for a real purpose in school—counting milk money, for example. Show them efficient techniques, such as starting with the coins that have the largest value, and grouping the coins in piles that equal 25¢, 50¢, or a dollar.

Making Geometric Patterns

What Happens

Session 1: Patterns with Mirror Symmetry
Using pattern blocks, pairs of students make designs that have a line of symmetry, and distinguish them from designs with no clear pattern. They also look for examples of symmetry in the classroom or outdoors environment.

Session 2: Patterns with Rotational Symmetry
Pairs of students construct pattern block designs that grow from a central hexagon and have rotational symmetry. The class discusses what makes a pattern a pattern.

Sessions 3 and 4: Patterns and Nonpatterns
On a bulletin board display of patterns and non-patterns, students post clippings brought from home along with the pattern block designs they have made. They play a game in which they try to build a design from oral descriptions. They write about one of the designs they made earlier, and work in groups to guess which description fits which design.

Sessions 5 and 6: Symmetrical Geoboard Patterns Using geoboards, students make designs with rotational symmetry. They also make a geoboard design with mirror symmetry, and copy half of their design onto dot paper for another student to complete. Students investigate the number of lines of symmetry in their designs. They finish the unit with an assessment, drawing one design with only mirror symmetry and one with only rotational symmetry, and writing about their work.

Mathematical Emphasis

- Distinguishing between geometric patterns and random designs
- Distinguishing between mirror symmetry and rotational symmetry
- Writing about designs

What to Plan Ahead of Time

Materials

- Pattern blocks: 1 bucket of 250 per 4–6 students (Sessions 1–6)
- Ruler or straightedge: 1 per pair (Session 1)
- Pencils, crayons, or markers in red, green, yellow, and blue (Sessions 1, 2, 5–6)
- Scraps of patterned fabric, wrapping paper, or wallpaper (Session 1, optional)
- Scissors: 1 per student (Session 2)
- Stick-on notes (Sessions 3–6)
- Geoboards with rubber bands in assorted colors: 1 per student or per pair (Sessions 5–6)
- Overhead projector (Sessions 1–6)
- Overhead pattern blocks (Sessions 1–4, optional)
- Resealable plastic bags: 1 per bucket of blocks (Session 1)
- Small mirror (Session 1, optional)

Other Preparation

- Prepare the pattern block sets by removing the narrow parallelograms and the squares, leaving hexagons, triangles, trapezoids, and wide parallelograms (diamonds), or plan to have students remove them in Session 1. Read the **Teacher Note,** Pattern Block Shapes (p. 70).
- Prepare a bulletin board where you can post student work and pictures or clippings they bring in to demonstrate patterns and nonpatterns. (Sessions 3–4)
- Duplicate student sheets and teaching resources (located at the end of this unit) in the following quantities. If you have Student Activity Booklets, copy only the item marked with an asterisk.

For Session 1

Triangle paper (p. 134): 2 per student (class), 2 per student (homework)

For Session 2

Student Sheet 11, Mirror Symmetry and Rotational Symmetry (p. 130): 1 per student

Triangle paper (p. 134): 1 per student

For Sessions 5–6

Student Sheet 12, Multiple Lines of Symmetry (p. 131): 1 per student (homework)

Shaded Geoboard Design* (p. 132): 1 transparency

Geoboard Dot Paper (p. 133): 4 per student (class), 2 per student (homework)

Triangle paper (p. 134): 2 per student (class), 2 per student (homework)

Patterns with Mirror Symmetry

Materials

- Pattern blocks (1 bucket per 4–6 students)
- Ruler or straightedge (1 per pair)
- Triangle paper (2 per student, class; 2 per student, homework)
- Pencils, crayons, or markers in red, green, yellow, and blue
- Overhead projector (optional)
- Overhead pattern blocks (optional)
- Scraps of fabric, wrapping paper, or wallpaper (optional)
- Resealable plastic bags or other containers (1 per bucket of blocks)
- Small mirror (optional)

What Happens

Using pattern blocks, pairs of students make designs that have a line of symmetry, and distinguish them from designs with no clear pattern. They also look for examples of symmetry in the classroom or outdoors environment. Their work focuses on:

- making patterns with mirror symmetry
- working cooperatively with a partner
- copying a pattern onto paper

 Ten-Minute Math: Exploring Data Continue to do Exploring Data as a Ten-Minute Math activity outside of math time. During this investigation, you might collect data related to the numbers of each pattern block that students use as they create designs. Small groups could be assigned to total the number of a given shape—for example, triangles—in all the designs.

Quickly graph the data using a line plot, list, table, or bar graph. Ask students to describe what they see in the data and make predictions about whether the data might be different if they were to gather it another time.

Alternatively, students in pairs can take turns choosing a question and collecting and recording the data. Or you could post a table or graph form on which students can record their own data any time during the day, and then discuss the gathered data as a whole class at the end of the day.

For a full description and variations on this activity, see p. 93.

Symmetry with Pattern Blocks

Distribute the buckets of pattern blocks to groups. If you haven't removed the narrow parallelograms and squares, students can do that now. Provide a plastic bag or other container to store these extra blocks.

For this activity, creating pattern block designs with a line of symmetry, each student will need a sheet of triangle paper. Have extras for students who have time to create more than one design. The first step is to darken one of the horizontal or diagonal lines near the middle of the page to use as a line of symmetry. This is done easily with a straightedge.

If you have an overhead projector, use it to demonstrate as you explain the activity. If not, use pattern blocks on a table or the floor where students can gather around to see. Make a line of symmetry by drawing a line or placing a stick. Students will enjoy participating in the demonstration on the overhead. If you don't have overhead pattern blocks, use regular pattern blocks and slightly separate adjacent blocks so students can see their outlines. A small mirror will be useful for supporting your demonstration of mirror symmetry.

Explain the procedure for this activity as follows:

You will be working in pairs to make symmetrical designs with pattern blocks. You'll be making more than one design, but you'll do each one together, working on one sheet of triangle paper until the design is finished.

Start with a sheet of triangle paper, marked with a line of symmetry. One side will be person 1's side, the other will be person 2's side. As you make your design, you will only work on your own side of the line.

- **Person 1 starts by putting a pattern block on the triangle paper, touching the line of symmetry along one side.**
- **Person 2 now puts the same kind of block in the mirror-image position on the other side of the line.**
- **Person 2 now gets to place a new block. Each block put down must touch either the line of symmetry or another block, at least by a corner if not a whole side.**
- **Person 1 puts a block in the mirror-image position.**

Continue to take turns like this. Use 12 blocks in all. You should each have three turns to place a new block in the design.

After each pair finishes one design, they leave those pattern blocks in place on the paper. Then they use 12 new pattern blocks to make a different design on the other sheet of triangle paper.

When they have finished both designs, partners can each color one design by lifting the blocks one at a time. Tell them to use colors that match the colors of the blocks. You may want to wait until pairs have finished both designs before you distribute the colored pencils, crayons, or markers.

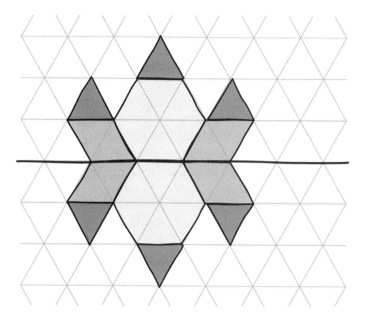

A Design Without Symmetry   If there is time, students can use pattern blocks and triangle paper to make designs that have no symmetry. They could make a picture or an abstract design, but it must *not* be the same on one side as the other.

Save the designs from this activity—both with and without symmetry—for posting on the bulletin board in Sessions 3–4.

Activity

Symmetry in the Environment

Allow a few minutes at the end of the session for students to look in the classroom or outside to find examples of symmetry. If you have scraps of fabric, wrapping paper, or wallpaper, these are often good sources. On the board, list the things they notice.

Ask students to indicate with their hands the lines of symmetry in each shape. Some designs may have more than one line of symmetry; some may have rotational or mirror symmetry.

If someone finds a design with rotational symmetry, begin a discussion of the difference between mirror and rotational symmetry to prepare students for the activities in Session 2. See the **Teacher Note,** Pattern and Symmetry (p. 71), for information about these types of symmetry.

Finding Examples of Symmetry   To collect items for your Patterns/No Patterns bulletin board in Sessions 3 and 4, ask students to bring in examples of symmetry they find, perhaps in advertisements, photographs, pieces of gift wrap, wallpaper, and fabric. Students may also make a list of other items they see outside of school that have symmetry but that can't be brought to class. Watch for some designs, such as clocks, where it is not clear whether or not there is symmetry. These will be especially useful for discussion.

Homework

Making a New Design   Send home triangle paper for students to make a new design, with or without symmetry. Save their work for posting on the Patterns/No Patterns bulletin board.

Making Symmetrical Linear and 3-D Designs   Some students may enjoy making linear designs (as can be seen in some beaded necklaces), starting in the middle, placing shapes on either side, and maintaining symmetry around the middle.

Extension

If you have or can borrow building blocks for the classroom, students enjoy building three-dimensional structures that have symmetry and balance— some have made very elaborate structures with perfect symmetry.

Pattern Block Shapes

The pattern block set is made up of six shapes: a hexagon, a square, a triangle, two parallelograms (rhombuses), and a trapezoid. In most sets, each shape comes in one color: the hexagons are yellow; the triangles are green; the squares are orange; the trapezoids are red; the narrower parallelograms or rhombuses (which your students will probably call diamonds) are tan; and the wider parallelograms or rhombuses are blue (although in some sets, they are so dark as to appear purple).

Pattern blocks are related mathematically in terms of side length and angle measures. For example, six of the triangles can be put together to make one hexagon; two of the trapezoids make one hexagon. Your students will see some of these relationships readily. Because of these

relationships, pattern blocks are useful for exploring many aspects of mathematics, including fractions, symmetry, and angles of polygons. They fit together to make beautiful and mathematically interesting patterns.

You may want to explore the pattern block relationships further by trying the following problem yourself:

> If the hexagon is one unit of area, what are the relative sizes of the other pieces?

While some of the relationships of the pieces are straightforward, you might find others challenging. Students who have done the *Investigations* grade 3 Fractions unit, *Fair Shares,* will be familiar with the use of pattern blocks to represent fractions, especially thirds and sixths.

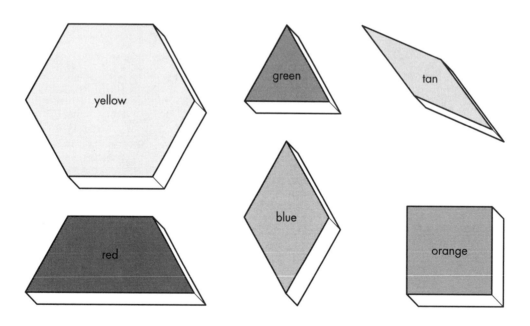

Pattern and Symmetry

A pattern creates a regularity that can be copied. When we speak of patterns in fabric, we may mean a design made from colors or textures. Plaids have a color pattern; corduroys have a texture pattern. A pattern in a mathematical sense has a relationship among its component parts—sometimes in number, sometimes in relationship among data, sometimes in visual shape.

Number A pattern exists in each of these series of number relationships, making it possible to predict the next steps:

$$10 \times 23 = 230 \qquad 5 + 8 = 13$$
$$100 \times 23 = 2300 \qquad 5 + 18 = 23$$
$$1,000 \times 23 = 23,000 \qquad 5 + 28 = 33$$
$$10,000 \times 23 = ? \qquad 5 + 38 = ?$$
$$? = ? \qquad ? = ?$$

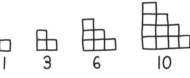

| 1 | 3 | 6 | 10 | ? |

Data A fourth grade class that collected bedtime and rising time data in their school concluded that younger children sleep for more hours than older children. Although this pattern had some remarkable exceptions—such as one first grader who reported to sleep only five and a half hours a night—the information allowed them to make generalizations about the number of hours of sleep required by students at different ages, and to make predictions about the sleep patterns of children younger and older than those in their survey.

Shape The designs that follow have patterns that allow you to know what piece is missing. Patterns in which one half can be flipped or folded over onto the other half have mirror symmetry. The two halves are reflections of one another. The first three designs have mirror symmetry (if the question mark in each is replaced with the appropriate shape).

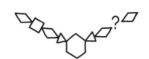

Mirror symmetry

Patterns that revolve around a central point have *rotational symmetry* or *circular symmetry*. A pattern with rotational symmetry can be turned a fraction of a circle—one-third, or 120° if it has three segments; one-fourth, or 90° if it has four segments; one-sixth, or 60° if it has six segments; one-twelfth, or 30° if it has twelve segments—and appear as though it hasn't moved at all. The two patterns below have rotational symmetry.

Only rotational symmetry

Mirror and rotational symmetry

A circle has infinite rotational symmetry; any turn will leave it looking the same. Some patterns with rotational symmetry—such as a circle, a regular hexagon like the yellow pattern block, any even-sided regular polygon, or the six-pointed star above—also have mirror symmetry. Others, such as the pinwheel design above and the trapezoid below, do not.

Mirror and rotational symmetry

Only mirror symmetry

Patterns with Rotational Symmetry

Materials

- Student Sheet 11 (1 per student)
- Scissors
- Buckets of pattern blocks
- Triangle paper (1 per student)
- Pencils, crayons, or markers in red, green, yellow, and blue

What Happens

Pairs of students construct pattern block designs that grow from a central hexagon and have rotational symmetry. The class discusses what makes a pattern a pattern. Their work focuses on:

- making patterns with rotational symmetry
- copying patterns onto paper
- thinking about other kinds of patterns

Activity

Two Symmetries: Which Is Which?

Before talking about the difference between rotational and mirror symmetry, let students tell about the symmetrical objects they found at home. Most of these objects will have mirror symmetry, but the discussion will give you a chance to introduce rotational symmetry. For an example of such a conversation, see the **Dialogue Box** Discussing Symmetry (p. 77).

Hand out Student Sheet 11, Mirror Symmetry and Rotational Symmetry. Students may cut, fold, or manipulate the two designs in any way that helps them determine what kind of symmetry each demonstrates.

If students have trouble identifying which design has rotational symmetry, suggest that they hold each design on the table with a finger or a pencil in the center, and turn the design some part of a circle to see if there is a point where it appears the same as it did at the beginning. Emphasize that the placement of their finger must be in the center of the design.

How far must each design be rotated to see the same view more than once?

A design that must be rotated in a full circle before the same view can be seen again does *not* have rotational symmetry. A design that can be rotated less than a full circle to see the same view has rotational symmetry.

Try this with the design with rotational symmetry: How many times can you see the same view before you have turned it around a full circle?

A design with mirror symmetry can be divided in half so that each side is a reflection of the other. Remind students of the symmetrical designs they made in Session 1.

In the design with mirror symmetry, where is the line of symmetry?

Students may color the two designs in ways that show their symmetry.

As students continue to work with symmetry in this session, they may discover that they can make designs with *both* mirror and rotational symmetry in the same design.

Note: During this investigation, we use a number of specialized words in discussing symmetry. Don't insist that students use them, either in their speaking or, later, in their writing about their designs. What's important is that students find ways to communicate their ideas so others understand. See the **Teacher Note,** Using Mathematical Vocabulary (p. 76), for a discussion of how to use such terms in your class.

Patterns Around Hexagons

Distribute either triangle paper or plain paper to students, who will be working together to draw two designs with rotational symmetry. As when drawing their designs with mirror symmetry in Session 1, students work in pairs, cooperating to make the two designs. They work first with pattern blocks and then color the designs on their paper.

For each pattern, students begin with a hexagon shape, either using a whole yellow hexagon or constructing a *single-color* hexagon from trapezoids, triangles, or wide parallelograms. They place this in the center of their paper.

Using one type of block at a time, they build around the hexagon, arranging the blocks in a regular pattern. A limit of 15 or 16 blocks will help keep the designs simpler. Students may leave spaces to create a lacy effect, but the blocks must be placed equally around the hexagon to form a pattern with rotational symmetry.

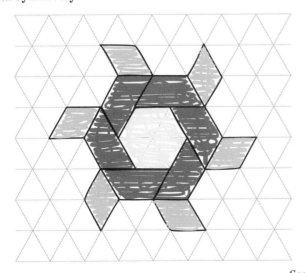

Checking for Rotational Symmetry As pairs finish their first design, students need to check to be sure that it has rotational symmetry.

Make a pencil mark at the bottom of one view of your design. Carefully rotate the triangle paper with the blocks on it, turning the paper in a circle around the center of the design. How far must you rotate it to see the same view of the design again?

If they need to rotate the paper a full turn (so that the pencil mark is at the bottom again), the design does not have rotational symmetry. Pattern block designs that do have rotational symmetry will need to be turned halfway, one-third of the way, or one-sixth of the way around to see the same view again.

Watch the pencil mark to keep track of how much you've turned the sheet. How much do you turn your design before it looks the same? Halfway around? One-third of the way? One-sixth of the way?

When each pair is sure their first design has rotational symmetry, they begin a second design. Again they start with a hexagon in the center, and use about 16 pattern blocks.

When students can confirm that they have two designs with rotational symmetry, they may record their work. Each student takes one design and, lifting one block at a time, colors the design on the paper, using colors that match the pattern blocks.

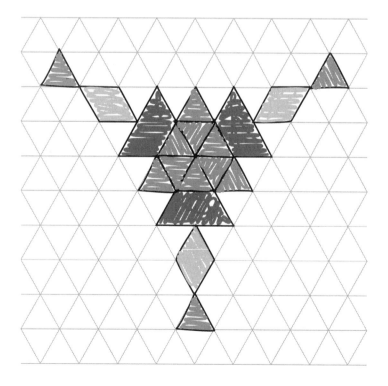

What Is a Pattern?

In the next session, students will be sorting collected items into patterns and nonpatterns for a classroom display. To prepare for this, allow 10 or 15 minutes at the end of this session to talk about pattern. Students should become familiar with the idea that a pattern allows us to predict the way something will repeat. We can cover up part of a visual pattern and know what is underneath.

You might show students examples of number or shape patterns and ask them to continue the patterns or to suggest others. See the **Teacher Note,** Pattern and Symmetry (p. 71), for some examples, or use patterns like the following:

Patterns in number series

    3, 6, 9, 12, ...

    1, 2, 4, 8, ...

Patterns that give clues to computation

$$3 \times 10 = 30$$

$$7 \times 10 = 70$$

$$14 \times 10 = ?$$

Patterns in the ones digits
(Related Problem Sets)

    $3 + 5 = 8$

    $23 + 5 = 28$

  $14,583 + 5 = ?$

Patterns of growing shapes

  1   4   9   16   ...

Patterns in a linear arrangement of shapes

 ?

As you present examples, ask students to continue the patterns. Challenge them to design another pattern of the same type.

Session 2 Follow-Up

Collecting Designs for Display   Students collect designs without symmetry for the classroom display. They may also finish designs they started in class that show mirror or rotational symmetry.

 **Homework**

 **Extension**

Pattern Puzzles   Students might enjoy making up puzzles based on number or shape series. They draw or write their pattern, leaving space at the end for the patterns to be extended. Pattern puzzles could be posted on a *What's the Pattern?* bulletin board. Other students may extend the patterns by adding one number or shape in pencil; the originator may erase it if it isn't the correct next step. If students show interest in this, you might post the display in a hall to share it with other classes, challenging viewers to try extending the patterns.

Teacher Note

Using Mathematical Vocabulary

Students learn mathematical words the same way they learn other vocabulary—by hearing them used correctly, frequently, and in context. Young children learn words by hearing their families use language appropriately. When they make mistakes—"Look at the big doggie," says a young child pointing at a horse—adults use the correct words, and the child gradually learns the distinctions among all the four-footed animals.

We don't ask young children to memorize definitions of *horse* or *dog;* rather, we find opportunities for them to hear words being used in meaningful ways. Learning mathematical vocabulary is no different. Students do not learn how to speak mathematics by memorizing definitions, but by hearing these words frequently and having many opportunities to use them in context.

Use mathematical vocabulary accurately and frequently, and connect it with more familiar words that students may know:

Let's look at Rafael's pattern block design. Does it have *mirror symmetry?* Is one side a *reflection* of the other? How can you tell? Is there anything in the classroom that is *symmetrical?*

What can you say about the number of people wearing shoes with laces *compared to* the number of people wearing sandals? You think there are 12 more people wearing shoes with laces? How did you figure out that the *difference* is 12?

Throughout the *Investigations* curriculum, we will point out mathematical terms that are important for you to use in context. Don't insist that students use these terms. What is important is that they express their ideas and describe their strategies for solving mathematical problems clearly and accurately, using whatever words are comfortable for them.

As you use mathematical terms frequently in context, students will become used to hearing them and will begin to use them naturally. Even young children can learn to use mathematical vocabulary accurately when they hear it used correctly and in the context of meaningful activities.

Discussing Symmetry

As the students in one class brought in from home their observations of things that have symmetry, the teacher took some time to discuss what they were finding.

Tell us some of the symmetrical things on your list that you saw but couldn't bring to class.

Kenyana: The smoke detector. It is round and you can cut it a few different ways and get it to be a mirror reflection.

B.J.: The curtains.

So there is one curtain on each side of the window, and they match each other?

B.J.: Yes.

Vanessa: A chair, but it matters how you split it. It is symmetrical only if you split the back and seat down the middle one way.

Marci: My cat.

Nick: No living thing is. I thought my dog was, but he's not because he has more spots on one side.

Marci: My cat is exactly the same on both sides.

Elena: The clock is symmetrical.

Is the clock symmetrical?

Dave: At 6 o'clock it is.

Marci: What about the second hand?

Vanessa: I don't think it is because of the numbers. If you took the numbers off, it might be symmetrical.

Marci: You'd have to take the hands off too. They are different lengths, and the second hand really gets in the way.

Does everybody agree that if we took the hands and numbers off, the clock would be symmetrical?

Nick: I have to think about it. It's hard for me to imagine it that way.

While you think about that, I have another question for you. If there is such a thing as a symmetrical cat, how many lines of symmetry does it have? How many ways could you cut it in half and have the same image on each side?

Tyrone: Only one way. You'd have to cut it between the ears and the long way down the tail.

That is an example of mirror symmetry. What else have we talked about that has mirror symmetry?

Marci: The chair, and probably the curtains.

Does anybody know what it means to rotate?

Nadim: To turn around?

I agree with that. Are there any items we mentioned that if you turn them a little bit you can get the same view as when you started? That is, are there any items that have rotational symmetry?

Kenyana: I think the smoke detector is like that. You can cut it a lot of different ways.

Marci: Maybe the clock without numbers and hands.

Tyrone: The chair?

If you were looking at a chair from above, how far would you have to rotate it to get the same view?

Tyrone: All the way around?

Nhat: A full circle.

An object has rotational symmetry when you can rotate it part way and it still looks the same. If you have to rotate it a full circle to get the same view, it doesn't have rotational symmetry.

Tyrone: But it might have mirror symmetry, right?

Patterns and Nonpatterns

Materials

- Collected designs and clippings from home
- Stick-on notes
- Pattern blocks
- Overhead projector (optional)
- Overhead pattern blocks (optional)

What Happens

On a bulletin board display of patterns and nonpatterns, students post clippings brought from home along with the pattern block designs they have made. They play a game in which they try to build a design from oral descriptions. They write about one of the designs they made earlier, and work in groups to guess which description fits which design. Their work focuses on:

- recognizing patterns
- describing a visual design orally and in writing
- building a design from oral instructions

Activity

Teacher Checkpoint

A Display of Patterns

The class begins a bulletin board with designs and pictures displayed in two groups: those that have patterns and those that don't. Ask the students to suggest headings, such as *Patterns* and *Pictures Without Patterns*. Students can add to the display the patterns and nonpatterns they brought from home as well as any pattern block designs they have completed during this investigation.

Allow time for students to examine the display. Supply stick-on notes that they can put on any items they think are placed in the wrong group. As a class, talk about designs that are controversial.

Use this activity as a checkpoint. While students are posting their pictures, examining the display, and talking about items that are controversial, notice the following:

- Can they distinguish between designs that have patterns and those that don't?
- Can they make designs with symmetry?
- Can they see symmetry in other people's designs?
- Can they indicate the line of symmetry in a pattern with mirror symmetry?

- Can they point to the center of a design with rotational symmetry?
- Can they point out how a pattern has rotational symmetry but not mirror symmetry?

Many of these ideas are sophisticated. However, some students are more able to see these attributes of visual patterns than their teachers—including students who have difficulty doing accurate computation. At the same time, students who do well with number work may have difficulty in visualization tasks.

Writing About Our Designs

Students now select one of the pattern block designs that they have colored during this investigation and, on notebook paper, write a description of it. The description should tell which blocks (shapes) they used and how many of each, how their pattern grows, the number of lines of symmetry, and, if appropriate, what part of a circle they need to rotate the design to see the view they started with.

Pairs can work together on designs they created cooperatively, or they can each pick a different design to describe.

Since writing in mathematics may be new to your students, you may want to start them off with a sentence such as "Here is how we built our pattern block design." The description need only be three or four sentences, but insist that students include all the important information. Ask them to check their work this way:

If someone read your description, could that person pick out your design from all the others on display?

❖ **Tip for the Linguistically Diverse Classroom** Offer students the option of writing their description in their native language. If they do so, have them include rebus drawings over key words, for example, for the shapes they used. If they have not yet acquired written language skills, pair them with English-proficient students. They can provide drawings for each sentence.

Collect these designs and written descriptions for use in the activity at the end of Session 4, Guessing from Descriptions (p. 82).

Draw the Hidden Design

For this activity, students need to have buckets of pattern blocks within their reach. They will work in small teams and take turns being the leader. The leader makes an arrangement of pattern blocks, hidden from the view of others, and then describes orally how to make it. The rest of the group tries to replicate the hidden design.

First demonstrate the activity to the whole class. Build a simple design with three or four blocks, hidden from the view of the class (for example, put it on the overhead projector with the projector turned off, or on a desk with books propped around it). The design may or may not have a pattern. (If you are working with real pattern blocks on the overhead, leave space between the pattern blocks so students will be able to clearly see each silhouetted shape when you show your design.)

Give the students an oral description of your design. Stop after each statement to give them time to build with their blocks what they think it looks like. Here is an example:

- **I put down a green triangle, with one point facing toward the left.**
- **To the right of the triangle, I put a blue diamond. One of its points is touching the middle of the side of the triangle.**
- **Then I put a red trapezoid above the other two blocks. One of its points touches the point where the green and blue blocks meet. It just fits.**
- **I put another red trapezoid block below the other blocks. The red blocks are mirror images of each other.**
- **There is a line of symmetry across the middle of my design. It looks like a flying creature with a green head, a blue body, and red wings.**

When you are finished with your directions, reveal your design. Hold a discussion about how clear the directions were. Ask students what you might have said to describe your design more clearly.

The object of this activity is for the leader and the rest of the team to collaborate—the leader is *not* trying to stump the others. The leader always tries to give a description that is as clear as possible; the rest of the team members listen carefully and ask good questions.

After you have demonstrated the activity, students divide into teams of three, or teams of four playing as pairs. The leader (or leader pair) for each team makes a hidden design. They might work behind a barrier, on a book or binder on one of their laps, or on a chair below the level of the desk or table where they're seated. The first design they try should have only 3 or 4 pieces.

When the design is finished, the leader describes it while the others try to follow the description and copy the design with pattern blocks. When they are finished, the design is revealed and compared with the copy.

Students take turns being the leader as they repeat the activity several times. If they are successful with three or four pieces, they can try a design with five or six pattern blocks.

❖ **Tip for the Linguistically Diverse Classroom** For this activity, group together students who speak the same native language. They can use their primary language to give the oral descriptions.

As you circulate, notice when the copied designs don't match the original. Encourage students to review the description that was given and try to understand what went wrong.

Three triangles are connected at a point. Blue diamonds are between them. The whole design is a big triangle. It is six blocks.

Guessing from Descriptions

In a new display, post only the designs students wrote about earlier. As students take turns reading their descriptions aloud, other students try to figure out which design is being described.

Doing this activity in small groups of five or six will help limit the number of choices. One teacher with a small class had each student come up to the front of the room and sit in "The Mathematician's Chair" while reading his or her description for others to guess the design.

Alternatively, you might post all the designs, each labeled with a number. Erase or cover any names that are written on the front of the designs. Compile and copy the written descriptions, *with* student names on them, and distribute these to the students. Students read each description and write the number of the matching design. Allow students to move around the room and consult with the authors of the descriptions for clarification.

❖ **Tip for the Linguistically Diverse Classroom** This activity should be comprehensible to everyone if the written descriptions included rebus drawings, as suggested on p. 79.

If it is too cumbersome for you to compile and copy all the descriptions, students could pass their written work around the class. Pairs of students could then work with two descriptions at a time, attempting to match them with the numbered designs.

My pattern looks like a diamond that would go on a ring. It is made up of mostly rhombuses. In the middle three triangles are connected. Connected to the triangles are red trapazoids. You have to turn it a third to get the same pattern. My pattern has no yellow hexagons. There are three triangles.

Symmetrical Geoboard Patterns

What Happens

Using geoboards, students make designs with rotational symmetry. They also make a geoboard design with mirror symmetry, and copy half of their design onto dot paper for another student to complete. Students investigate the number of lines of symmetry in their designs. They finish the unit with an assessment, drawing one design with only mirror symmetry and one with only rotational symmetry, and writing about their work. Their work focuses on:

- making symmetrical patterns
- copying patterns from the geoboard to dot paper
- finding symmetry in other students' patterns

Materials

- Geoboards and rubber bands (1 set per student or per pair)
- Transparency of Shaded Geoboard Design
- Overhead projector
- Geoboard dot paper (4 per student, class; 2 per student, homework)
- Colored pencils, crayons, or markers
- Triangle paper (2 per student, class; 2 per student, homework)
- Stick-on notes
- Pattern blocks
- Student Sheet 12 (1 per student, homework)

Activity

Before you pass out rubber bands for the geoboard activities, discuss with students how to handle the rubber bands appropriately (for example, they are not to use them for shooting).

After distributing the geoboards and rubber bands, allow students some time to make designs and become accustomed to working with the geoboard. When students seem ready, tell them to put away all but four rubber bands for each geoboard. Students may work on this activity in pairs if you don't have enough geoboards for individual work.

This Teacher Checkpoint activity has two parts, one for rotational symmetry and one for mirror symmetry.

Teacher Checkpoint

Symmetry on the Geoboard

Rotational Symmetry

To introduce rotational symmetry on the geoboard, display the Shaded Geoboard Design on the overhead projector and ask students what kind of symmetry they see in it. (It has rotational symmetry and not mirror symmetry.) Rotate the design one-fourth (90°) for students to see that it looks the same from that viewpoint.

To demonstrate that the design does not have mirror symmetry, ask students to imagine a vertical line of symmetry through it.

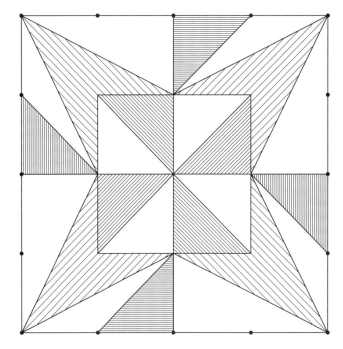

If you fold it over on this line, or imagine the reflection, what happens? Does the design on both sides of the line match up? Try a different line of symmetry—horizontal or diagonal. Does that work?

See if students agree that this design has only rotational symmetry. Then direct them to their geoboards.

Make a design on your geoboard that has rotational symmetry. Ignore the color of the rubber bands. Just use whatever colors you have.

Many students may make designs that have both mirror and rotational symmetry. It is particularly challenging to create a design on the square geoboard that has rotational symmetry but *not* mirror symmetry.

When students have completed their designs, they exchange them and look for the rotational symmetry in each other's designs. A good way to check is to actually turn the geoboards around the center point. If the students can do this and find the same view of the design in less than one full turn, the design has rotational symmetry.

While students are working, circulate to do a quick check of their designs. Ask some students (not only those who have made mistakes) to show you how their designs rotate.

Distribute geoboard dot paper for students to copy their designs. Allow time for students to go quietly around the room to look at the designs their classmates have made.

Mirror Symmetry

Students now use the geoboard to make mirror symmetrical designs. Distribute more geoboard dot paper for this part of the activity.

When students have completed a design that has mirror symmetry, they check the symmetry with a partner (or, if working in pairs, with another pair). When they are satisfied that they have a symmetrical pattern, they copy *half* of their design onto geoboard dot paper.

To clarify the idea of drawing only half of the design, draw a symmetrical geoboard design on the board and erase half of it, leaving only the dots.

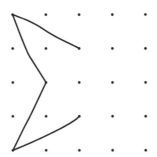

Students now trade half-designs with someone. (If two students have created a design together, they each make a copy of half of their design and trade with different students.) They then try to complete the design given to them. The geoboards are kept out of sight (or face down) during this step, and then brought out again when students are ready to check the accuracy of the completed drawing. The originator of the design corrects the drawing as necessary so that it has the symmetry that was planned.

Looking for Lines of Symmetry   Students may color their designs for both rotational and mirror symmetry, then add them to the classroom display of designs with patterns. While students are coloring, ask some of them to show you the symmetry in their designs.

How many lines of symmetry do your designs have? Where are they?

Some students may have difficulty producing drawings that have mirror or rotational symmetry. However, all students should be able to do the following:

- Identify a design that has mirror symmetry and show that if you fold it, flip it, or look at the opposite sides, you can see that it is the same.

- Identify a design with rotational symmetry and explain how you can hold the center still and turn it a fraction of a whole circle to see that it looks the same from another view.

Check to be sure that students are aware of these differences in the two types of symmetry before they do the assessment at the end of the unit.

Counting Lines of Symmetry

Use the classroom display of finished designs as a focal point for more exploration. You might post the following questions near the display for students to consider:

- Which designs have only one line of symmetry?
- Which designs have four lines of symmetry?
- Do any of these designs have exactly two lines of symmetry?
- Which of the mirror designs also have rotational symmetry?

Students might use stick-on notes to indicate, near each design, how many lines of symmetry they find in it. Take some time for the class to discuss what they found out.

Do designs with four lines of symmetry always have rotational symmetry? How can you make a design that has mirror symmetry but not rotational symmetry?

Students can continue this investigation of lines of symmetry for homework, as suggested on p. 88.

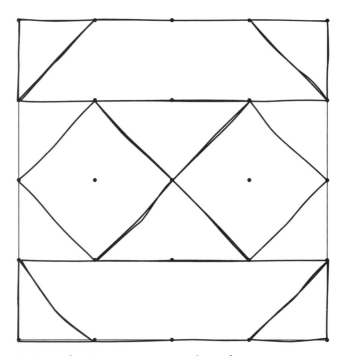

Design with mirror symmetry —two lines of symmetry.
Also rotational symmetry.

There is no student sheet for this assessment, but students may want to use triangle paper or geoboard dot paper for their designs. Make these available. Students may also work on plain paper. They are also free to use pattern blocks or geoboards for planning their designs. Introduce the assessment task to the class.

Now I have a challenge for you. I want you to make two designs:

■ The first design must have mirror symmetry *but not* rotational symmetry.
■ The second design must have rotational symmetry *but not* mirror symmetry.

The hard part is making designs that have only one kind of symmetry, not the other. You may use pattern blocks or geoboards to work out your design and then copy it onto paper. Or, you may draw your design right on your paper.

When they have completed their drawings, the students write on the same page how they know that their design has rotational or mirror symmetry. Write these questions on the board for reference:

How would you explain to someone else that your design has mirror symmetry?

How would you explain to someone else that your design has rotational symmetry?

Collect student work for review. See the **Teacher Note,** Assessment: Mirror and Rotational Symmetry (p. 89), for guidelines on assessing student responses.

Choosing Student Work to Save

As the unit ends, you may want to use one of the following options for creating a record of students' work on this unit.

■ Students look back through their folders or notebooks and write about what they learned in this unit, what they remember most, and what was hard or easy for them. You might have students do this work during their writing time.

■ Students select one or two pieces of their work as their best work, and you also choose one or two pieces of their work, to be saved in a portfolio for the year. You might include students' written solutions to the assessments Numbers and Money (p. 61) and Mirror and Rotational Symmetry (p. 87). Students can create a separate page with brief comments describing each piece of work.

■ You may want to send a selection of work home for families to see. Students write a cover letter, describing their work in this unit. This work should be returned if you are keeping year-long portfolios.

Sessions 5 and 6 Follow-Up

Homework

Multiple Lines of Symmetry After Session 5, send home Student Sheet 12 along with geoboard dot paper, triangle paper, or plain paper for students to make designs with different numbers of lines of symmetry. For homework, they:

Make one design with only one line of symmetry.

Make one design with two lines of symmetry.

Make one design with four lines of symmetry.

All of their designs will have mirror symmetry, but which have rotational symmetry and which do not? See if they can tell. They might add their designs to the class display for discussion at the beginning of Session 6.

Extension

Displaying More Patterns You might keep a bulletin board area all year to exhibit examples of patterns, both those made by students and those found ready-made. As students provide new patterns, take others down and return them. Include number patterns as well as visual designs.

Assessment: Mirror and Rotational Symmetry

By the end of Investigation 4, most fourth grade students are able to make a design with mirror symmetry and a design with rotational symmetry. However, very few students that we observed made designs that had only rotational symmetry. Here is a beautifully simple example that one student produced:

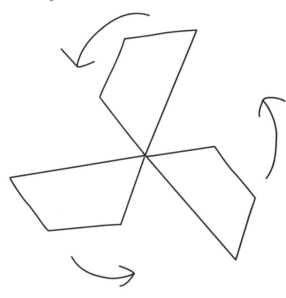

Many more students are able to make designs that have only mirror symmetry, like this one:

Some students will start with a line of symmetry (for a mirror design) or with a hexagon (for a circular design), then just add to the design until it has the kind of symmetry they are seeking. They then describe the symmetry they meant to draw, without considering whether the other kind of symmetry is also there. Thus, many ended up with designs that had both kinds of symmetry:

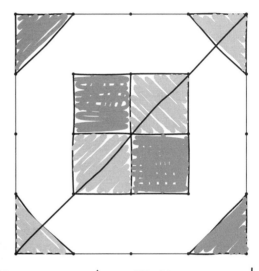

Mirror symmetry — It's the same on both sides of the line.

Rotational — turn the page and see the same thing.

A few students have difficulty with some parts of the task. They may show some idea of symmetry, but will make a design with one line of symmetry and say it has rotational symmetry. A student like this may be thinking of rotating the design around a point at its base, rather than a point in its center.

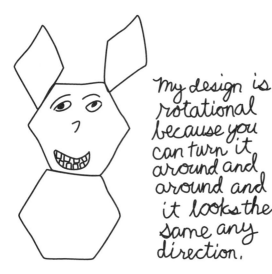

My design is rotational because you can turn it around and around and it looks the same any direction.

Other students will attempt a symmetric pattern but not execute it accurately.

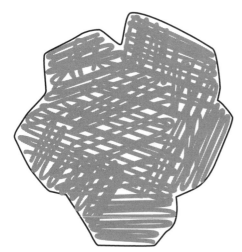

My design is rotational because It goes in a circle.

In assessing the written work, look to see how well students convey the basic characteristics of mirror and rotational symmetry. Here are some good reasons students have given for knowing why their designs have mirror symmetry:

> My design is symmetrical because it is a mirror.
>
> My design is symmetrical because if you fold it, it will end up on the same side.
>
> My design is symmetrical because I used the same shapes on both sides of my design.

And here are some clear reasons for knowing why a design has rotational symmetry:

> My design is rotational because you can turn it around and you can see the same thing.
>
> My design can turn around. It's spinning like a merry go round.
>
> My design is the same on every side when you rotate it.

If used as part of the suggested grade 4 Investigations sequence, this is the first unit of the year. This final investigation has given your students a chance to try some visual/spatial work, and for you to see which students are especially comfortable with this kind of work and which students have more difficulty. You may find, as we have, that throughout the year some students who have difficulty with number work will shine at spatial work. More visual/spatial work is offered in the units *Seeing Solids and Silhouettes* (3-D Geometry) and *Sunken Ships and Grid Patterns* (2-D Geometry). In addition, the unit *Different Shapes, Equal Pieces* takes a very visual approach to fractions.

Estimation and Number Sense

Basic Activity

Students mentally estimate the answer to an arithmetic problem that they see displayed for a short time. They discuss their estimates. Then they find a precise solution to the problem by using mental computation strategies.

Estimation and Number Sense provides opportunities for students to develop strategies for mental computation and for judging the reason-ableness of the results of a computation done on paper or with a calculator. Students focus on:

- looking at a problem as a whole
- reordering or combining numbers within a problem for easier computation
- looking at the largest part of each number first (looking at hundreds before tens, thousands before hundreds, and so forth)

Materials

Calculators (for variation)

Procedure

Step 1. Present a problem on the chalkboard or overhead. For example.

$$9 + 62 + 91 + 30$$

Step 2. Alow 15 to 20 seconds for students to think about the problem. In this time, students come up with the best estimate they can for the solution. This solution might be-but does not have to be-an exact answer. Students do not write anything down or use the calculator during this time.

Step 3. Cover the problem and ask students to discuss what they know. Ask questions like these: "What did you notice about the numbers in this problem? Did you estimate an answer? How did you make your estimate?"

Encourage all kinds of statements and strategies. Some will be estimates; others may be quite precise:

"It's definitely bigger than 100 because I saw a 90 and a 60."

"It has to be 192 because the 91 and the 9 make 100 and the 30 and the 62 make 92."

Be sure that you continue to encourage a variety of observations, especially the "more than, less than" statements, even if some students have solved it exactly.

Step 4. Uncover the problem and continue the discussion. Ask further: "What do you notice now? What do you think about your estimates? Do you want to change them? What are some mental strategies you can use to solve the problem exactly?"

Variations

Problems that can be Reordered Give problems like the following examples, in which grouping the numbers in particular ways can help solve the problem easily:

$$6 + 2 - 4 + 1 - 5 + 4 + 5 - 2$$
$$36 + 22 + 4 + 8$$
$$112 - 30 + 60 - 2$$
$$654 - 12 + 300 + 112$$

Encourage students to look at the problem as a whole before they start to solve it. Rather than using each number and operation in sequence, they see what numbers are easy to put together to give answers to part of the problem. Then they combine their partial results to solve the whole problem.

Problems with Large Numbers Present problems that require students to "think from left to right" and to round numbers to "nice numbers" in order to come up with a good estimate. For example.

$230 + 343 + 692$	$5.13
3.15×9	$6.50
$8 + 1200 + 130$	+ $3.30

Continued on next page

Present problems in both horizontal and vertical formats. If the vertical format triggers a rote procedure of starting from the right and "carrying" encourage students to look at the numbers as a whole, and to think about the largest parts of the numbers first. Thus, for the problem 230 + 343 + 692, they might think first, "About how much is 692? – 700." Then thinking in terms of the largest part of the numbers first (hundreds), they might reason: "300 and 700 is a thousand, and 200 more is 1200, and then there's some extra, so I think it's a little over 1200."

Fractions Pose problems using fractions and ask students to estimate the number of wholes the result is closest to. Start by posing problems such as $1/2 + 1/4$ or $1/2 + 3/4$, and ask,, "Is the answer more than or less than one? Eventually, you can include fractions with larger results and expand the question to " Is the answer closer to 0.1 or 2?" Begin to include problems such as $5 \times 1/4$ and $3 \times 1/8$. Use fractions such as $9/4$, $50/7$, $100/26$, or $63/20$, an d ask, "About how many wholes are in this fraction?"

Is It Bigger or Smaller? Use any of the kinds of problems suggested above, but pose a question about the result to help students focus their estimation: " Is this bigger than 20? Is it smaller than $10.00? If I have $20.00, do I have enough to buy these four things?"

Using the Calculator The calculator can be used to check results. Emphasize that it is easy to make mistakes on a calculator, and that many people who use calculators all the time often make mistakes. Sometimes you punch in the wrong key or the wrong operation. Sometimes you leave out a number by accident, or key sticks on the calculator and doesn't register. However, people who are good at using the calculator always make a mental estimate so they can tell whether their result is reasonable.

Pose some problems like this one:

> I was adding 212, 357, and 436 on my calculator. "The answer I got was 615. Was that a reasonable answer? Why do you think so?

Include problems ion which the result is reasonable and problems in which it is not. When the answer is unreasonable, some students might be interested in figuring out what happened. For example, in the above case, you might say: I accidentally punched in 46 instead of 436.

Related Homework Options

Problems with Many Numbers Give one problem with many numbers that must be added and subtracted. Students show how they can reorder the numbers in the problem to make it easier to solve. They solve the problem using two different methods to double-check their solution. One way might be using the calculator. Here is an example of such a problem:

$$30 - 6 + 92 - 20 + 56 + 70 + 8$$

Exploring Data

Basic Activity

You or the students decide on something to observe about themselves. Because this is a Ten-Minute Math activity, the data they collect must be something they already know or can observe easily around them. Once the question is determined, quickly organize the data as students give individual answers to the question. The data can be organized as a line plot, a list, a table, or a bar graph. Then students describe what they can tell from the data, generate some new questions, and, if appropriate, make predictions about what will happen the next time they collect the same data.

Exploring Data is designed to give students many quick opportunites to collect, graph, describe, and interpret data about themselves and the world around them. Students focus on:

- describing important features of the data
- Interpreting and posing questions about the data

Procedure

Step 1. Choose a question. Make sure the question involves data that students know or can observe: How many buttons are you wearing today? What month is your birthday? What is the best thing you ate yesterday? Are you wearing shoes or sneakers or sandals? How did you get to school today?

Step 2. Quickly collect and display the data. Use a list, a table, a line plot, or a bar graph. For example, a line plot for data about how many buttons students are wearing could look something like this:

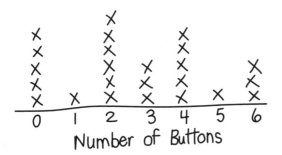

Step 3. Ask students to describe the data. What do they notice about it? For data that have a numerical order (How many buttons do you have today? How many people live in your house? How many months until your birthday?), ask questions like these: Are the data spread out or close together? What is the highest and lowest value? Where do most of the data seem to fall? What seems typical or usual for this class?"

For data in categories (What is your favorite book? How do you get to school? What month is your birthday? ask questions like these: "Which categories have a lot of data? Few data? none? Is there a way to categorize the data differently to get other information?"

Step 4. Ask students to interpret and predict. Why do you think that the data came out this way? Does anything about the data surprise you? Do you think we'd get similar data if we collected it tomorrow? next week? in another class? with adults?"

Step 5. List any new questions. Keep a running list of questions you can use for further data collection and analysis. You may want to ask some of these questions again

Variations

Data from Home Students might collect data about routines at home: What time do your brothers and sisters go to bed? What do you usually eat for breakfast?.

Data from Another Class or Other Teachers Depending on your school situation, you may be able to assign students to collect data from other classrooms or other teachers. Students are always interested in surveying others about questions that interest them, such as this one: When you were little, did you like school?

Continued on next page

Categories If students take surveys about "favorites"—flavor of ice cream, breakfast cereal, book, color-or other data that fall into categories, the graphs are often flat and uninteresting. There is not too much to say, for example, about a graph like this:

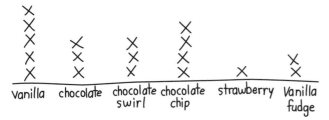

It is more interesting for students to group their results into more descriptive categories so that they can see other things about the data. In this case, even though vanilla seems to be the favorite in the graph above, another way of grouping the data seems to show that flavors with some chocolate in them are really the favorites.

Chocolate flavors   ⲋⲎⲎ   ⲋⲎⲎ   ∣∣

Flavors without chocolate   ⲋⲎⲎ   ∣

The following activities will help ensure that this unit is comprehensible to students who are acquiring English as a second language. The suggested approach is based on the *Natural Approach: Language Acquisition in the Classroom* by Stephen D. Krashen and Tracy D. Terrell (Alemany Press, 1983). The intent is for second-language learners to acquire new vocabulary in an active, meaningful context.

Note that *acquiring* a word is different from learning a word. Depending on their level of proficiency, students may be able to comprehend a word upon hearing it during an investigation, without being able to say it. Other students may be able to use the word orally, but not read or write it. The goal is to help students naturally acquire targeted vocabulary at their present level of proficient.

We suggest using these activities just before the related investigations. The activites can also be led by English-proficient students.

Investigation 1

the numbers 1 to 300

1. Create action commands that ask students to nonverbally identify numbers on the board.

   Put your finger on the number 96.

   Cover the number 225.

2. Use classroom items (paper clips, rubber bands) to help students count to 100.

3. Write the hundreds on the board: 100, 200, 300, 400, 500, 600, 700, 800, 900. Count by 100's with the students as you point to each number.

4. Challenge students to write different numbers that you call out.

   Write the number 279.

   Write the number 138.

   Write the number 205.

same, different, compare

1. Show students a set of Numeral Cards. Pick out two 3's. Trace the shape of each 3 with you finger, and tell students that when you compare these numbers, they look the *same*. Then pick out two 4's and say that these two are also the same. Ask the students to compare the cards and put into groups all those that are the *same*.

2. Pick out a 2 and a 9. Say that when you compare these numbers, you can see that they are not the same-they are *different*. As you select pairs of cards, ask students to compare them and tell you if they are the same or different.

3. Provide other items from the unit to compare-plastic coins, pattern block, interlocking cubes put together in simple shapes. Students should be able to identify items that are the same and items that are different.

add, plus, subtract, minus, difference

1. Give students different numbers of cubes, and ask them to count and report how many they have. Then move together two students cubes into one pile

   If I add Pinsuba's cubes and Tuong's cubes, how many will be in the new pile?

   Is the answer 15 because we added 7 + 8?

2. Write on the board the number problem that represents the adding of cubes you just did. Identify the plus sign.

3. Challenge students to add two different piles of cubes and find the total. Ask someone to write on the board the corresponding number problem.

4. Count out a pile of 12 cubes. Then remove 5 from the pile. Tell the students that when you subtract 5 cubes from the 12, you have 7 left. The *difference* between 12 and 5 is 7.

5. Write 12 − 5 = 7 on the board, and identify the minus sign.

6. Regroup the 12 cubes, and ask students to find the difference between 12 and 6. Have someone write the problem on the bard and read it.

7. Continue creating simple addition and subtraction problems with cubes, writing the number problems for each. When you are using the calculator in class have students find the plus, minus and equals keys.

lowest, close to

1. Write the following numbers on the board: 2, 9, 21, 39. Point to the 2 as you identify it as having the lowest value of these three numbers.

2. Ask students to find and mark 2, 9, 21, and 39, on the 100 chart. Point out that the 9 is *close* to

10. Point to 11, and say that 11 is another number that is close to 10.

Which of the numbers you marked is close to 20?

Which of the numbers is close to 1.

Which of the numbers is close to 40

3. Write several groups of numbers on the board; for example, 102, 115, 126; 23, 35, 54; 287, 288, 289. Point to a number in one of the series and ask if it is the lowest number of that group. (It may or may not be.) If it is not the lowest, have students nod affirmatively; if it is not the lowest, have students shake their heads negatively. Repeat with different numbers.

4. Indicating the numbers on the board, challenge students to find a number that is close to 100, a number that is close to 50, and a number this is close to 300.

5. Ask students to point to the lowest of all the numbers you wrote on the board.

Investigation 2

Money: coins, cents, penny, nickel, dime, quarter, dollar.

1. Use a dollar, quarter, dime, and nickel—real, play money, or both—along with action commands to help familiarize students with these words.

   Put a quarter in your hand.

   Give me a dime.

   Put the nickel under the dollar.

   Put all the coins in a pile.

   Fold the dollar in half.

2. Create action commands that require students to identify coins bu their value.

   Take a coin that is worth 5 cents.

   Give me a coin that is worth 10 cents.

   Show me which coin is worth the most money.

Investigation 3

pattern

1. Start a clapping pattern (hit knees, hit knees, clap; hit knees, hit knees, clap). Ask students to join in. Then change the pattern.

Try this pattern with me.

Who wants to show us a new pattern?

2. Give students two colors of interlocking cubes. Show them a pattern of cubes in a line, such as blue, red, red, blue, red, red. Ask students to make their own patterns.

3. Draw or write patterns on the board, identify them, and ask students to continue them.

This is a pattern of shapes; what comes next?

□ △ ○ □ △ ○ □ △ ○

This a pattern in numbers; what comes next? *[Write the numbers in order, then circle and say aloud each even number, pausing at 8.]*

1 ②3 ④5 ⑥7 ⑧9 10 11 12...

This is another kind of number pattern; what comes next? *[Write the numbers in a column .]*

   3

  13

  23

  33

Investigation 4

shape, triangle, square, hexagon, trapezoid, diamond.

1. Using pattern blocks, point out that different blocks have different shapes. Draw or trace fine shapes on the board-triangle, square, hexagon, trapezoid, and diamond-and identify each.

2. Let students each take a handful of pattern blocks. Ask students to hold up one of each shape as you name it. Point to the shapes on the board for the first round; for a second round, erase the shapes you have drawn and just call for the pieces by name, using action commands.

Find a triangle.

Give a hexagon to someone else.

Put a trapezoid in the middle of the table.

Show me all the blue diamonds.

Blackline Masters

_____ , 20 ___

Dear Family,

We are beginning a unit called *Mathematical Thinking at Grade 4*. This unit will help your child get used to solving problems that take considerable time, thought, and discussion. While solving these problems, your child will be using materials like coins, cubes, and calculators, and will be writing, drawing, and talking about how to do the problems. Emphasis during this unit will be on thinking hard and reasoning carefully to solve mathematical problems.

During this unit your child will estimate how many hundreds are in a group of objects. The class will also be figuring out ways to count coins efficiently, creating symmetrical designs, and looking for patterns in their environment. In what we call *working with data,* the class will be collecting and organizing information about themselves. Your child will have a math folder, notebook, or journal for keeping track of work.

While our class is working on this unit and throughout the year, you can help in several ways:

- Your child will have assignments to work on at home. Sometimes they will need your participation. For example, your child will be teaching you several games that can be played cooperatively. Later in the unit, your child will be asked to look for patterns in magazines or newspapers or on pieces of fabric, gift wrap, or wallpaper.

- During this unit, students will be solving problems involving money. When working at home, it would help them to have an assortment of coins to work with. You can also involve your child in solving problems about money: How much will two items cost together? How much change will you get for $1.00? What is the total value of all the coins in a purse or pocket?

One of the most important things you can do is to show genuine interest in the ways your child solves problems, even if they are different from your own. We are looking forward to an exciting few weeks as we create a mathematical community in our classroom.

Sincerely,

How Many Cubes in Each Object?

Name of maker	Name of object	Estimate	Count

Tell about what you enjoyed in math class today.

Suppose someone was trying to estimate how many cubes were in an object. What advice would you give that person?

Making Hundreds

1. Make a drawing to show how you grouped
   100 cubes. (If you arranged 100 in more than
   one way, show both ways.)

2. How do you know you have exactly 100 cubes?

3. What other ways could you have arranged 100 cubes?

How Many Cubes in the Class?

Number of cubes in each group	About how many hundreds altogether? Estimate.	Add the numbers to find the exact total.
	Show or explain how you got your answer.	Is the total close to the number of hundreds you estimated? If they are very different, try to find out why.

A Design with 100 Squares

On graph paper, make a design using exactly
100 squares.

Finish the sentence below:

I know my design is 100 squares because _____

_____

_____

_____

_____

_____

How Many Hundreds?
How Many Altogether?

These are the numbers of cubes that groups in two classes counted.

Number of cubes in each group	About how many hundreds altogether? Estimate.	Add the numbers to find the exact total.
46 22 74 51 98 113	100 or 200 or 300 or 400? How did you decide?	
131 271 197 204	600 or 700 or 800 or 900? How did you decide?	

Problems for Close to 100

Pretend you are dealt these hands in the game
Close to 100. What numbers would you make
to get sums as close to 100 as possible?

Score

1. | 3 | 4 | 6 | 9 | 2 | 7 |

____ ____ + ____ ____ = _____   _____

2. | 1 | 7 | 0 | 8 | 2 | 9 |

____ ____ + ____ ____ = _____   _____

3. | 4 | 3 | 6 | 0 | 2 | 7 |

____ ____ + ____ ____ = _____   _____

4. | 9 | 8 | 3 | 1 | WILD CARD | 2 |

____ ____ + ____ ____ = _____   _____

5. | 9 | 8 | 3 | 1 | 3 | 2 |

____ ____ + ____ ____ = _____   _____

TOTAL SCORE _____

CHART FOR HOW MANY CUBES?

Group	Estimates	Counts

Investigation 1 • Resource
Mathematical Thinking at Grade 4

Materials
- One deck of Numeral Cards
- Close to 100 Score Sheet for each player

Players: 1, 2, or 3

How to Play

1. Deal out six Numeral Cards to each player.

2. Use any four of your cards to make two numbers. For example, a 6 and a 5 could make either 56 or 65. Wild Cards can be used as any numeral. Try to make numbers that, when added, give you a total that is close to 100.

3. Write these two numbers and their total on the Close to 100 Score Sheet. For example: 42 + 56 = 98.

4. Find your score. Your score is the difference between your total and 100. For example, if your total is 98, your score is 2. If your total is 105, your score is 5.

5. Put the cards you used in a discard pile. Keep the two cards you didn't use for the next round.

6. For the next round, deal four new cards to each player. Make more numbers that come close to 100. When you run out of cards, mix up the discard pile and use those cards again.

7. Five rounds make one game. Total your scores for the five rounds. LOWEST score wins!

Scoring Variation

Write the score with minus and plus signs to show the direction of your total away from 100. For example: If your total is 98, your score is –2. If your total is 105, your score is +5. The total of these two scores would be +3. Your goal is to get a total score for five rounds that is close to 0.

Ways to Count Money

Below are three handfuls of coins. Find the total value of each. Try it in two or three different ways.

- Try it mentally or with coins.
- Try it with a calculator.
- Try it with paper and pencil.

1. 2 quarters
   3 dimes
   2 nickels
   3 pennies
   Total value: _____

2. 1 half dollar
   1 quarter
   1 dime
   7 nickels
   Total value: _____

3. 3 quarters
   4 pennies
   5 nickels
   3 dimes
   Total value: _____

4. What is the best way to find the total value of a handful of coins? What advice would you give to a friend about this?

_____

_____

_____

_____

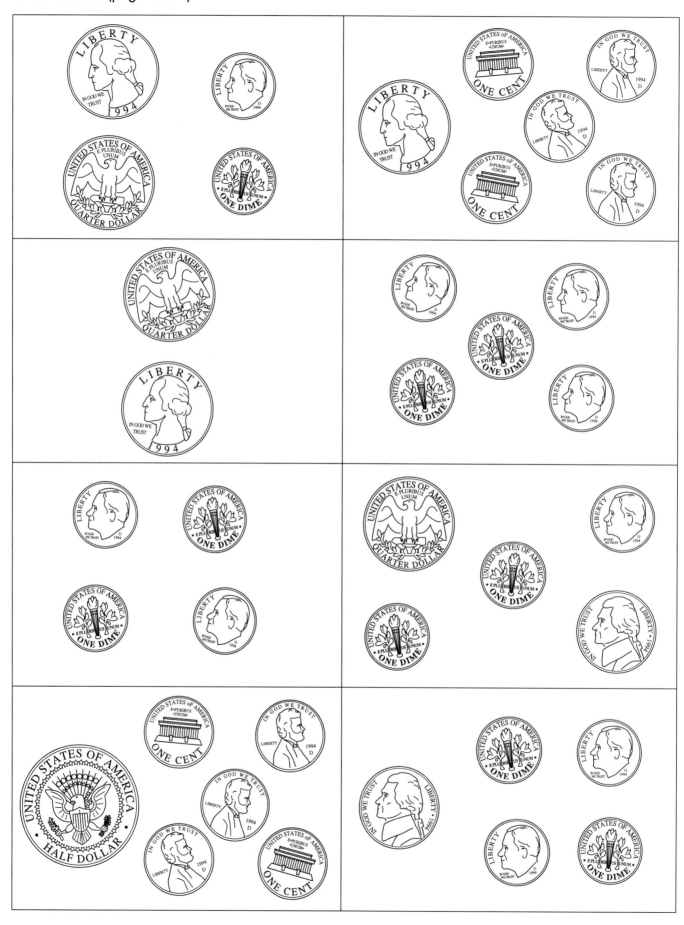

Materials
- One deck of Coin Cards

Players: 2 or 3

How to Play

1. Deal out 8 Coin Cards face up. Put the rest of the pack in a pile face down.
2. Take turns finding pairs of cards that equal one dollar.
3. If everyone agrees that no combinations of the 8 cards make one dollar, shuffle all 8 back in the pack and deal 8 new cards.
4. At the end of your turn, draw new cards from the pack to replace the cards that you used. The next player should have 8 cards to choose from.
5. The goal is to collect as many pairs of cards (dollars) as possible.
6. The game ends when all the cards have been paired.

Scoring Variation
Make combinations of cards that equal any whole number of dollars. For example, a player could take three cards with 50¢, 70¢, and 80¢ for a total of $2.00. You may decide to score by number of dollars collected or by number of cards collected.

Materials
- One dollar in real coins: 2 quarters, 3 dimes, 3 nickels, and 5 pennies
- A small paper bag you can *reach* into but not *see* into. Put the coins in the bag.

Players: 2 or 3 (can also be a solitaire game)

How to Play
1. Players agree on a sum of money less than $1.00 that one player will try to pick from the bag. Some easy amounts require only 1 or 2 coins—for example, 10¢ or 35¢. More difficult amounts require more coins—for example, 23¢, 47¢, 66¢, or 92¢.
2. Reach into the bag and take out one coin at a time until you have the target amount of money. If you take a coin that will not help you make the target amount, put it back.
3. When all players agree that the target amount has been picked out, return the coins to the bag.
4. Choose a different amount of money, and start again. Take turns.

Variation
After one player picks out the right amount, the next player tries to make the same amount of money with different coins.

If no other way is possible, that player picks out the same selection of coins the first player chose.

300 Chart (page 1 of 3)

1	2	3							10
11					16				20
		23			26				
		33				37			
41	42								
		53	54						60
			65						
	72								
81									90
						97			100

Trim along bottom of chart. Tape to next page.

300 Chart (page 2 of 3)

Tape bottom of page 1 along here.

			104						
	112	113							120
			125		127				
131									140
		143	144						150
			155	156					
161									170
			175						
	182	183							190
							199		

Trim along bottom of chart. Tape to next page.

Investigation 3 • Sessions 1–2
Mathematical Thinking at Grade 4

300 Chart (page 3 of 3)

Tape bottom of page 2 along here.

		203			207			
211			214					220
			225					
	232							240
		243	244					
251				256				
		264						
271								
							289	290
				297				

Investigation 3 • Sessions 1–2
Mathematical Thinking at Grade 4

Related Problem Sets (page 1 of 6)

	How I solved this set
3 + 5 = _____	
13 + 5 = _____	
43 + 5 = _____	
83 + 5 = _____	
103 + 5 = _____	

	How I solved this set
4 + 15 = _____	
4 + 16 = _____	
4 + 17 = _____	
4 + 18 = _____	
4 + 19 = _____	

Related Problem Sets (page 2 of 6)

How I solved this set

4 + 10 = _____

14 + 10 = _____

24 + 10 = _____

24 + 20 = _____

24 + 30 = _____

How I solved this set

35 − 5 = _____

35 − 6 = _____

35 − 7 = _____

35 − 17 = _____

35 − 27 = _____

Related Problem Sets (page 3 of 6)

	How I solved this set
32 + 10 = _____	
32 + 20 = _____	
32 + 40 = _____	
32 + 70 = _____	
32 + 80 = _____	

	How I solved this set
80 + _____ = 100	
180 + _____ = 200	
280 + _____ = 300	
180 + _____ = 300	

Related Problem Sets (page 4 of 6)

1 quarter = _____ pennies

2 quarters = _____ pennies

3 quarters = _____ pennies

4 quarters = _____ pennies

5 quarters = _____ pennies

How I solved this set

---

1 dime = _____ nickels

2 dimes = _____ nickels

5 dimes = _____ nickels

10 dimes = _____ nickels

20 dimes = _____ nickels

How I solved this set

Investigation 3 • Session 3
Mathematical Thinking at Grade 4

Related Problem Sets (page 5 of 6)

How I solved this set

1 quarter = _____ nickels

2 quarters = _____ nickels

3 quarters = _____ nickels

4 quarters = _____ nickels

8 quarters = _____ nickels

How I solved this set

1 dollar = _____ pennies

1 dollar = _____ nickels

2 dollars = _____ nickels

1 dollar = _____ dimes

3 dollars = _____ dimes

Related Problem Sets (page 6 of 6)

Write the total value for each of these groups of coins.

How I solved this set

2 nickels =

3 nickels =

5 nickels =

6 nickels =

7 nickels =

How I solved this set

1 quarter and 1 nickel =

1 quarter and 1 dime =

2 quarters and 1 dime =

3 quarters =

3 quarters and 1 nickel =

Numbers and Money (page 1 of 2)

1. Here are 6 Numeral Cards:

| 0 | 2 | 3 | <u>6</u> | 7 | 8 |

Use four of the numbers. Make two 2-digit numbers that you can add to make a number close to 100. Can you get 100 exactly? How close can you get?

2. Write the answers to these counting problems in the blanks:

a. Start with 58. Count up by 10's by adding 10 each time.

58 ___ ___ ___ ___ ___ ___ (+ 10 each time)

b. Start with 4. Count up by 20's.

4 ___ ___ ___ ___ ___ ___ (+ 20 each time)

c. Start with 137. Count backward by 10's.

137 ___ ___ ___ ___ ___ ___ (− 10 each time)

d. What advice would you give to someone who was trying to count by 10's and 20's?

Numbers and Money (page 2 of 2)

3. Count and make groups of coins.

a. What is the total value of these coins?

b. What is the total value of 3 quarters, 2 dimes, 2 nickels, and 2 pennies?

c. Show what coins you could use to make 63¢.

d. Show a different way to make 63¢.

Materials
- 101 to 200 Bingo Board
- One deck of Numeral Cards
- One deck of Tens Cards
- Colored pencils, crayons, or markers

Players: 2

How to Play
1. Each player takes a 1 from the Numeral Card deck and keeps this card throughout the game.

2. Shuffle the two decks of cards. Place each deck face down on the table.

3. Players use just one Bingo Board. You will take turns and work together to get a Bingo.

4. To determine a play, draw two Numeral Cards and one Tens Card. Arrange the 1 and the two other numerals to make a number between 100 and 199. Then add or subtract the number on your Tens Card. Circle the resulting number on the 101 to 200 Bingo Board.

5. Wild Cards in the Numeral Card deck can be used as any numeral from 0 through 9. Wild Cards in the Tens Card deck can be used as + or − any multiple of 10 from 10 through 70.

6. Some combinations cannot land on the 101 to 200 Bingo Board at all. Make up your own rules about what to do when this happens. (For example, a player could take another turn, or the Tens Card could be *either* added or subtracted in this instance.)

7. The goal is for the players together to circle five adjacent numbers in a row, in a column, or on a diagonal. Five circled numbers is a Bingo.

101	102	103	104	105	106	107	108	109	110
111	112	113	114	115	116	117	118	119	120
121	122	123	124	125	126	127	128	129	130
131	132	133	134	135	136	137	138	139	140
141	142	143	144	145	146	147	148	149	150
151	152	153	154	155	156	157	158	159	160
161	162	163	164	165	166	167	168	169	170
171	172	173	174	175	176	177	178	179	180
181	182	183	184	185	186	187	188	189	190
191	192	193	194	195	196	197	198	199	200

+10	+10	+10	+10
+20	+20	+20	+20
+30	+30	+30	+40
+40	+50	+50	+60
+70	WILD CARD	WILD CARD	WILD CARD

Investigation 3 • Resource
Mathematical Thinking at Grade 4

-10	**-10**	**-10**	**-10**
-20	**-20**	**-20**	**-20**
-30	**-30**	**-30**	**-40**
-40	**-50**	**-50**	**-60**
-70	**WILD CARD**	**WILD CARD**	**WILD CARD**

Investigation 3 • Resource
Mathematical Thinking at Grade 4

Mirror Symmetry and Rotational Symmetry

One of these designs has mirror symmetry.
The other design has rotational symmetry.
Cut out the designs. Try turning and folding them.
Can you tell which design has mirror symmetry?
Which design has rotational symmetry?

Draw the line of symmetry in the
design with mirror symmetry.
Put a dot in the center of
the design with rotational
symmetry.

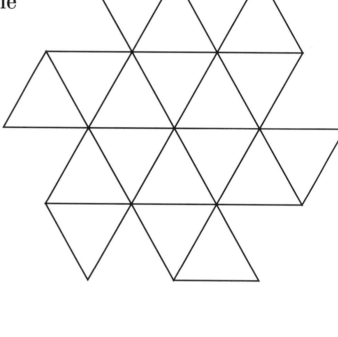

Color the designs to
show the symmetry.

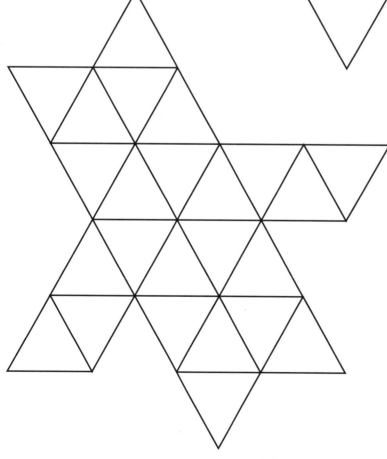

Investigation 4 • Session 2
Mathematical Thinking at Grade 4

Multiple Lines of Symmetry

Use geoboard dot paper, triangle paper, or plain paper
to make the following designs:

Make one design with only one line of symmetry.

Make one design with two lines of symmetry.

Make one design with four lines of symmetry.

Label the lines of symmetry in your designs.

SHADED GEOBOARD DESIGN

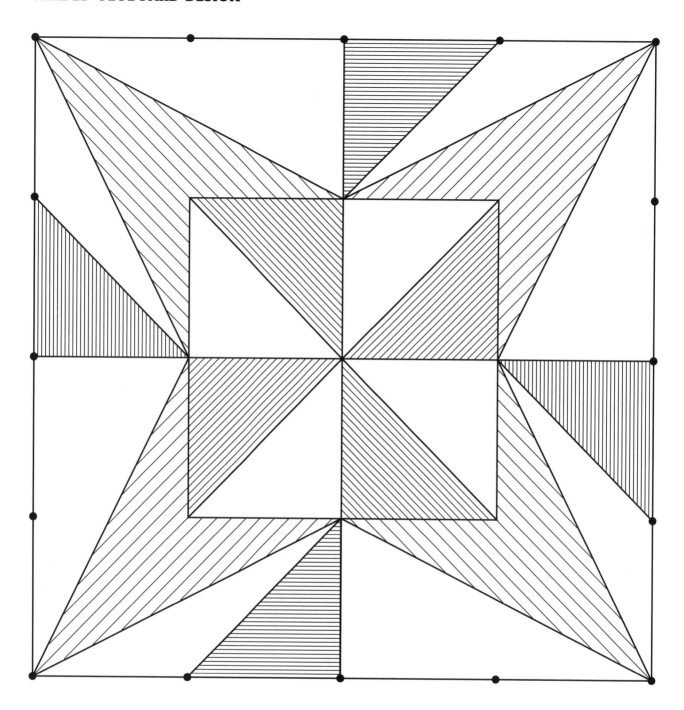

132

GEOBOARD DOT PAPER

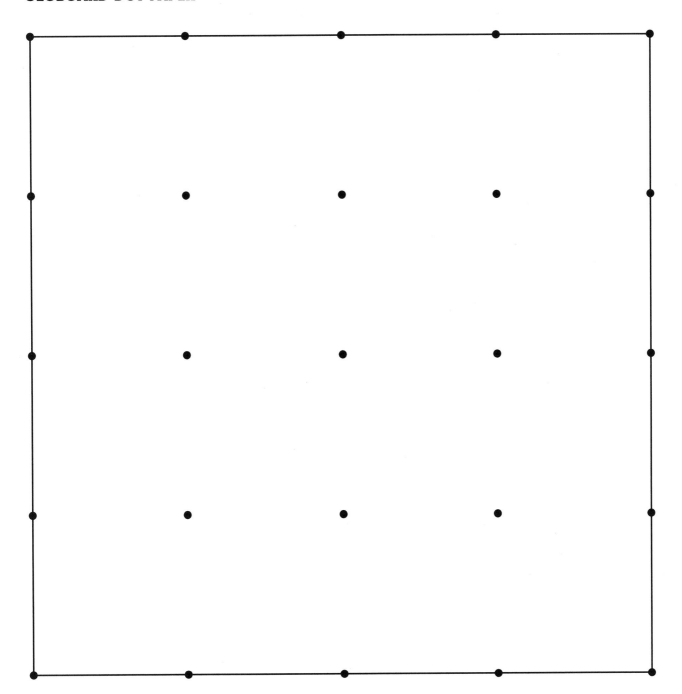

TRIANGLE PAPER

Name _____

GAME 1   Score

Round 1:   ____ ____ + ____ ____ = _____   _____

Round 2:   ____ ____ + ____ ____ = _____   _____

Round 3:   ____ ____ + ____ ____ = _____   _____

Round 4:   ____ ____ + ____ ____ = _____   _____

Round 5:   ____ ____ + ____ ____ = _____   _____

                              TOTAL SCORE _____

Name _____

GAME 2   Score

Round 1:   ____ ____ + ____ ____ = _____   _____

Round 2:   ____ ____ + ____ ____ = _____   _____

Round 3:   ____ ____ + ____ ____ = _____   _____

Round 4:   ____ ____ + ____ ____ = _____   _____

Round 5:   ____ ____ + ____ ____ = _____   _____

                              TOTAL SCORE _____

0	0	1	1
0	0	1	1
2	2	3	3
2	2	3	3

Unit Resource
Mathematical Thinking at Grade 4

4	4	5	5
4	4	5	5
<u>6</u>	<u>6</u>	7	7
<u>6</u>	<u>6</u>	7	7

8	8	<u>9</u>	<u>9</u>
8	8	<u>9</u>	<u>9</u>
WILD CARD	**WILD CARD**		
WILD CARD	**WILD CARD**		

Unit Resource
Mathematical Thinking at Grade 4

COIN VALUE STRIPS

half dollar 50¢   quarter 25¢   dime 10¢   nickel 5¢   penny 1¢

half dollar 50¢   quarter 25¢   dime 10¢   nickel 5¢   penny 1¢

half dollar 50¢   quarter 25¢   dime 10¢   nickel 5¢   penny 1¢

Unit Resource
Mathematical Thinking at Grade 4

Name _____

Activity Choice	✔ When Finished
1. _____	☐
2. _____	☐
3. _____	☐
4. _____	☐
5. _____	☐
6. _____	☐
7. _____	☐
8. _____	☐

Practice Pages

This optional section provides homework ideas for teachers who want or need to give more homework than is assigned to accompany the activities in this unit. The problems included here provide additional practice in learning about number relationships and in solving computation and number problems. For number units, you may want to use some of these if your students need more work in these areas or if you want to assign daily homework. For other units, you can use these problems so that students can continue to work on developing number and computation sense while they are focusing on other mathematical content in class. We recommend that you introduce activities in class before assigning related problems for homework.

Solving Problems in Two Ways   Solving problems in two ways is emphasized throughout the *Investigations* fourth grade curriculum. Here, we provide four sheets of problems that students solve in two different ways. Problems may be addition, subtraction, multiplication, or division. Students record each way they solved the problem. We recommend you give students an opportunity to share a variety of strategies for solving problems before you assign this homework.

Story Problems   Story problems at various levels of difficulty are used throughout the *Investigations* curriculum. The three story problem sheets provided here help students review and maintain skills that have already been taught. You can also make up other problems in this format, using numbers and contexts that are appropriate for your students. Students solve the problems and then record their strategies.

Practice Page A

Solve this problem in two different ways, and write about how you solved it:

$$90 + 45 =$$

Here is the first way I solved it:

Here is the second way I solved it:

Practice Page B

Solve this problem in two different ways, and write about how you solved it:

75 − 16 =

Here is the first way I solved it:

Here is the second way I solved it:

Practice Page C

Solve this problem in two different ways, and write
about how you solved it:

11 × 7 =

Here is the first way I solved it:

Here is the second way I solved it:

Practice Page D

Solve this problem in two different ways, and write about how you solved it:

$$32 \div 4 =$$

Here is the first way I solved it:

Here is the second way I solved it:

145

Practice Page E

The football team scored 4 touchdowns. They got 7 points for each touchdown. How many points do they have?

Show how you solved this problem. You can use numbers, words, or pictures.

Practice Page F

James and I made chocolate chip cookies to sell.
We made 2 batches. Each batch makes 24 cookies. How
many cookies can we sell?

Show how you solved this problem. You can use
numbers, words, or pictures.

Practice Page G

There are 6 people in my family. We bought 2 pizzas. Each pizza has 12 slices. If we share equally, how many slices of pizza will each person get?

Show how you solved this problem. You can use numbers, words, or pictures.

Department of Economic and Social Affairs
Statistics Division

The World's Women 2005
Progress in Statistics

United Nations
New York, 2006

DESA

The Department of Economic and Social Affairs of the United Nations Secretariat is a vital interface between global policies in the economic, social and environmental spheres and national action. The Department works in three main interlinked areas: (i) it compiles, generates and analyses a wide range of economic, social and environmental data and information on which States Members of the United Nations draw to review common problems and to take stock of policy options; (ii) it facilitates the negotiations of Member States in many intergovernmental bodies on joint courses of action to address ongoing or emerging global challenges; and (iii) it advises interested Governments on the ways and means of translating policy frameworks developed in United Nations conferences and summits into programmes at the country level and, through technical assistance, helps build national capacities.

Note

Symbols of United Nations documents are composed of capital letters combined with figures.

ST/ESA/STAT/SER.K/17
ISBN 92-1-161482-1

United Nations publication
Sales No. E.05.XVII.7
Copyright © United Nations, 2006
All rights reserved
Printed by the United Nations
Publishing Section
New York

Message from the Secretary-General

Ten years after the adoption of the Beijing Declaration and Platform for Action, the lack of reliable national statistics on gender issues persists in many parts of the world. In recent years, efforts to monitor the Millennium Development Goals further revealed the inadequacy of those statistics that were available. That is why *The World's Women 2005* focuses on the state and progress of statistics. Based on what countries report to the international statistical system, it analyzes their capacity to produce statistics on gender issues, and highlights progress made in reporting those statistics over the past three decades.

The analysis shows that despite some improvements over the years, much more needs to be done to develop adequate statistics that address gender concerns. This report is intended as a guide to help Governments and other stakeholders strengthen statistical systems, mainstream gender statistics, and further develop concepts and methods for collecting statistics on gender concerns. I urge Governments, non-governmental organizations, researchers, academics and activists around the world to make full use of this valuable tool.

Kofi A. Annan
Secretary-General

Preface

In accordance with the Beijing Platform for Action, adopted at the Fourth World Conference of Women in 1995, the United Nations prepares a new issue of *The World's Women* at regular five-year intervals and distributes it widely. The first issue was published in 1991, and the current one, *The World's Women 2005: Progress in Statistics,* is the fourth in the series.

During the 10 years since the adoption of the Beijing Platform for Action, there has been an increasing demand for sex-disaggregated data and statistical information that adequately reflect the situation of women and men in all aspects of their life. The Platform put gender equality firmly on the policy agenda and laid out the actions required from all stakeholders to improve gender statistics in order to measure and monitor progress towards the achievement of the goals of the Platform.

To monitor progress in gender equality and the advancement of women and to guide policy, it is crucial that reliable and timely statistics be available. Yet official national data on basic demographic and social topics for gender analysis are at times deficient or unavailable. Consequently, much of the trend analysis in the previous editions of *The World's Women* published in 1991, 1995 and 2000 either limited coverage to countries that had reasonably good data over time or relied on national and regional estimates prepared by the international statistical system.

The direction and focus of *The World's Women 2005: Progress in Statistics* is on the state of national statistics useful for addressing gender concerns. That focus is necessary in order to know the extent to which official national statistics, as differentiated from internationally prepared estimates, are available to address various gender concerns. The report reviews the current availability of data and assesses progress made in the provision of gender statistics during the past 30 years. It also identifies areas, such as violence against women, power and decision-making and human rights, where statistics are particularly difficult to obtain owing to their nature or to a lack of well-defined and established concepts, definitions and/or methods of data collection. In addition, it offers suggestions for a way forward in building national statistical capacity, mainstreaming gender statistics and developing and refining concepts and methods relevant to the production of gender statistics. The fourth edition of *The World's Women* therefore takes a somewhat different track from its predecessors, looking at progress rather than trends in statistics.

As in the three previous editions of *The World's Women,* non-technical language has been used to make the publication accessible to a large audience and respond to the needs of different users, including policy makers, non-governmental organizations, researchers, academics and gender specialists.

The World's Women 2005 was prepared by the United Nations Statistics Division of the Department of Economic and Social Affairs (DESA). The Office of the Special Adviser on Gender Issues and Advancement of Women and the Division for the Advancement of Women of DESA provided substantive support for the report. United Nations Regional Commissions and specialized agencies provided statistics, information and guidance in their respective fields of expertise, including the Population Division of DESA, the International Labour Office, the UNESCO Institute for Statistics, the World Health Organization, the Joint United Nations Programme on HIV/AIDS, the office of the United Nations High Commissioner for Refugees, the International Organization for Migration and the United Nations Office on Drugs and Crime.

The Governments of Italy and Germany and the World Food Programme provided financial support for the publication.

Assistance in preparing the report was provided by the following consultants: Lorraine Corner, who drafted some chapters; Tina Johnson, who edited the first drafts; and Nicki Adler and Jim Eschinger, who designed the text pages of this publication.

José Antonio Ocampo
Under-Secretary-General
   for Economic and Social Affairs
December 2005

Executive summary

Why report on progress in statistics?

The World's Women 2005: Progress in Statistics focuses on the state of statistics for addressing gender concerns. It reviews the current availability of national data and assesses progress in data reporting from 1975 to 2003, based on the information that national statistical authorities report to the international statistical system.[1] The statistics reviewed include those related to population, health, education and work. Also reviewed in the report is the current state of statistics in some of the relatively newer areas, namely violence against women; poverty; power and decision-making; and human rights.

The focus on official national statistics, as differentiated from internationally prepared estimates, reveals the extent to which Governments are able to produce statistics to address various gender concerns. By so doing, the report provides Governments with the means to assess progress, identify gaps and design strategies to improve the national collection and dissemination of gender statistics needed for policy formulation and programme planning and evaluation.

It is hoped that such assessment of national capacity to report on various topics can assist national statistics offices to obtain the increased budgetary and human resources needed for sustainable improvements in statistics. The assessment can reveal the realistic level of statistical capacity to produce sex-disaggregated Millennium Development Goal indicators at the country level. This would help pinpoint the areas where technical support is most crucial. Gender specialists can also use the report as an advocacy tool for the improvement of gender statistics.

The current situation 1995-2003

The capacity of countries to report sex-disaggregated official national statistics during the period 1995–2003 has been mixed. This is illustrated by the reporting of 204 countries or areas on some basic topics. Chart A shows the number of countries that have reported data on those topics for at least one year during the period 1995-2003. It also shows the

number that reported the data by sex. As the chart shows, population and enrolment are widely reported, with more than 180 countries reporting population and primary and secondary enrolment. Statistics on births, deaths and economic activity are not as widely reported, with between 100 and 160 countries reporting the data. The large number of countries unable to provide data by sex on wages, births and deaths is a cause for concern.

Chart A

Number of countries or areas that reported data on selected topics at least once during the period 1995–2003

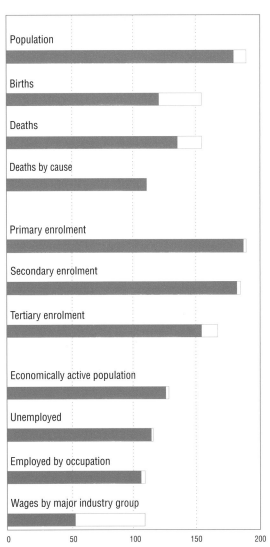

■ By sex
□ Not by sex

Population

Births

Deaths

Deaths by cause

Primary enrolment

Secondary enrolment

Tertiary enrolment

Economically active population

Unemployed

Employed by occupation

Wages by major industry group

0   50   100   150   200

Number of countries or areas

Sources:
See chapter 1, table 1.A; chapter 2, table 2.A; chapter 3, table 3A; and chapter 4, table 4.A.

Reporting of data varies greatly by geographic region. Europe has the highest reporting and Africa the lowest. Other regions fall between the two extremes. Similarly, the more developed regions report the most data and the least developed countries the least.

The situation in Africa is such that well over half of the countries provided sex-disaggregated data on population and on primary, secondary and tertiary enrolment at least once between 1995 and 2003. However, less than a third were able to provide data on births, deaths and the economic characteristics of the population by sex. Additional details for Africa and the other regions are provided in summary tables available at the end of each chapter. Annex tables A1 to A4 present detailed national data on the same topics.

A review of three decades
1975-1984, 1985-1994 and
1995-2003

A global review of three decades of reporting by Governments shows fairly limited progress in the reporting of official national statistics worldwide. Assessment of progress for the most recent period is, however, inconclusive owing to delays in national reporting by statistical systems. Countries often take several years or longer to report their most recent statistics. The review finds that to a great extent countries that reported data thirty years ago continue to do so today. Similarly, many countries that did not report thirty years ago still do not report. However, a number of countries move from reporting in one period to not reporting in the next, and vice versa. On balance, the result is illustrated in chart B below, which shows the reporting of total population, economically active population and number of deaths, by sex and age.

Comparing the two graphs in chart B, it is evident that fewer countries are able to report annual data frequently (i.e. for at least 5 years in a 10-year period[2]) by sex and age. Two types of gaps are evident from the graphs: first, the gap between reporting at least once and frequent reporting, represented by those countries that report data for less than five years in a period; second, the gap representing those countries that did not report at all.

Frequent reporting of annual data on the economically active population by sex and age has increased over the three periods. However, reporting of the economically active population has not yet reached the levels of reporting that are available for total population or for number of deaths.

The report also noted that a number of countries have initiated the collection of data on new topics important to the study of gender. More countries now have some data on violence against women, the participation of women and men in the informal sector and time use of women and men. However, data collection on those issues remains largely ad hoc and has not been incorporated into the regular statistical work programme of the national statistics offices. For developing countries, it is often dependent on external resources or, in some cases, the support of national women's machineries.

Chart B

Number of countries or areas that reported sex- and age-disaggregated statistics for at least one year and for at least five years, for three periods

Population

Economically active population

Deaths

Sources:
Prepared by the United Nations Statistics Division, Department of Economic and Social Affairs, based on data from the International Labour Office, LABORSTA database and the United Nations *Demographic Yearbook* system.

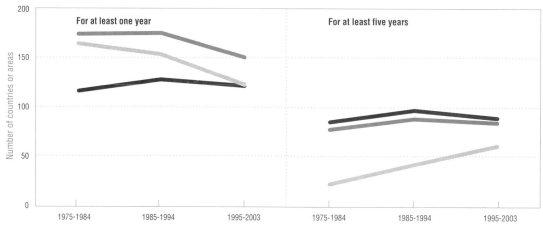

Contents

oped: poverty, power and decision-making, and human rights. The conclusion offers a number of strategies to help improve the capacity of national statistical systems to meet the demand for gender statistics.

Most of the basic data presented in the substantive chapters are contained in much greater detail in Annex 1 at the end of the report. The first four tables in the statistical annex contain the data analyzed in the chapters on national reporting of selected statistics to the international statistical system, by country. The remaining six tables in the statistical annex present the most recent statistics and indicators on the situation of women and men in the areas of concern reviewed in the present volume. These data are included to allow comparisons over time with data reported in prior editions of *The World's Women*.

Notes

1   Examples include the four regional handbooks in the *Women of the World* series published between May 1984 and February 1985 by the Office of Women in Development, Bureau of Program and Policy Coordination, United States Agency for International Development, under contract with the United States Bureau of the Census.

2   *Report of the World Conference to Review and Appraise the Achievements of the United Nations Decade for Women: Equality, Development and Peace, Nairobi, 15-26 July 1985* (United Nations publication, Sales No. E.85.IV.10), paras. 122 and 130.

3   Sweden has been promoting the development and production of gender statistics nationally and globally through technical cooperation and support provided by Statistics Sweden and the Swedish development assistance agency, SIDA. *Women and Men in Sweden: Facts and Figures,* first published in 1985 by Statistics Sweden, has been a model for publications in countries in Africa, Asia, Europe and Latin America.

4   *Report of the Fourth World Conference on Women, Beijing, 4–15 September 1995* (United Nations publication, Sales No. E.96.IV.13), chap. I, resolution 1, annex II, para. 206 (a).

5   Resolution S-23/3, annex, para. 77.

6   *Official Records of the Economic and Social Council, 2005, Supplement No. 7* (E/2005/27 and Corr. 1), chap. I, sect. D, resolution 49/4, para. 5.

7   See *Official Records of the Economic and Social Council, 2005, Supplement No. 4* (E/2005/24), chap. VI, para. 24 (a).

8   Office of the Special Advisor on Gender Issues and Advancement of Women, "Gender mainstreaming: strategy for promoting gender equality" (New York, United Nations, August 2001). Available from http://www.un.org/womenwatch/osagi/pdf/factsheet1.pdf.

9   Ibid.

10   See *Report of the Fourth World Conference on Women, Beijing, 4-15 September 1995* (United Nations publication, Sales No. E.96.IV.13), chap. I, resolution 1, annex II, paras. 206–209.

11   Definition of gender mainstreaming adopted by the Economic and Social Council in July 1997. See *Official Records of the General Assembly, 1997, Supplement No. 3* (A/52/3/Rev.1 and Add.1), chap. IV, sect., A, agreed conclusions 1997/2.

12   See http://www.un.org/special-rep/ohrlls/ldc/list.htm

13   United Nations, *World Population Prospects: The 2004 Revision,* Comprehensive CD-Rom edition (United Nations publication, Sales No. E.05.XIII.11).

14   *Principles and Recommendations for Population and Housing Censuses, Revision 1* (United Nations publication, Sales No. E.98.XVII.8 and Corr.), para. 1.1.

Chapter 1
Population, households and families

"… gender inequities have significant influences on, and are in turn influenced by, demographic parameters such as population growth, structure and distribution."
Programme of Action of the International Conference on Population and Development

Information on population, households and families contributes to a better understanding of gender inequities in many aspects of life. The size and composition of a population can reveal gender differences in migration, births, deaths and related processes. Information on marriages and divorces sheds light on the formation and dissolution of families. Data on households and families can improve understanding of the opportunities and resources available to women and men at different stages in life. Detailed statistics on population, households and families are, therefore, essential for addressing some of the gender concerns voiced at international conferences and summits.

The present chapter reviews the reporting by Governments of statistics on the following four topics: population; births; marriage and divorce; and households.

Current state of statistics 1995-2003

Population

The size and sex-age composition (numbers of females and males in various age groups) of a population and how they change over time have important implications for the situation of women and men. They determine to a great extent the current needs of the population and needs that are likely to arise in the future. Information on population by sex and age is also essential for the calculation of rates, ratios, proportions, percentages and other measures used to facilitate comparisons over time and across countries or among subnational groups, including comparisons between women and men.

Population censuses are the primary source of information on the size and composition of the population. Most countries conduct at least one population census every ten years. For the census decade 1995-2004, however, 26 countries or areas out of the

204 included in the present review did not conduct a population census (box 1.1).

To aid policymaking and planning, as well as to provide the population base for calculating annual rates and measures, it is essential that a country estimate periodically its population size. Between censuses, national statistical offices prepare estimates of their country's population, usually disaggregated by sex and age (box 1.2). Ideally, population estimates are produced on an annual basis for use in planning and policy formulation.

Box 1.1

	All countries or areas	Conducted a census	Did not conduct a census
Census taking worldwide			

It is recommended that countries conduct at least one population census every ten years.[a] In the most recent census decade (1995-2004), the vast majority of countries or areas in the world—178 out of 204—conducted a population census. Of the 26 that did not conduct one, most are in Africa, where 16 out of 55 countries or areas did not conduct a census.

	All countries or areas	Conducted a census	Did not conduct a census
World	**204**	178	26
Africa	**55**	39	16
North America	**27**	26	1
South America	**13**	11	2
Asia	**50**	44	6
Europe	**42**	41	1
Oceania	**17**	17	0

a *Principles and Recommendations for Population and Housing Censuses, rev. 1* (United Nations publication, Sales No. E.98.XVII.8), para 1.9.

Between 1995 and 2003 the vast majority of countries—189 out of 204—reported total population at least once. For population data to be most useful in addressing gender concerns, it needs to be

Detailed statistics on population, households and families are essential for addressing gender concerns

For the census decade 1995-2004, 26 countries or areas did not conduct a population census

Box 1.2

National population estimates

To produce a population estimate, information or benchmark population data for a specified date is needed. The data are taken from a census, a population register, compulsory registration, or a large-scale national population survey. Additional information is then used to adjust the benchmark population data and arrive at a current estimate. Some of the more common adjustment methods that countries use include the following:

- **Adjustment by continuous registers.** This is possible in countries that have comprehensive civil or population registration systems. Such systems serve as a basis for producing national population estimates or for evaluating estimates produced using other methods;

- **Adjustment based on the calculated balance of births, deaths and migration.** This method involves adding births and immigrants to and subtracting deaths and out-migrants from the last population count or the latest previous estimate;

- **Adjustment by assumed rate of population increase.** This method is used by some countries that have no reliable information on population change. In this case, the base population may be from a census, a partial registration system or an estimate from a sample survey. To produce a current population estimate, the base population is updated using an assumed rate of population increase.

Types of estimates that national statistical offices prepare include the total population of a country or area and particular groups of the population in the area, classified by sex, age, marital status, employment status, educational attainment, ethnicity, and so on. The most common estimates are of total population disaggregated by sex and age. They are usually produced at the national level and for major administrative subdivisions. An estimate may be evaluated by comparing it with another estimate produced by a different method and, at times, by using different information.

---

further disaggregated by sex and by sex and age. Compared to the number of countries reporting total population, a smaller number reported the information by sex and by sex and age at least once. Indeed, chart 1.1 shows that the number of countries reporting statistics on population at least once decreases as more detailed information is called for. Of the 204 countries or areas, 179 reported total population by

sex at least once and 151 provided the data further disaggregated by age.

Considerable differences exist among geographic regions and development groups in the reporting of total population disaggregated by sex and age at least once. Among the six regions, Africa and Oceania have the smallest relative number of countries or areas reporting such data: 23 of the 55 countries or areas in Africa and 9 of the 17 in Oceania. In terms of development groups, the lowest reporting is among the least developed countries where 17 out of the 50 countries provided total population by sex and age at least once (see table 1.A).

When considering the frequency of reporting, there is a significant drop in the number of countries providing total population by sex and age frequently (at least five out of nine years) compared to the number providing the data at least once. Of the 204 countries or areas reviewed, 83 reported total population by sex and age frequently, representing 66 per cent of the world population (chart 1.1 and table 1.B).

Differences between regions and development groups are also apparent in the case of frequent reporting of total population by sex and age. Again, the geographic regions with the smallest relative

Chart 1.1

Number of countries or areas that reported population data between 1995 and 2003

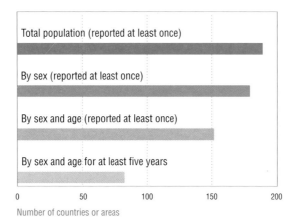

number of countries reporting the information frequently are Africa and Oceania. In Africa, 8 of the 55 countries or areas provided total population by sex and age frequently. The corresponding number in Oceania is 4 out of 17 countries. In terms of development groups, frequent reporting of total population by sex and age is lowest among the least developed countries: just 5 of the 50 countries provided the information for at least five years (see table 1.A).

Births

One of the key determinants of population change is fertility—the number of births that occur to an individual or in a population. Information on fertility is needed for projecting the rate of population growth or decline. In addition, knowing the number of births taking place within a country and some of their key characteristics such as the sex and place of birth is crucial for informed national policy-making and planning.

For example, an area of concern in some countries is the practice of prenatal sex selection and female infanticide, owing to a strong preference for sons. Prenatal sex selection and female infanticide[1] can lead to a sex ratio at birth that strongly favours males over females. Data on the number of births by sex can point to those discriminatory practices against girls.

Likewise, statistics on the number of births by age of the mother can be used to monitor changes in the ages at which women tend to have children. Early childbearing is a concern highlighted in the Beijing Platform for Action, which notes that pregnancy at very young ages increases the risk of maternal death and of complications during pregnancy and delivery[2]—a problem also faced by women giving birth towards the end of their reproductive years. Furthermore, early childbearing can severely curtail the educational and employment opportunities of women thereby limiting improvements in their educational, economic and social status.[3]

The main source of information on births is the civil registration system of a country. Countries that have a civil registration system derive information on births from vital statistics based on the registration system, even if the civil registration system is known to be deficient (see box 1.3). Countries may also estimate the total number of births from censuses or surveys.

Of the 204 countries or areas included in the review, 111 reported births from a civil registration system said to cover at least 90 per cent of the coun-

Just 5 of the 50 least developed countries provided data on population by sex and age for at least five years

Examining the number of births by sex can point to discriminatory practices against girls

Box 1.3

Civil registration and vital statistics

Statistics on births, deaths and marriages are collectively referred to as **vital statistics**. In most countries, they are compiled from birth certificates, death certificates or marriage certificates that are issued by civil authorities when individuals report births and deaths or apply for a marriage license. The recording of these events is called civil registration. **Civil registration** is defined as the continuous, permanent, compulsory and universal recording of occurrence and characteristics of vital events, most notably births, deaths and marriages.

Governments have a vested interest in the proper functioning of the civil registration system: documents issued by civil registrars are legal tenders that entitle the bearer to a number of services such as school enrolment, medical care, family benefit programmes, social protection, pensions and inheritances, among others.

An effective civil registration system provides a continuous and important source of information on fertility, mortality and marriage. For example, the civil registration system, in issuing a birth certificate, may require information on the characteristics of (a) the mother: age, marital status, nationality, place of birth, place of usual residence, number of previous births, date of last birth, date of marriage, occupation; (b) the father: age, marital status, nationality, place of birth, place of usual residence, occupation; and (c) the child: sex, place and date of birth, birth order. All of the preceding information is transferred to official statistics, which removes individual identifiers (name, personal identification number) and aggregates them into a set of vital statistics. For vital statistics to be most effective as policy tools, there needs to be a well-functioning civil registration system that is universal (i.e., with coverage of at least 90 per cent of all events) and a vital statistics system that produces and disseminates statistical information about births, deaths and marriages in a timely manner.

Source:
Principles and Recommendations for a Vital Statistics System, Rev. 2 (United Nations publication, Sales No. E.01.XVII.10), paras. 301 and 423.

try's total births (see table 1.A). The issue of coverage is crucial to the quality of the information and can vary widely across countries. Some birth registration systems may be limited to births only in urban areas or to those taking place in hospitals. In many countries, limited coverage can result in a large proportion of births not being counted (see box 1.4).

Out of 204 countries or areas, 153 reported the total number of births at least once and 124 reported the information frequently. As in the case with reporting of population statistics, a smaller number of countries reported the more detailed statistics on births compared with the number reporting total births. Out of the 204 countries or areas, 120 reported the number of births by sex and 113 the number of births by age of mother at least once. The pattern of fewer countries reporting detailed birth statistics is observed across all geographic regions and development groups (see table 1.A).

The national reporting of births by sex at least once varies across geographic regions and development groups. Europe, North America and South America have the highest relative number of countries reporting total births by sex at least once whereas Africa and Oceania have the smallest relative num-

Box 1.4

Setting up a civil registration system: a major commitment

Setting up and maintaining a civil registration system requires a major commitment by the government, if the system is to be continuous and universal. For many countries, the process is incremental. Colombia, for example, initiated a civil registration system in January 1998, after years spent in its development. However, the system has yet to achieve 90 per cent coverage for births and deaths. In Accra, the capital of Ghana, births and deaths are registered when they take place in major hospitals, but not when these events take place elsewhere. At present, less than 30 per cent of births are registered in the country.

ber reporting with 14 out of 55 in Africa and 6 out of 17 in Oceania (see table 1.A). In Asia, 30 out of the 50 countries reported such information. However, among those not reporting are China, India and Indonesia—the three most populous countries in the continent. As a result, at 19 per cent, Asia has the lowest percentage of the regional population living in a country that reported births by sex at least once (chart 1.2).

Among development groups, whereas 45 of the 47 countries in the more developed regions reported births by sex at least once, just 6 of the 50 least developed countries did so. In the less developed regions excluding the least developed countries, 69 of the 107 countries reported the information (see table 1.A).

The pattern of reporting births by age of mother at least once across geographic regions and development groups is similar to that of births by sex (see table 1.A).

Marriage and divorce

Marriage and divorce are vital events that have important implications for the situation of women and men, for the organization of society, and for population change. As key events in the formation and dissolution of families, marriage and divorce strongly influence many aspects of the lives of women and men including their access to resources and opportunities and their living arrangements. Detailed statistics on marriage and divorce are, therefore, crucial for revealing disparities between women and men in many areas as well as for planning and for the allocation of programmes and services, including those

Chart 1.2

Percentage of the population in countries or areas that reported births by sex of child at least once between 1995 and 2003, by region

Source:
Table 1.B

related to housing and a wide variety of family benefits.

For example, information on first marriages by age of bride and groom is important for monitoring changes in the ages at which women and men first marry and in the age gap between spouses. Early marriage, in particular, is a stated concern of the Beijing Platform for Action.[4] Information on marriages by previous marital status is likewise important for revealing gender differences in remarriage.

Different sources of information are required for statistics to capture the diversity of marriage and divorce practices within and across countries and regions.[5] The results presented below refer to statistics on registered marriages and divorces produced by national vital statistics systems from civil registers of marriages and divorces (see box 1.5). In some cases, information on registered divorces may also be obtained from court records.

At the global level, 134 out of 204 countries or areas reported the total number of marriages at least once and 107 reported such information frequently (table 1.A). A much smaller number of countries reported statistics on marriage disaggregated by characteristics of the bride and groom. For example, 85 countries or areas reported the number of first marriages by age of the bride and groom and 84, the total

Chart 1.3

Percentage of the population in countries or areas that reported information on marriages between 1995 and 2003

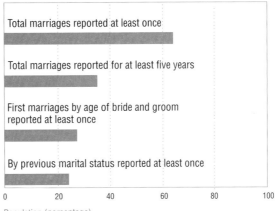

Total marriages reported at least once

Total marriages reported for at least five years

First marriages by age of bride and groom reported at least once

By previous marital status reported at least once

Population (percentage)

Source:
Table 1.B

number of marriages by previous marital status of the bride and groom. The percentage of the world population in countries that reported such marriage statistics is shown in chart 1.3.

Fewer countries or areas reported total divorces compared to marriages. Of the 204 countries or areas, 119 reported the number of divorces at least once and 94 reported such information frequently (see table 1.A). A smaller number of countries reported divorce statistics further disaggregated by other characteristics—64 reported at least once the total number of divorces by number of dependent children and 78, the total number of divorces by length of marriage. As a result, 23 per cent of the world population is in countries that reported, at least once, those detailed divorce statistics.

Wide differences exist in the reporting of marriage and divorce statistics among geographic regions (see table 1.A). In terms of marriage, all of the countries in Europe, and nearly all of the countries in North America and South America reported total marriages at least once. In Asia, 36 of the 50 countries reported such information at least once. Africa and Oceania have the smallest relative number of countries reporting total marriages: 12 out of 55 in Africa and 9 out of 17 in Oceania. Although about half of the countries in Oceania did not report total marriages at least once, 80 per cent of the continent's population lives in a country reporting such statistics (table 1.B). This is because among those reporting are Australia and New Zealand which together account for 74 per cent of the continent's population.

Box 1.5

Definition of marriage and divorce for the production of vital statistics

The recommended statistical definitions for the production of vital statistics on marriage and divorce are as follows:

Marriage is the act, ceremony or process by which the legal relationship of husband and wife is constituted. The legality of the union may be established by civil, religious or other means as recognized by the laws of each country.

Divorce is the final legal dissolution of a marriage, that is, that separation of husband and wife that confers on the parties the right to remarriage under civil, religious and/or other provisions, according to the laws of each country.

Source:
Principles and Recommendations for a Vital Statistics System, Rev. 2 (United Nations publication, Sales No. E.01.XVII.10), para. 57.

23 per cent of the world population is in countries that reported detailed divorce statistics

All countries in Europe and nearly all countries in North and South America reported total marriages

In terms of divorce, the regional variation in reporting follows a similar pattern as that observed for the reporting of marriage statistics, although the levels of reporting are lower (table 1.A). Chart 1.4 shows the percentage of the regional population in countries reporting divorce statistics. In all regions, fewer countries reported divorces by number of dependent children and by length of marriage as compared to the number reporting total divorces (table 1.A).

Among the least developed countries, the reporting of marriage and divorce statistics is rare. Only six and four countries in this group reported, respectively, the total number of marriages and divorces. None of the 50 least developed countries

reported statistics on marriage or divorce beyond total numbers (see table 1.A).

Households

Statistics on households are required for planning the supply, distribution and allocation of a wide variety of programmes, products and services, including such basic necessities as food and housing. When information such as the sex and age of the household head (see box 1.6 for definition) and the size of the household is available, household statistics can also be used to study gender differences in headship. A rise in female-headed households is a stated concern of the Beijing Platform for Action owing to the association between female-maintained households and poverty.[6]

> Among the least developed countries, the reporting of marriage and divorce statistics is rare

Chart 1.4

Percentage of the population in countries or areas that reported total divorces, divorces by length of marriage and divorces by number of dependent children at least once between 1995 and 2003

Total divorces ▮

Divorces by length of marriage ▮

Divorces by number of dependent children ▮

Source:
Table 1.B

Population (percentage)

Box 1.6

Definitions: household and head of household

For data collection purposes, there are two primary definitions of **household**. The most commonly used definition is that based on the housekeeping concept which classifies households as either (a) a one-person household, that is, a person who makes provision for his/her own food or other essentials for living without combining with any other person to form part of a multi-person household, or (b) a multi-person household, that is, a group of two or more persons who make common provision for food or other essentials for living. According to this definition, the persons in the group may pool their incomes and have a common budget to a greater or lesser extent; they may be related or unrelated persons or a combination of both. Alternatively, based on the house-dwelling concept, a household is defined as consisting of all persons living together in a housing unit.

For establishing relationships among household members, a common practice is to first identify the household head or a reference person. The **head of household** is defined as that person in the household who is acknowledged as such by the other members. The **reference person** is chosen solely for the purpose of establishing relationships, with no implication of headship. At present, there is no common definition of reference person. However, it is recommended that the term be used in situations where spouses are considered equal in household authority and responsibility.

Source:
Population and Housing Censuses, Rev.1 (United Nations publication, Sales No. E.98.XVII.8), paras. 2.61-2.70

For data collection purposes, the concept of "household" is more often used than that of the "family", and the two do not always overlap. Household information largely comes from population and housing censuses. This information is often complemented by information from household surveys.

Reporting of statistics on households from population censuses since 1995 has been slow. Thus far only 59 countries or areas, representing 43 per cent of the world population, have reported the total number of households from a census. Household data disaggregated by sex and age of the head of household was reported by an even smaller number of countries—42, representing 20 per cent of the world population. Statistics further disaggregated by size of household were reported by 39 countries or areas, representing 19 per cent of the world population (table 1.A and chart 1.5).

In terms of geographic regions, Europe has the highest relative number of countries reporting household statistics followed by Asia; whereas Oceania has the lowest relative number with just one country reporting household statistics from the census since 1995 (table 1.A). North and South America are the regions with the highest percentage of the population living in countries that reported household statistics (chart 1.5). This is primarily because the most populous countries in those regions are among those that reported the information (Canada and the United States in North America, and Brazil in South America).

Progress in statistics
1975-2003

Population

Reporting of population statistics by sex and age appears to have remained fairly stable between 1975 and 2003. Chart 1.6 shows that a similar number of countries reported total population by sex and age at least once in the first two periods: 175 in 1975-1984 and 176 in 1985-1994. Compared to the first two periods, a smaller number of countries or areas reported such data at least once in the most recent period (1995-2003). However, this is likely the result of the following two factors and, therefore, may not reflect a real decline in reporting. First, the most recent period is shorter by one year compared to the first two periods. Second, data for the more recent years may not have been reported by 2003 due to delays in data processing and reporting.

Chart 1.5

Percentage of the population in countries or areas that reported selected household statistics at least once between 1995 and 2003, by region

Population (percentage)

Total households

Households by sex and age of head

Housenholds by sex and age of head and size of household

Source:
Table 1.B

Amidst the overall stability in reporting, improvements are observed in the frequency of reporting across periods. Between the periods 1975-1984 and 1985-1994, the number of countries or areas reporting total population by sex and age frequently increased from 76 to 87. A smaller number of countries or areas—83—reported the information frequently in the most recent period. This is likely due to the factors described above and may not reflect a real decline in frequent reporting over time (chart 1.6).

Indeed, a closer look reveals that between the periods 1985-1994 and 1995-2003, 19 countries or areas progressed from reporting infrequently (1-4 years in the 10-year period) to reporting frequently (at least 5 years).[7] An additional 3 coun-

Reporting of statistics on households from of population censuses has been slow

Reporting of population statistics by sex and age appears to have remained fairly stable between 1975 and 2003

Chart 1.6

Distribution of countries or areas by frequency of reporting population by sex and age, for three periods

Frequency of reporting	1975 – 1984		1985 – 1994		1995 – 2003	
	Number of countries or areas	Population (%)	Number of countries or areas	Population (%)	Number of countries or areas	Population (%)
All countries or areas	204	100	204	100	204	100
At least 5 years	76	48	87	51	83	66
1-4 years	99	48	89	45	68	24
Not reported	29	4	28	4	53	10

Source:
Prepared by the United Nations Statistics Division, Department of Economic and Social Affairs,
based on data from the *Demographic Yearbook* system (November 2004).

National reporting of statistics on births was fairly consistent in the three periods considered

The majority of countries that reported statistics on births frequently did so consistently across all three periods

tries (Cambodia, Grenada and Mongolia) progressed from not reporting in the 1985-1994 period to reporting data for at least five years in the most recent period. On the other hand, five countries (Andorra, Bosnia and Herzegovina, Burundi, Chad and Eritrea) that reported frequently in the period 1985-1994 did not report once in the most recent period.

Births

National reporting of statistics on births was fairly consistent in the three periods considered. In addition, there are signs of improvement over time in the reporting of total births and of births by sex at least once (chart 1.7). As in the case of population statistics, a shorter most recent period and delays in reporting are likely the reasons behind the decrease in the number of countries reporting total births and births by sex at least once in the most recent period compared to the second period.

The trends in frequent reporting of births statistics are mixed. There was a slight decline in the number of countries or areas reporting the total number of births for at least five years between the first and second periods. At the same time, there was an increase in the number of countries reporting births by sex (chart 1.7).

It is important to note that the majority of countries that reported statistics on births frequently did so consistently across all three periods. Of the 204 countries or areas, 118 consistently reported total births for at least five years in each of the three periods. In the case of births by sex, 70 countries consistently reported the information frequently in each of the three periods. At the same time, out of the 204 countries or areas, 29 have never reported total births and 53 have never reported births by sex since 1975 (chart 1.8).

Chart 1.7

Number of countries or areas reporting births at least once and for at least five years, for three periods

	1975 - 1984	1985 - 1994	1995 - 2003
All countries or areas	204	204	204
Total, at least once	150	160	153
By sex, at least once	128	135	120
Total, for at least five years	135	131	124
By sex, for at least five years	99	111	95

Source:
Prepared by the United Nations Statistics Division, Department of Economic and Social Affairs, based on data from the United Nations *Demographic Yearbook* system (November 2004).

Chart 1.8

Number of countries or areas that reported frequently and that never reported births in all three periods considered

	All countries or areas	Frequency of reporting	
		Frequent	Never
Total births	204	118	29
By sex	204	70	53

Source:
Prepared by the United Nations Statistics Division, Department of Economic and Social Affairs, based on data from the United Nations *Demographic Yearbook* system (November 2004).

Marriage and divorce

Globally, the reporting of marriage and divorce statistics has changed only slightly since 1975 (chart 1.9). After a peak in reporting in the early 1980s, there has been a slight but steady decline in the number of countries reporting marriage and divorce statistics each year. The steeper decline observed from 1999 onward in chart 1.9 is partially the result of delays in reporting which can range between two and five or more years from the time of data registration.

Since 1975, the gap between the number of countries reporting total marriages each year and the number reporting the more detailed statistics on marriages has remained roughly the same. Each year, less than half of the countries that report total marriages report marriages by previous marital status of bride and groom or first marriages by age of bride and groom.

Likewise, there continues to be a gap in the number of countries each year reporting total marriages and the number reporting total divorces. That gap, however, appears to have become smaller in the more recent years.

Households

In terms of household information, the global trend in the last three decades has been one of overall decline in reporting. Between the periods 1975-1984 and 1985-1994, the number of countries or areas reporting at least once total households by sex and age of head from censuses declined from 66 to 53. For the most recent period, the number of countries or areas reporting such data at least once further declined to 42. It is important to note, however, that the time lag in reporting household data is generally longer than for other census data. Household data may not be disseminated for several years after a census is conducted. Countries that conducted their census late in the period would not have had the opportunity to disseminate household data by the end of 2004.

Challenges

For many countries, developing the capacity to produce basic demographic statistics—and consequently gender statistics—on a regular and timely basis remains a major challenge. At the minimum, this would require the implementation of a population and housing census every 10 years and the setting up and maintenance of a well-functioning civil registration system. Both programmes require extensive resources and long-term commitment from the highest levels of government, which may not be available in the least developed countries.

The reporting of marriage and divorce statistics has changed only slightly since 1975

For many countries, developing the capacity to produce basic demographic statistics remains a major challenge

Chart 1.9

Number of countries or areas that reported statistics on marriages and divorces, from 1975 through 2003

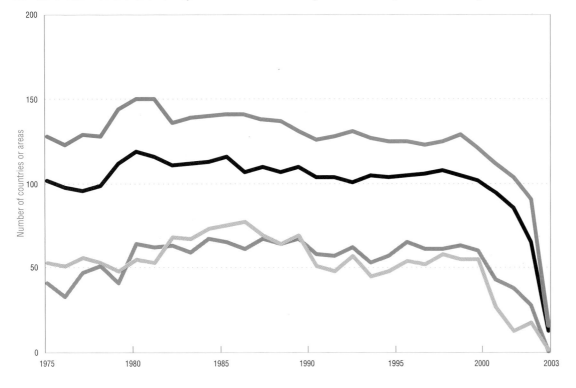

— Total marriages

— Total divorces

— Marriages by previous marital status

— First marriages by age of bride and groom

Source:
Prepared by the United Nations Statistics Division, Department of Economic and Social Affairs, based on data from the *United Nations Demographic Yearbook* system (November 2004).

A challenge for gender
specialists, is to help
maximize the value
of censuses for gender
analysis

Maintaining a civil
registration system is a
considerable challenge
for less developed
countries

A population and housing census is one of the most important statistical activities undertaken by Governments. The census can be a rich source of gender statistics—if the concepts, definitions and methods used in the collection and analysis of data are gender-sensitive. A challenge for gender specialists, therefore, is to help maximize the value of censuses for gender analysis by ensuring that a gender perspective is mainstreamed into all stages of the census. The planning of the 2010 round of population censuses provides opportunities for gender specialists and women's groups to assert their information needs and advocate for the use of concepts, definitions and methods that incorporate a gender perspective.

Maintaining a civil registration system that allows the timely and regular production of statistics on births and deaths is a considerable challenge for less developed countries. An effective civil registration and vital statistics system is very costly and its development is a long-term process that resource-poor countries generally find very difficult to sustain. In many of those countries, civil registration systems miss large segments of the population. In some cases, registration is limited to persons residing in urban areas. A practical way for governments seeking to improve the coverage of civil registration systems is to proceed incrementally.

As a component of population change, migration is perhaps even more difficult to measure than births and deaths. With globalization, international migration has grown in importance throughout the world. Concurrent to that, there has been increasing interest in many countries to improve data on international migration. While international guidelines on the collection of data on international migration exist,[8] many concepts and methods need to be further improved and/or elaborated. The fact that women constitute half of international migrants[9] and the differences in personal and migration characteristics between women and men dictate that data collection on migration and migrants be planned with a gender perspective.

Table 1.A
Number of countries or areas that reported data on selected demographic characteristics, 1995 – 2003

		Geographic region						Development group		
	World	Africa	North America	South America	Asia	Europe	Oceania	More developed regions	Less developed regions [a]	Least developed countries
All countries or areas	204	55	27	13	50	42	17	47	107	50
Population										
Total, at least once	189	43	27	13	47	42	17	47	103	39
By sex, at least once	179	35	27	13	47	41	16	46	100	33
By sex and age, at least once	151	23	26	11	43	39	9	44	90	17
By sex and age, for at least five years	83	8	12	6	21	32	4	37	41	5
Births										
Total, at least once	153	22	25	11	39	42	14	47	91	15
From civil registration system[b]	111	9	19	6	26	42	9	47	62	2
Total, for at least five years	124	13	22	10	32	39	8	44	76	4
By sex, at least once	120	14	21	9	30	40	6	45	69	6
By age of mother, at least once	113	8	22	10	27	38	8	43	68	2
Marriages										
Total, at least once	134	12	25	10	36	42	9	47	81	6
Total, for at least five years	107	7	20	8	28	39	5	44	63	0
First marriages by age of bride and groom, at least once	85	5	12	6	21	38	3	42	43	0
By previous marital status, at least once	84	4	15	6	19	36	4	40	44	0
Divorces										
Total, at least once	119	11	25	7	32	39	5	44	71	4
Total, for at least five years	94	5	18	6	25	36	4	40	54	0
By number of dependent children, at least once	64	3	8	2	17	32	2	36	28	0
By length of marriage, at least once	78	4	12	6	20	33	3	37	41	0
Households										
Total, for at least one year	59	5	5	3	22	23	1	27	27	5
By sex and age of head, at least once	42	3	5	1	11	21	1	25	15	2
By sex and age of head and size of household, at least once	39	1	5	1	10	21	1	25	14	0

Source:
Prepared by the United Nations Statistics Division, Department of Economic and Social Affairs, based on data from the
United Nations *Demographic Yearbook* system (November 2004).

a   Excluding the least developed countries.
b   Reported births at least once from a civil registration system with 90 per cent or better coverage of births.

Table 1.B
Percentage of the world and regional populations in countries or areas that reported data on selected demographic characteristics, 1995 – 2003

	World	Africa	North America	South America	Asia	Europe	Oceania	More developed regions	Less developed regions [a]	Least developed countries
All countries or areas	100	100	100	100	100	100	100	100	100	100
Population										
Total, at least once	98	87	100	100	99	100	100	100	99	85
By sex, at least once	97	80	100	100	99	100	100	100	99	79
By sex and age, at least once	90	59	100	98	93	99	79	99	95	38
By sex and age, for at least five years	66	18	73	68	74	76	75	85	69	16
Births										
Total, at least once	68	43	97	98	60	100	98	100	63	41
From civil registration system[b]	30	18	74	23	13	100	79	100	15	0.1
Total, for at least five years	60	26	95	96	52	99	77	99	58	3
By sex, at least once	40	28	96	88	19	99	76	99	29	6
By age of mother, at least once	39	20	97	96	18	98	76	99	28	0
Marriages										
Total, at least once	64	31	97	86	58	100	80	100	59	30
Total, for at least five years	35	14	95	76	15	99	75	99	23	0
First marriages by age of bride and groom, at least once	27	15	34	59	11	100	75	76	18	0
By previous marital status, at least once	24	15	15	66	11	78	75	63	16	0
Divorces										
Total, at least once	59	27	97	66	51	100	76	100	55	11
Total, for at least five years	27	9	36	61	12	98	75	75	18	0
By number of dependent children, at least once	23	14	29	53	9	84	74	66	14	0
By length of marriage, at least once	23	15	32	66	9	71	75	59	16	0
Households										
Total, for at least one year	43	12	85	51	46	34	12	58	45	7
By sex and age of head, at least once	20	6	85	49	10	31	12	56	12	6
By sex and age of head and size of household, at least once	19	0	85	49	9	31	12	56	12	0

Source:
Prepared by the United Nations Statistics Division, Department of Economic and Social Affairs, based on data from the United Nations *Demographic Yearbook* system (November 2004).

a   Excluding the least developed countries.
b   Reported births at least once from a civil registration system with 90 per cent or better coverage of births.

Notes

1   The birth of a female infant subjected to infanticide is often not registered and, therefore, not included in official records.

2   *Report of the Fourth World Conference on Women, Beijing, 4-15 September 1995* (United Nations publication, Sales No. E.96.IV.13), chap. I, resolution 1, annex II, para. 268.

3   Ibid.

4   Ibid., para. 263.

5   Marriage and divorce are defined in terms of laws and customs, making it difficult to arrive at universally applicable statistical definitions. In some countries, for example, marriage is governed by civil law, which may or may not be supplemented with religious rites; in other countries, unions by mutual consent, without ceremonial or legal rites, constitute formal and legally binding contracts. Likewise, the laws and regulations relating to divorce range from total prohibition to the granting of divorce in response to a simple statement or desire or intention.

6   *Report of the Fourth World Conference on Women, Beijing, 4-15 September 1995* (United Nations publication, Sales No. E.96.IV.13), chap. I, resolution 1, annex II, para. 22

7   The 19 countries or areas are: China, Costa Rica, El Salvador, Estonia, Guatemala, Kazakhstan, Kyrgyzstan, Lesotho, Lithuania, Macao Special Administrative Region of China, Malawi, Republic of Moldova, Morocco, Netherlands Antilles, Saint Kitts and Nevis, Slovakia, Tonga, Turkey and Uruguay.

8   See *Recommendations on Statistics of International Migration, Revision 1* (United Nations publication, Sales No. E.98.XVII.14).

9   *World Survey on the Role of Women in Development: Women and International Migration* (United Nations publication, Sales No. E.04.IV.4).

Chapter 2
Health

"Health is a state of complete physical, mental and social well-being and not merely the absence of disease or infirmity."
World Health Organization

The health status of a population is, ironically, often reflected and measured by information about deaths. Data on deaths by sex and age are commonly used to monitor programs and policies aimed at improving health; and also used to calculate age and sex-specific death rates and life expectancies. While women tend to live longer than men, differences in death rates can point to differences in women's and men's position in the household and society, including gender inequality in terms of access to food, health care and other sources of well-being. Death rates by cause help reveal the different patterns of disease for women and men.

The present chapter asks how well countries are doing in providing the basic information needed to monitor the health status of women and men over time. In other words, how countries are faring in terms of reporting their basic health statistics: deaths, illnesses, levels of human functioning and disability. It therefore focuses on the following three main areas:

1. **Mortality**
   a. Total deaths
   b. Infant deaths
   c. Deaths by cause
      i. Maternal deaths
      ii. Deaths due to AIDS

2. **Morbidity**
   a. Prevalence of HIV/AIDS

3. **Human functioning and disability**

Deaths are recorded in civil registration systems that are maintained by Governments for purposes of recording and registering vital events (see chapter 1, box 1.3). Information on deaths is then compiled to produce death statistics. In addition, national demographic and health surveys, and sometimes censuses, also provide data on mortality as well as on morbidity, human functioning and disability. Disease registers and surveillance systems are also important sources of data in some countries or areas.

At the international level, official national statistics on mortality are collected by the United Nations Statistics Division. Statistics on morbidity and causes of death are collected by the World Health Organization. Plans are in place for basic data on human functioning and disability to be collected at the international level by the United Nations Statistics Division.

In the period 1995-2003, even basic statistical data such as the number of deaths of women and men and girls and boys are not being reported for many countries or areas. More than a third of the 204 countries or areas examined did not report the number of deaths by sex even once for the period 1995 to 2003. About half did not report deaths by cause, sex and age at least once in the same period. Moreover, from 1975 to 2003 there has been limited progress in the reporting of deaths and their causes.

Current state of statistics
1995-2003

Mortality

Total deaths

Age and sex-specific death rates are used in calculating life expectancy at birth, which is defined as the average number of years of life a newborn girl or boy is expected to live, if she or he is subject to the age-specific mortality rates prevailing in the year to which the life expectancy refers. In general, women live longer than men, partly for biological reasons, but their natural advantage is significantly reduced in societies where female infant mortality is higher than male infant mortality owing to discrimination against girls. Social and economic disadvantages also have important repercussions in health outcomes.

However, even basic statistical data such as deaths are not available for many countries. In total, 155 countries or areas representing 69 per cent of the world's population reported total number of

Differences in death rates can point to differences in women's and men's position in the household and society

More than a third of all countries or areas do not report the number of deaths by sex. About half do not report deaths by cause, sex and age deaths at least once during the period 1995-2003. Fewer countries or areas reported deaths by sex at least once and fewer still reported by sex and age (see chart 2.1).

There are major differences in the reporting of deaths across geographic regions (see chart 2.2 and table 1.B). The region with the lowest proportion of countries or areas reporting deaths by sex is Africa. Only 18 out of 55 countries or areas, comprising 35 per cent of the region's population, reported national

Chart 2.1

Number of countries or areas that reported deaths for the period 1995 – 2003

All countries or areas	204
Deaths	
Total, at least once	155
By sex, at least once	134
By sex and age, at least once	121
By sex and age, at least five years	88

Source: Table 2.A

data on deaths by sex at least once in the period 1995-2003. In Asia, 33 countries or areas, representing 55 per cent of the region's population, and in Oceania 7 countries or areas, representing 76 per cent of the region's population, reported deaths by sex. The number of countries or areas that reported deaths by sex in the other regions is comparatively higher representing at least 95 per cent of the region's population.

There are a few countries or areas in each region that reported total deaths but did not report them by sex: four in Africa, three in North America, one in South America, seven in Asia, and six in Oceania.[1]

Deaths by sex and age are reported by most countries or areas in North America, South America and Europe. In those regions, the countries or areas reporting the data at least once between 1995 and 2003 account for over 95 per cent of the population of the respective regions.

Substantial differences exist between development groups in the reporting of deaths by sex (chart 2.3). In the more developed regions, all countries reported deaths and did so by sex in the period 1995-2003. In less developed regions, the capacity to report data on deaths is lower, and there is even less capacity to report the data by sex. Excluding the least developed countries, 94 out of the 107 countries or areas in less developed regions reported total deaths and 78 reported deaths by sex in the period 1995-2003. The lowest reporting is among the least developed countries: only 14 of 50 countries reported total deaths, and just 9 of them reported deaths by sex at least once in the same period.

Policymakers and planners increasingly demand that data be annually reported and that these data are current. However, that is not the situation observed in most countries or areas during the period 1995-2003. While 121 out of 204 countries or areas reported deaths by sex and age at least once in the period, only 88 countries or areas reported those data for at least five years out of nine (chart 2.1). Limited reporting is therefore affecting the continuous availability of up-to-date annual information for a number of countries. For recent years the number of countries or areas reporting data is substantially lower than for earlier years. This is largely due to delays in data compilation and dissemination.

Infant deaths

According to the Beijing Platform for Action, son preference is one factor that contributes to differen-

Chart 2.2

Number of countries or areas that reported deaths for the period 1995 – 2003, by geographic region

	Africa	North America	South America	Asia	Europe	Oceania
All countries or areas	55	27	13	50	42	17
Deaths						
Total, at least once	22	25	13	40	42	13
By sex, at least once	18	22	12	33	42	7
By sex and age, at least once	15	21	11	28	40	6
By sex and age, at least five years	4	15	8	20	36	5

Source: Table 2.A

Chart 2.3

Number of countries or areas that reported deaths for the period 1995 – 2003, by development group

	More developed regions	Less developed regions[a]	Least developed countries
All countries or areas	**47**	**107**	**50**
Deaths			
Total, at least once	47	94	14
By sex, at least once	47	78	9
By sex and age, at least once	45	71	5
By sex and age, at least five years	41	46	1

Source: Table 2.A
a Excluding the least developed countries.

tial mortality by sex. As a result, in some countries it is estimated that men outnumber women by 5 in every 100.[2] A preference for sons remains deeply rooted in many societies and girls may have less access to nutrition, preventive care (such as immunization) and health care.[3] Data on infant deaths by sex are needed to see where excess mortality among girls exists so that it can be addressed and eliminated.

While total infant deaths were reported by 143 countries or areas in the period 1995-2003, fewer—114, representing 40 per cent of the world population—reported infant deaths by sex (chart 2.4). The pattern of low reporting in Africa and Asia and high reporting in the other geographic regions, as seen with reporting deaths by sex, also prevails for infant deaths (see table 2.A).

In all regions, there are countries that reported total infant deaths at least once in the period but did not break the data down by sex: seven in Africa, four in North America, two in South America, seven in Asia, two in Europe and seven in Oceania.[4]

Deaths by cause

In terms of reporting statistics on the cause of death, 110 out of 204 countries or areas, representing 59 per cent of the world population, reported cause of death data at least once in the period 1995-2003, whereas 109 countries or areas, also representing 59 per cent of world population, reported cause of death statistics by sex and age at least once in the same period. However, only 87 countries or areas, representing 53 per cent of the world population, reported data for at least five of the nine years (see tables 2.A and 2.B).

The pattern of low reporting from Africa and Asia and high reporting in the other regions that was observed for all deaths and infant deaths can also be observed in the reporting of deaths by cause. The region with the lowest proportion of countries or areas reporting deaths by cause, sex and age is Africa.

Countries or areas that reported causes of death did so at a detailed level (see box 2.1 for examples of the causes of death reported). Among the causes reported are maternal deaths and deaths due to injury, as well as deaths caused by AIDS, malaria and other diseases. The following analysis will focus on two major issues for women's health: maternal deaths and deaths caused by AIDS.

The region with the lowest proportion of countries or areas that report deaths by cause, sex and age is Africa

Chart 2.4

Number of countries or areas that reported infant deaths for the period 1995 – 2003

All countries or areas	**204**
Infant Deaths	
Total, at least once	143
By sex, at least once	114
By sex at least five years	81

Source: Table 2.A

Maternal deaths

According to the Beijing Platform for Action, complications related to pregnancy and childbirth are among the leading causes of death and morbidity of women of reproductive age in many parts of the developing world.[5] The maternal mortality ratio, or number of maternal deaths per 100,000 live births, is a widely used indicator of reproductive health. It is an approximation of the risk of death of women for reasons related to pregnancy and childbirth. Maternal mortality ratio is one of the indicators under the Millennium Development Goals for monitoring improvements in maternal health.[6]

Box 2.1

Main divisions of cause of death and selected subdivisions for presentation of statistics[a]

Disease	ICD-10 code
All causes	A00-Y89
Certain infectious and parasitic diseases	A00-B99
Intestinal infectious diseases	A00-A09
Tuberculosis	A15-A19
Tetanus[b]	A33, A35
Diphtheria	A36
Whooping cough	A37
Meningococcal infection	A39
Septicaemia	A40-A41
Acute poliomyelitis	A80
Measles	B05
Viral hepatitis	B15-B19
Human immunodeficiency virus [HIV] disease	B20-B24
Malaria	B50-B54
Neoplasms	C00-D48
Malignant neoplasms	C00-C97
Malignant neoplasm of lip, oral cavity and pharynx	C00-C14
Malignant neoplasm of oesophagus	C15
Malignant neoplasm of stomach	C16
Malignant neoplasm of colon, rectosigmoid junction, rectum, anus and anal canal	C18-C21
Malignant neoplasm of liver and intrahepatic bile ducts	C22
Malignant neoplasm of pancreas	C25
Malignant neoplasm of trachea, bronchus and lung	C33-C34
Malignant neoplasm of female breast	C50
Malignant neoplasm of cervix uteri	C53
Malignant neoplasm of prostate	C61
Malignant neoplasm of lymphoid, haematopoietic and related tissue	C81-C96
Disorders of the blood and blood-forming organs and certain disorders involving the immune mechanism	D50-D89
Anaemias	D50-D64
Endocrine, nutritional and metabolic diseases	E00-E88
Diabetes mellitus	E10-E14
Malnutrition	E40-E46
Mental and behavioural disorders	F01-F99
Diseases of the nervous system	G00-G98
Diseases of the circulatory system	I00-I99
Acute rheumatic fever and chronic rheumatic heart diseases	I01-I09
Hypertensive diseases	I10-I13
Ischaemic heart diseases	I20-I25
Cerebrovascular diseases	I60-I69

Box 2.1 continued

Main divisions of cause of death and selected subdivisions for presentation of statistics [a]

Diseases of arteries, arterioles and capillaries	I70-I79
Diseases of the respiratory system	J00-J98
Influenza	J10-J11
Pneumonia	J12-J18
Chronic lower respiratory diseases	J40-J47
Diseases of the digestive system	K00-K92
Gastric and duodenal ulcer	K25-K27
Diseases of the liver	K70-K76
Diseases of the musculoskeletal system and connective tissue	M00-M99
Diseases of the genitourinary system	N00-N98
Disorders of kidney and ureter	N00-N28
Hyperplasia of prostate	N40
Pregnancy, childbirth and the puerperium	O00-O99
Pregnancy with abortive outcome	O00-O07
Other direct obstetric causes [b]	O10-O92, O95, A34
Indirect obstetric causes	O98-O99
Certain conditions originating in the perinatal period	P00-P96
Congenital malformations, deformations and chromosomal abnormalities	Q00-Q99
Symptoms, signs and abnormal clinical and laboratory findings, not elsewhere classified	R00-R99
All other diseases	H00-H95, L00-L98
External causes	V01-Y89
Accidents	V01-X59
Transport accidents	V01-V99
Falls	W00-W19
Accidental drowning and submersion	W65-W74
Exposure to smoke, fire and flames	X00-X09
Accidental poisoning by and exposure to noxious substances	X40-X49
Intentional self-harm	X60-X84
Assault	X85-Y09
All other external causes	Y10-Y89

Source:
United Nations *Demographic Yearbook 2002* (United Nations publication, Sales No. E.05.XIII.1),
table 21-2, based on the *International Statistical Classification of Diseases and Related Health Problems,
10th revision* (Geneva, 1992).

a   For a full detailed list of classifications of cause of death and disease, see
World Health Organization, *International Statistical Classification of Diseases and Related Health Problems,
10th revision* (Geneva, 1992).

b   In ICD-10 obstetrical tetanus is classified to A34 but in this table it is included with the
"Other direct obstetric causes".

Reliable estimates of maternal mortality are still difficult to obtain for many countries (box 2.2). There are often the problems of significant underreporting and misclassification of maternal deaths. Even where deaths are derived from a civil registration system with complete coverage,[7] maternal deaths may be missed or not correctly identified, thus compromising the reliability of such statistics. Maternal deaths are hard to identify because information is needed about (a) deaths among women of reproductive age, (b) pregnancy status at or near the time of death and (c) the medical cause of death. The deaths can be misclassified if, for example, the pregnancy status of the woman was not known, or if the cause of death was wrongly attributed or deliveries are outside of a medical health system.

In the period 1995-2003, among the 110 countries reporting deaths by cause, all reported maternal deaths by age at least once. Almost all 110 countries that reported maternal deaths also reported maternal deaths due to abortion. Two countries, Mongolia and the Syrian Arab Republic, reported maternal deaths but did not report deaths due to abortion.

Box 2.2

The availability of reliable maternal mortality data

Experience in developing international estimates of maternal mortality illustrates the many difficulties that countries face in measuring maternal mortality. The accuracy of data on maternal deaths depends largely on the existence and reliability of national civil registration systems, which are the primary source of data on deaths. Of the 173 countries considered in the preparation of the 2000 estimates, 60 countries (accounting for only 13 per cent of total births worldwide) reported up-to-date maternal mortality statistics based on complete civil registration systems having good attribution of cause of death. For 51 other countries, which together account for 59 per cent of global births, available data from civil registration systems, surveys, censuses and other sources of information were used to derive statistics on maternal mortality for the 2000 estimates. For the remaining 62 countries, covering 27 per cent of the births worldwide, there was no recent national data on maternal mortality that could be used to derive an estimate.[a]

a UNICEF, UNFPA and WHO, *Maternal Mortality in 2000: Estimates Developed by WHO, UNICEF and UNFPA* (Geneva, World Health Organization, 2004).

Deaths due to AIDS

The number of deaths caused by AIDS, when reported by sex, can highlight male and female differences in the spread of HIV/AIDS. However, only 80 of the 110 countries or areas that reported deaths by cause at least once in the period 1995-2003 reported deaths attributable to AIDS. All countries that reported deaths caused by AIDS in the period 1995-2002[8] reported the data by sex and age.

Morbidity

The Beijing Platform for Action notes the devastating effect of HIV/AIDS and other sexually transmitted diseases on women's health, particularly on the health of adolescent girls and young women.[9] HIV prevalence among 15 to 24-year-old pregnant women is one of the indicators for Millennium Development Goal 6, which calls for stopping and reversing the spread of HIV/AIDS, malaria and other major diseases including tuberculosis. To track the spread and incidence of diseases, accurate statistics on morbidity are necessary. However, morbidity statistics are difficult to obtain, and countries and international organizations often have to rely on estimates. HIV/AIDS statistics are a good example.

Prevalence of HIV/AIDS

The Joint United Nations Programme on HIV/AIDS (UNAIDS) disseminates, on a regular basis, estimates of the prevalence of HIV, but difficulties in obtaining reliable estimates of HIV prevalence have been documented (see box 2.3). Moreover, it is not always possible to obtain estimates of HIV prevalence by sex. Estimates of the number of adults living with HIV/AIDS were available for 149 countries or areas in 2003, but separate estimates for women and men were available for only 128 countries or areas.

UNAIDS also disseminates, on a regular basis, knowledge and behaviour indicators regarding HIV/AIDS. For the preparation of the 2003 UNAIDS progress report,[10] UNAIDS asked countries for breakdowns by sex for a number of key indicators, but fewer than one in five countries provided that information.[11] In the 2004 UNAIDS report, many indicators continue to be unavailable by sex, including estimated prevalence of AIDS among children aged 0–14, estimated deaths due to AIDS, estimated number of orphans due to AIDS and HIV prevalence in groups with high-risk behaviours in capital cities.[12]

Box 2.3

Prevalence of HIV/AIDS: data sources and estimation methods

Determining the prevalence levels of HIV/AIDS presents considerable challenges. The three most common sources of data for estimating HIV prevalence are (a) sentinel surveillance systems that undertake periodic surveys among specific population groups; (b) national population-based surveys; and (c) case reports from health facilities. As the methods and assumptions used to make these estimates have been continually evolving, the estimates cannot be readily compared over time.

There are difficulties in estimating prevalence levels even in regions with high prevalence rates. In sub-Saharan Africa, a subregion with an estimated 66 per cent of the HIV cases worldwide, estimates of HIV/AIDS prevalence are based largely on information gathered from pregnant women attending selected antenatal clinics. The assumption that HIV prevalence among pregnant women is the same as that among both women and men in the surrounding communities may not be valid in all countries. Recently, some improvements have been achieved in the collection of data on HIV prevalence: several countries in sub-Saharan Africa conducted national population-based surveys with HIV testing of respondents, some of which were Demographic and Health Surveys. Examples include Burundi, Kenya, Mali, Niger, South Africa, Zambia and Zimbabwe.

Source:
UNAIDS, *2004 Report on the Global AIDS Epidemic* (Geneva, 2004).

Human functioning and disability

The Beijing Platform of Action stresses that diseases of ageing and the interrelationships of ageing and disability among women require particular attention.[13] It requests that action be taken to improve concepts and methods of data collection on the participation of women and men with disabilities.[14]

A considerable number of countries already collect official national statistics on disability. According to the United Nations Statistics Division, at least 80 countries collected such data in the 1990s, and more than 70 countries have included a question on disability in their census since 1995. However, owing to differences in the concepts and methods used in the questions to identify persons with disabilities, prevalence rates are not comparable across countries.

Progress in statistics 1975-2003

Overall, little progress has been made in national reporting between 1975 and 2003 for deaths, infant deaths and cause of death statistics in every geographic region. The number of countries or areas reporting deaths by sex and age has remained approximately the same every year. Occasionally, some countries reported total deaths but the data were not disaggregated by sex.

Similarly, lack of progress was observed in the reporting of deaths by cause. In general, countries fall into one of two groups: either they have a strong statistical capacity and have been able to report mortality data almost every year by sex, age and cause; or their reporting capacity is very limited and has not improved since 1975. Moreover, there is a clear association between the national reporting of mortality data by sex and age and the level of development. This is, at least partially, a consequence of the lack of well-functioning civil registration systems that record births and deaths in the less developed regions. However, there have been some notable improvements. There has been better reporting of deaths caused by HIV/AIDS. In addition, the implementation of international programmes such as Multiple Indicator Cluster Surveys and Demographic and Health Surveys have contributed to a wider availability of national data on some aspects of mortality, morbidity and disability.

Chart 2.5 displays the number of countries or areas that reported total deaths; deaths by sex; and deaths by sex and age, for each year between 1975 and 2003. From 2000 onwards, the results should be regarded as preliminary, as many countries have delays in the reporting of data. Each year from 1975 to 2000, about 130 countries or areas reported the total number of deaths; about 100 reported deaths by sex; and only about 90 reported deaths by sex and age. Every year, between 20 and 30 countries or areas reported total deaths without reporting deaths by sex.

Some countries reported deaths by sex and age at very sparse intervals; others reported data frequently, i.e. for at least five years in a period. An improvement, albeit small, was observed in the period 1985-1994 (chart 2.6). The number of countries or areas reporting data for at least one year increased from 116 in 1975-1984 to 128 in 1985-1994. Fewer countries have reported the data for 1995-2003, possibly due to delays in reporting caused by the time required to process the data. Similarly, the number of countries or areas that reported data frequently

The number of countries reporting deaths due to AIDS by sex to the World Health Organization increased substantially between 1995 and 2000

More than 70 countries have included a question on disability in their census since 1995

Chart 2.5

Number of countries or areas that reported statistics on deaths, 1975 – 2003

Deaths
Deaths by sex
Deaths by sex and age

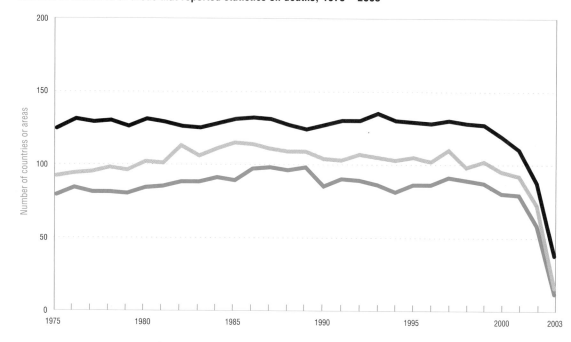

Source:
Prepared by the United Nations
Statistics Division, Department of
Economic and Social Affairs,based
on data from the United Nations
Demographic Yearbook system
(November 2004).

increased from 84 in 1975-1984 to 96 in 1985-1994. Again, a lower number—88—is seen to have reported frequently in 1995-2003.

The number of countries or areas that reported annual deaths by cause, sex and age for at least one year has also remained about the same over the last three decades: 106 in 1975-1984, 109 in 1985-1994 and 109 in 1995-2003. Countries or areas that reported deaths by cause in those three periods usually also provided the data disaggregated by sex and age. It is important to note, however, that there have been improvements in some aspects of reporting over the three periods. For example, during the period

Chart 2.6

Number of countries or areas that reported deaths by sex and age, by number of years data were reported, for three periods.

5+ years
1-4 years

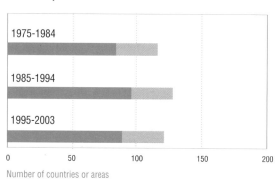

1975-1984

1985-1994

1995-2003

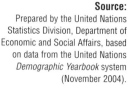

0   50   100   150   200

Number of countries or areas

Source:
Prepared by the United Nations
Statistics Division, Department of
Economic and Social Affairs, based
on data from the United Nations
Demographic Yearbook system
(November 2004).

1975-1984, a total of 10 countries or areas reported data disaggregated by sex but not by age.[15] During the periods 1985-1994 and 1995-2003, only one country reported data disaggregated by sex but not by age.[16]

Another area in which there has been improvement is the national reporting of deaths due to AIDS. The number of countries reporting deaths due to AIDS by sex to the World Health Organization increased substantially between 1995 and 2000 (chart 2.7). Among the 87 countries or areas that reported deaths by cause in 1995, only 38 reported deaths caused by AIDS. In the following years the number steadily increased and, in 2000, out of 75 countries or areas that reported deaths by cause, 68, or almost all of them, reported deaths caused by AIDS.[17] The increase in reporting deaths due to AIDS is in part due to the gradual implementation by countries or areas of the Tenth Revision of the International Classification for Diseases (ICD-10), which was published in 1992 and went into effect in 1993. ICD-10 includes HIV as a cause of death, whereas the previous revision (ICD-9) did not.[18]

The availability of data on HIV/AIDS prevalence for adults has improved between 2001, when estimates were available for 132 countries or areas, and 2003, when estimates were available for 149 countries or areas. However, there has been only minimal improvement in the availability of data by sex. Estimates of the number of women and men living with HIV/AIDS were available for 127 countries or areas in 2001 and for 128 countries or areas in 2003.[19]

In recent years, there has been some improvement in the availability of health-related data in countries that had very little data in the past through international programmes such as Demographic and Health Surveys and Multiple Indicator Cluster Surveys, which have made it possible to conduct a large number of nationally representative surveys in developing countries (see box 2.4). The surveys focus on many aspects of health and are especially designed to capture data on women and children.

A significant development in the methodological work on disability measurement is the adoption of the WHO's International Classification of Functioning, Disability and Health (ICF) in 2001.[20] The ICF serves as a framework for developing measures for data collection on disability. Guided by this framework, the Washington Group on Disability Statistics is currently developing measures on disability for use in national censuses and surveys.[21]

Chart 2.7

Number of countries or areas that reported statistics, by sex, on deaths by cause and deaths due to AIDS, 1995 – 2002

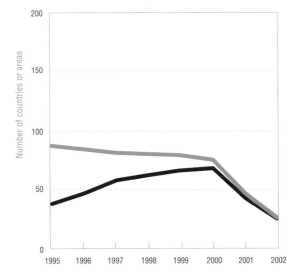

— Deaths by cause and sex
— Deaths due to AIDS, by sex

Source:
Prepared by the United Nations Statistics Division, Department of Economic and Social Affairs, based on data provided by the World Health Organization for the United Nations *Demographic Yearbook* system (November 2004).

Box 2.4

Demographic and Health Surveys and Multiple Indicator Cluster Surveys

Demographic and Health Surveys (DHS) are nationally representative household surveys with large sample sizes that have provided data on the population, health and nutrition of women and children in countries in less developed regions since the 1980s. DHS are meant to be conducted every five years to allow comparisons over time, and the DHS project has coordinated close to 200 surveys in more than 70 countries over the last 20 years. The standard DHS consists of a household questionnaire, which collects information on all members of the household, and a questionnaire for women aged 15-49 years. In general, the surveys include questions on contraception, maternal health, HIV/AIDS and nutrition. Special modules can also be added to questionnaires in order to meet host country and donor data needs. Data from the DHS are available online (see website at the end of the box).

The Multiple Indicator Cluster Survey (MICS) is a household survey programme that has assisted countries in filling data gaps for monitoring the situation of children and women. The first round of the MICS was conducted around 1995 in more than 60 countries, and

a second round of surveys was conducted in 2000 for about 65 countries. The MICS includes a set of modules to collect data on the health and nutrition status of women and children, child rights and other areas of concern. It consists of three questionnaires that can be customized to the needs of a country: a household questionnaire, a questionnaire for women 15-49 years of age and a questionnaire on the situation of children under the age of 5 (addressed to the caretaker of the child).

Both DHS and MICS are based on large national samples and in particular cover countries in less developed regions where health data is usually the scarcest. The surveys produce internationally comparable estimates, although countries sometimes modify the questions to meet their national data needs. The surveys do have some limitations, however, because of the age range of the population covered (15-49 for most of the questions related to women) and their lack of coverage of the adult male population (not covered at all in MICS and covered only in some of the DHS surveys).

Sources:
See http://www.measuredhs.com and http://www.childinfo.org/.

The result will be a set of questions that can be used to collect harmonized data across culturally diverse countries.

Another recent development in the area of disability is the international collection and dissemination of statistics on disability by the United Nations Statistics Division. Beginning in 2005, national data including metadata on human functioning and disability will be systematically collected and disseminated through the United Nations *Demographic Yearbook*. This initiative will contribute to the availability, at the international level, of disability statistics on women and men.

Challenges

Building statistical capacity

The ability of Governments to report health-related statistics by sex and age is closely tied to the existence of comprehensive national statistical systems. A key challenge, therefore, is strengthening those systems in countries where deficiencies in reporting are most apparent. In particular, efforts need to be directed at the development and integration of national civil registration and vital statistics systems.

Civil registers can provide the requisite information on deaths according to sex, age and reported cause of death, among other characteristics. Although a majority of countries have a national civil registration system that records deaths, many are incomplete in their coverage, have late registration or errors in reporting or in classifying the cause of death, especially in the less developed regions and among the least developed countries. Political will and ample resources are needed to improve these aspects of national systems.

Incomplete coverage and late registration limit the ability of Governments to monitor the health of women and men. This is particularly the case with rural women and those who are members of a disadvantaged group, as deaths among them are more likely to go unregistered or to be registered late. Expanding coverage to make it universal requires a concerted effort by Governments to ensure that deaths occurring outside of hospitals, in rural or in remote areas and among disadvantaged groups are properly recorded.

Lack of reliable information on the cause of death represents a serious obstacle to monitoring

health problems that affect women, such as maternal mortality and contagious diseases like HIV/AIDS. Underreporting and misclassification of maternal deaths are greatest in countries where maternal mortality is suspected to be highest and where civil registration and vital statistics systems are weakest. To improve the accuracy and reliability of cause of death information, Governments need to establish and standardize reporting and coding practices. Critical to that effort is the provision of training in death certificate completion for those involved in the certification process.

In addition, for information gathered through civil registers to be useful in the design of health policies and programmes that incorporate gender concerns, Governments must also devote resources to the establishment and maintenance of a well-functioning national vital statistics system. Two key challenges here are (a) establishing close integration between the civil registration and vital statistics systems and (b) developing the capacity to produce and disseminate statistics on deaths regularly broken down by sex, age and cause of death.

Close integration between the two systems is vital to ensure that key information from civil registers such as age, sex and cause of death is preserved and used in the production of vital statistics. Such integration requires Governments to allocate resources to streamline and harmonize the technology and processes used by each system, and to establish appropriate channels for communication and collaboration between their respective staffs. The second challenge requires sustained political commitment to maintain the resources needed to support national vital statistics systems.

Improving concepts and methods of data collection

In the absence of reliable vital statistics, practical and cost-effective approaches are needed in the short term to improve the national availability of data for monitoring the health of women and men. In the case of maternal mortality, several methods of data collection and estimation have been developed. However, maternal mortality ratio is just one indicator of women's reproductive health. There is a pressing need to monitor morbidity and disability due to pregnancy and childbirth—there is currently no systematic reporting of such data internationally. Only

Lack of reliable information on the cause of death represents a serious obstacle to monitoring health problems that affect women

The ability of Governments to report health-related statistics by sex and age is closely tied to the existence of comprehensive national statistical systems

Governments must devote resources to the establishment and maintenance of a well-functioning national vital statistics system

There is a pressing need to monitor morbidity and disability due to pregnancy and childbirth

some related risk factors, such as early child-bearing and adolescent fertility rates, are internationally reported (see chapter 1). In addition, some aspects highlighted in the Beijing Platform of Action, such as unsafe abortions[22], remain practically unmonitored. In brief, better and more comprehensive data on a wider range of reproductive health outcomes are needed.

Growing interest also exists in the use of population censuses as a source of data to estimate maternal deaths and deaths caused by AIDS in the most affected countries and where death registration is poor or non-existent.[23] Further research is needed to evaluate the usefulness of population censuses in producing reliable information on these issues. At the same time, clear guidelines need to be developed specifying both the types of questions that countries should include in a census to capture deaths due to maternal causes and AIDS and the methods to estimate mortality using those data.

Reliable data on morbidity, health-care practices and access to and use of health-care services are also necessary to fully assess improvements in the health status of women and men. In the case of maternal health, process indicators—i.e. measures of the services the health system is actually providing—such as attendance by skilled health personnel at delivery and utilization of emergency obstetric care facilities can be used for healthcare planning purposes. In the case of HIV/AIDS, research on the links between HIV infection and condom use, sexual and other high-risk behaviour, knowledge of HIV/AIDS, etc. are needed to better understand the spread of the disease and inform efforts to prevent its further spread.

Data on morbidity of women and men from other causes are also scant. When estimates are available, they are seldom available by sex. Even for diseases that have been highlighted by the Millennium Development Goals, such as malaria and tuberculosis, data on prevalence—i.e. the proportion of the population with the disease—often are not available. There are examples of efforts to collect certain morbidity data in countries. For instance, in some countries cancer prevalence is assessed through registries that record all cancer cases;[24] DOTS, the internationally recommended tuberculosis control strategy programme,[25] has also contributed to better monitoring of that disease. However, these efforts are not widespread. Further methodological work is required to improve the collection, availability and quality of morbidity data.

The concept of human functioning is becoming increasingly important to the study of aging of women and men. An important challenge related to human functioning and disability involves harmonizing the definitions, concepts and methods used in data collection across countries. The International Classification of Functioning, Disability and Health and the disability measures being developed by the Washington Group for inclusion in censuses and national surveys represent important steps towards such harmonization. Further research is needed to test fully the reliability of such new concepts and measures as well as their applicability in different country settings.

Reliable data on morbidity, health-care practices and access to and use of health-care services are necessary to fully assess improvements in the health status of women and men

Further research is needed to test fully the reliability of new disability concepts and measures as well as their applicability in different country settings

Table 2.A
Number of countries or areas that reported selected mortality statistics, 1995 – 2003

	World	Geographic region						Development group		
		Africa	North America	South America	Asia	Europe	Oceania	More developed regions	Less developed regions [a]	Least developed countries
All countries or areas	204	55	27	13	50	42	17	47	107	50
Deaths										
Total, at least once	155	22	25	13	40	42	13	47	94	14
By sex, at least once	134	18	22	12	33	42	7	47	78	9
By sex and age, at least once	121	15	21	11	28	40	6	45	71	5
By sex and age, for at least five years	88	4	15	8	20	36	5	41	46	1
Infant deaths										
Total, at least once	143	19	24	11	35	41	13	46	85	12
By sex, at least once	114	12	20	9	28	39	6	44	63	7
By sex, for at least five years	81	5	13	6	22	31	4	36	44	1
Deaths by cause										
Total, at least once	110	5	22	10	27	39	7	44	63	3
By sex, at least once	110	5	22	10	27	39	7	44	63	3
By sex and age, at least once	109	5	22	10	26	39	7	44	62	3
By sex and age, for at least five years	87	3	16	9	18	37	4	42	44	1

Sources:

Prepared by the United Nations Statistics Division, Department of Economic and Social Affairs: for deaths and infant deaths, based on data from the United Nations *Demographic Yearbook* system (November 2004); for deaths by cause, based on data from World Health Organization, *WHO Mortality Database* (December 2004).

a   Excluding the least developed countries.

Table 2.B
Percentage of the world and regional populations in countries or areas that reported selected mortality statistics, 1995 – 2003

| | | Geographic region | | | | | | Development group | | |
	World	Africa	North America	South America	Asia	Europe	Oceania	More developed regions	Less developed regions [a]	Least developed countries
All countries or areas	100	100	100	100	100	100	100	100	100	100
Deaths										
Total, at least once	69	46	97	100	61	100	98	100	64	47
By sex, at least once	63	35	96	98	55	100	76	100	61	15
By sex and age, at least once	61	33	96	98	52	100	76	100	58	13
By sex and age, for at least five years	33	12	94	88	10	98	75	99	19	0
Infant deaths										
Total, at least once	46	40	97	98	25	100	98	100	32	41
By sex, at least once	40	35	96	88	17	99	76	99	27	18
By sex, for at least five years	28	16	94	78	10	60	75	76	18	0
Deaths by cause										
Total, at least once	59	16	98	97	51	100	78	100	56	1
By sex, at least once	59	16	98	97	51	100	78	100	56	1
By sex and age, at least once	59	16	98	97	51	100	78	100	56	1
By sex and age, for at least five years	53	10	96	97	43	98	77	99	49	0

Sources:
Prepared by the United Nations Statistics Division, Department of Economic and Social Affairs: for deaths and infant deaths, based on data from the United Nations *Demographic Yearbook* system (November 2004); for deaths by cause, based on data from World Health Organization, *WHO Mortality Database* (December 2004).

a   Excluding the least developed countries.

Notes

1   In Africa: Chad, Côte d'Ivoire, Ethiopia, Mauritania; in North America: Dominica, Jamaica and Netherlands Antilles; in South America: Bolivia; in Asia: Bangladesh, Iran (Islamic Republic of), Iraq, Lebanon, Oman, Tajikistan, Turkey, Turkmenistan and United Arab Emirates; in Europe: Albania; in Oceania: Fiji, French Polynesia, Micronesia (Federated States of), Nauru, Papua New Guinea and Samoa.

2   See *Report of the Fourth World Conference on Women, Beijing, 4-15 September 1995* (United Nations publication, Sales No. E.96.IV.13), para. 259.

3   Ibid.

4   In Africa: Botswana, Burundi, Côte d'Ivoire, Malawi, Mauritania, Seychelles and Swaziland; in North America: Dominica, Guadeloupe, Jamaica and Martinique; in South America: Bolivia and Peru; in Asia: Bangladesh, Iran (Islamic Republic of), Oman, Tajikistan, Turkey, Turkmenistan and United Arab Emirates; in Europe: Albania and Bosnia and Herzegovina; in Oceania: Fiji, French Polynesia, Micronesia (Federated States of), Nauru, Palau, Papua New Guinea and Samoa.

5   See *Report of the Fourth World Conference on Women, Beijing, 4-15 September 1995* (United Nations publication, Sales No. E.96.IV.13), chap. I, resolution 1, annex II, para. 97.

6   "Road map towards the implementation of the United Nations Millennium Declaration" Report of the Secretary-General (A/56/326) annex. Available from http://unstats.un.org/unsd/mi/mi_links.asp.

7   Civil registration systems with 90 per cent or better coverage of deaths.

8   Data for 2003 were not available.

9   See *Report of the Fourth World Conference on Women, Beijing, 4-15 September 1995* (United Nations publication, Sales No. E.96.IV.13), chap. I, resolution 1, annex II, para. 98.

10   UNAIDS, *Progress Report on the Global Response to the HIV/AIDS Epidemic 2003* (Geneva, 2003).

11   UNAIDS, *2004 Report on the Global AIDS Epidemic* (Geneva, 2004).

12   Ibid.

13   See *Report of the Fourth World Conference on Women, Beijing, 4-15 September 1995* (United Nations publication, Sales No. E.96.IV.13), chap. I, resolution 1, annex II, para. 101.

14   Ibid. para. 206 (k).

15   Belize, Colombia, Grenada, Guadeloupe, Haiti, Honduras, Jamaica, Papua New Guinea, Saint Lucia and Seychelles.

16   Sri Lanka for some years in 1985-1994 and in 1995-2003.

17   From 2000 onwards, the results should be regarded as preliminary as many countries or areas have not yet had enough time to report the data.

18   In 1995 only 4 countries had adopted the new standard. By 2003, 75 countries had adopted the new standard. See Mathers et.al. *Counting the dead and what they died from: an assessment of the global status of cause of death data.* Bulletin of the World Health Organization 2005, 83: 171-177.

19   UNAIDS, *2004 Report on the Global AIDS Epidemic* (Geneva, 2004), p. 189-207.

20   World Health Organization, International Classification of Functioning, Disability and Health (Geneva, 2001).

21   For information on the Washington Group and its work, see "Report of the Washington Group on Disability Measurement", note by the Secretary-General (E/CN.3/2003/8).

22   *Report of the Fourth World Conference on Women, Beijing, 4-15 September 1995* (United Nations publication, Sales No. E.96.IV.13), chap. I, resolution 1, annex II, para. 97.

23   "Topics of emerging policy relevance and suggested minimum and essential census topics: implications for updating *Principles and Recommendations for Population and Housing Censuses*" (ESA/STAT/AC.98/1), paper presented at the Expert Group Meeting to Review Critical Issues Relevant to the Planning of the 2010 Round of Population and Housing Censuses, 15-17 September 2004 New York.

24   Cancer registries exist in many countries worldwide. See http://www.iacr.com.fr.

25   DOTS combines five elements: political commitments, microscopy services, drug supplies, surveillance and monitoring systems, and use of highly efficacious regimes.

Chapter 3
Education and training

"Education is a human right and an essential tool for achieving the goals of equality, development and peace."
Beijing Platform for Action

The Fourth World Conference on Women in 1995 recognized that "investing in formal and non-formal education and training for girls and women, with its exceptionally high social and economic return, has proved to be one of the best means of achieving sustainable development and economic growth", and through the Beijing Platform for Action, called on Governments to ensure equal access to education and to eradicate illiteracy among women.[1] Through the Millennium Development Goals in 2000 Governments reiterated their commitment to achieve universal primary education (Goal 2) and to eliminate gender disparity at all levels of education by 2015 (Goal 3, Target 4). To assess progress towards the attainment of those strategic objectives and goals, women's and girls' access to education and educational outcomes must be monitored through the collection, analysis and dissemination of data.

The statistical data reviewed in the present chapter address some of the strategic objectives on education formulated in the Beijing Platform for Action, including the following: to ensure equal access to education; to eradicate illiteracy among women; to improve women's access to vocational training, science and technology; and the Millennium Development Goals 2 and 3, as stated above.

The capacity of countries to monitor progress towards gender equality in education is assessed below with regard to both access to and outcomes of the educational process, using the following statistics (see box 3.1 for definitions):

Access to educational services
- Enrolment by level of education, sex and age
- School attendance by sex and age
- Number of teachers by sex

Outcomes of education experience
- Literacy by sex and age
- Educational attainment by sex and age

National statistical information on access to educational services and their outcomes are collected through (a) school administrative records gathered annually by the school systems and reported to ministries of education; (b) population and housing censuses; and (c) national household or other sample surveys. At the international level, national data on school enrolment and teachers as well as on literacy and educational attainment are reported to the United Nations Educational, Scientific and Cultural Organization (UNESCO). National census data on school attendance, literacy and educational attainment are reported to the United Nations Statistics Division. Country reporting to international organizations is an indication of national capacity to disseminate education information in a regular and timely way.

Since 1995 most countries or areas have reported the number of students enrolled in primary and secondary school at least once, but only less than a quarter have reported school attendance. Also, fewer than half have reported statistics on literacy and educational attainment from censuses.

Current state of statistics
1995-2003
Access to educational services

It is widely believed that millions of young girls never attend school and millions more never complete their education. According to the Beijing Platform for Action, "discrimination in girls' access to education persists in many areas, owing to customary attitudes, early marriages and pregnancies, inadequate and gender-biased teaching and educational materials, sexual harassment and lack of adequate and physically and otherwise accessible schooling facilities".[2] In order to assess the continuing validity of these statements and devise appropriate policies, data are needed on enrolment, school attendance and school completion, combined with other information such as the number and qualifications of teachers and the availability of teaching materials.

Women's and girls' access to education and educational outcomes must be monitored through the collection, analysis and dissemination of data

Since 1995 most countries have reported the number of students enrolled in primary and secondary school

Fewer than half of the countries have reported statistics on literacy and educational attainment from censuses

Box 3.1

Definitions

Enrolment refers to the number of pupils or students officially enrolled or registered in a given grade or level of education, regardless of age. Typically, these data are collected at the beginning of the academic year.

School attendance is defined as attendance at any regular accredited educational institution or programme, public or private, for organized learning at any level of education.

Technical and vocational education refers to a type of programme that is designed mainly to lead pupils to acquire the practical skills, know-how and understanding necessary for employment in a particular occupation or trade (or class of occupations or trades). Successful completion of such programmes normally leads to a labour-market relevant vocational qualification recognized by the competent authorities (e.g. Ministry of Education, employers' associations, etc.) in the country in which it is obtained.

Teaching staff (teachers) are persons employed full-time or part-time in an official capacity for the purpose of guiding or directing the learning experience of pupils

and students, irrespective of his/her qualification or the delivery mechanism (i.e. whether face-to-face and/or at a distance). It excludes educational personnel who have no active teaching duties (such as headmasters, head-mistresses or principals who do not teach) or who work occasionally or in a voluntary capacity in educational institutions.

A literate person is one who can, with understanding, both read and write a short simple statement on his or her everyday life.

An illiterate person is one who cannot, with understanding, both read and write such a simple statement.

Educational attainment is defined as the highest grade completed within the most advanced level attended in the educational system of the country where the education was received.

Sources:
Principles and Recommendations for Population and Housing Censuses, rev. 1 (United Nations publication, Sales No. E.98.XVII.8), paras. 2.145, 2.150 and 2.153; and definitions provided by the UNESCO Institute for Statistics.

Enrolment

Administrative records from the formal education system provide a major source of information on access to education, particularly on official enrolment levels, and are essential for planning the education process in terms of human and economic resources. Enrolment data by level of education and sex are needed to monitor progress towards the Millennium Development Goals of achieving universal primary education (Goal 2) and promoting gender equality (Goal 3).

The present chapter considers data on enrolment from six academic years: 1995/1996, 1996/1997 and 1998/1999 to 2001/2002. The academic year 1997/1998 was excluded owing to a lack of data disseminated by UNESCO following changes in the International Standard Classification of Education (ISCED)[3] system in 1997 and other institutional issues. Data for the years 2002/2003 to 2004/2005 were not yet available at the time when the present analysis was conducted.[4] Countries or areas were considered as being able to report

the number of students enrolled unless the data provided were deemed by UNESCO to be incomplete, inconsistent or to require an adjustment. Because the primary objective of the present analysis is to examine the capacity of Governments to report quality data, estimates and data adjustments by UNESCO Institute for Statistics (UIS) are not included in the analysis.[5]

In general, there was a high level of reporting of enrolment data to the international statistical system, with most of the 204 countries or areas reporting the number of children enrolled in both primary and secondary[6] education at least once for the six academic years considered (chart 3.1). Relatively fewer countries or areas reported the number of students in tertiary education.[7]

Most of the countries or areas reporting enrolment data also provided data broken down by sex. Of the total reporting, only 2 did not provide this breakdown for primary education, 3 for secondary education and 12 for tertiary education. In most cases, however, enrolment data by sex was missing for

Most countries reporting enrolment data also provided data broken down by sex

Chart 3.1

Number of countries or areas that reported enrolment data, by level of education, for the academic years 1995/1996 – 2001/2002[a]

	Primary	Secondary		Tertiary	
		Total	Vocational	Total	By field
All countries or areas	**204**	**204**	**204**	**204**	**204**
Enrolment					
Total, at least once	189	185	163	166	127
By sex, at least once	187	182	157	154	118
Total, at least three years	160	151	112	116	63
By sex, at least three years	155	143	104	104	62

Source:
Prepared by the United Nations Statistics Division, Department of Economic and Social Affairs, based on data provided by the UNESCO Institute for Statistics excluding UIS estimates (November 2004).

[a] The academic year 1997/1998 was excluded from analysis owing to a lack of data.

the analysed time period because countries did not report any data on enrolment at all: 15 did not report in the case of primary education, 19 in secondary education and 38 in tertiary education. It is important to note, however, that of the 38 countries or areas not reporting any data on enrolment in tertiary education, 11 do not provide tertiary education within their territories.[8]

In addition, not all the countries or areas reporting enrolment were able to do so frequently (i.e. for at least three out of the six academic years considered) and thus provide timely data necessary for evidence-based policies. Of a total of 204 countries or areas, 155 frequently reported the number of students by sex for primary education, 143 for secondary education and 104 for tertiary education. The population of the concerned countries or areas represents 92, 85 and 59 per cent of the world population respectively. Data for higher instruction seems to have been less systematically collected, processed and disseminated as compared with secondary and primary education.

Analysis by geographic region revealed that most of the countries in each region were able to provide, at least once, enrolment data by sex for primary and secondary education (table 3.A). However, a smaller proportion of countries from Africa, North America and Oceania were able to report enrolment data by sex frequently compared to countries from other geographic regions. In addition, a smaller proportion of the countries from the less developed regions including the least developed countries, were able to provide data frequently compared to countries from more developed regions (table 3.A).

Besides the need for enrolment data to be disaggregated by sex and level of education, monitoring progress towards achieving universal primary education requires that statistics on enrolment be further disaggregated by age of the student or pupil. Available data covering the academic years 1998/1999 to 2001/2002, shows that while most countries reported the number of girls and of boys in primary education at least once in the four academic years covered, far fewer (138 countries or areas comprising 61 per cent of the world's population) provided enrolment data by sex and age for primary education at least once (chart 3.2 and table 3.B). For secondary education, less than half the world's countries or areas (101) comprising only 30 per cent of its population reported this data by age and sex at least once (table 3.A).

Chart 3.2

Number of countries or areas that reported enrolment data at least once, by level of education, for the academic years 1998/1999 – 2001/2002

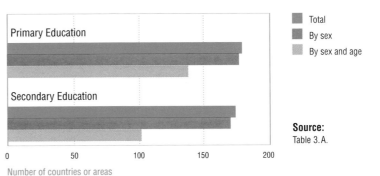

Primary Education

Secondary Education

0   50   100   150   200
Number of countries or areas

■ Total
■ By sex
■ By sex and age

Source:
Table 3.A.

Data for higher instruction seems to have been less systematically collected, processed and disseminated as compared with secondary and primary education

Striking regional
disparities were apparent
in the reporting of
enrolment data by
sex and age

Striking regional disparities were also apparent in the reporting of enrolment data by sex and age. The region with the lowest proportion of countries reporting such data was Oceania, where, out of 17 countries, only 6 reported enrolment data broken down by sex and age for primary education and 5 for secondary education. Africa also showed relatively low levels of reporting with 39 out of 55 countries or areas reporting data on enrolment in primary education by sex and age and with 18 providing similar information for secondary education (table 3.A).

Finally, a special issue highlighted by the Beijing Platform for Action with respect to women's education concerns their access to technical vocational programmes and to fields of study that are traditionally male-dominated. Specifically, the Platform for Action called for improving women's access to vocational training, science and technology to help improve their employment opportunities.[9] This requires further breakdown of enrolment data by field of study, which fewer countries were able to provide (chart 3.1). Data for the six academic years showed that 104 countries or areas frequently provided the numbers of female and of male students enrolled in technical vocational programmes,[10] while only 62 countries or areas frequently provided the number of tertiary students by sex and field of study.

School attendance

Apart from school administrative records, another way to measure access to education—to know whether girls and boys are in school—is through the use of school attendance questions in population censuses and household surveys. School administrative data typically provide information for only those children who have officially enrolled in school and often provide limited information about children who are enrolled but who are not attending school. School attendance questions from censuses and surveys can fill in that gap by providing information on both school-age children who are participating in education and those who are not.

Between 1995 and 2003,
only 40 countries or areas
representing a mere
14 per cent of the world's
population reported
census data on school
attendance by sex
and age

Moreover, data on school attendance combined with other basic information collected at the same time in a census or survey can give a picture of family and household factors that contribute to gender inequality in access to schooling. Surveys can be particularly useful in examining the factors that limit access to education, as they can accommodate more detailed questions on educational services and outcomes. Box 3.2 highlights some of the advantages and limitations of using household surveys to measure school attendance.

Box 3.2

Household surveys and school attendance

An important feature of household surveys is that they can provide detailed information on the characteristics of school-age children who are not participating in education, their families and the households they belong to. Such data is necessary to examine the factors underlying inequality in school participation. There are often sizeable differences in educational participation depending on the population subgroup. In Guinea, for example, children who live in rural areas or in households that score low on the household asset index, as well as those who have a mother with no education, are much less likely to report having attended school in the last year. Moreover, there are important interactions with residence, well-being and gender. One in eight girls from poor households attends school, compared to one in four boys from poor households.

This type of information is helpful in targeting national policy efforts, although it is important to appreciate that survey data may be weak in relation to severely disadvantaged groups since those groups are frequently underrepresented in household surveys. Poor coverage of such groups as migrants, refugees, the homeless, those in orphanages and other institutions or people from ethnic minorities may affect evaluations of the scope of a problem such as out-of-school children.

Inquiring about attendance at school is also not as straightforward as it might appear, and often surveys will produce markedly different estimates of attendance owing to differences in the methodology or in the survey timing in relation to the school year.

Source:
Global Education Digest 2003: Comparing Education Statistics across the World (Montreal, UNESCO Institute for Statistics, 2003).

Between 1995 and 2003, only 40 countries or areas representing a mere 14 per cent of the world's population reported census data on school attendance by sex and age (tables 3.A and 3B). Three additional countries reported census information on school attendance, but did not disaggregate the data by sex or age. Finally, one additional country provided school attendance data by sex, but did not break it down by age.

Important differences in the reporting of census data on school attendance by sex and age were evident among geographic regions and across development groups. Compared to other regions, a greater number of countries or areas from Europe (17 out of

42) and Asia (11 out of 50) reported census data on school attendance broken down by sex and age. By contrast, in Oceania only one out of 17 countries or areas had, by 2003, reported school attendance data by sex and age from the census. In Africa, the figure was three out of 55 countries or areas (table 3.A).

In terms of development groups, greater reporting of census data on school attendance disaggregated by sex and age was apparent among countries in the more developed regions (19 out of 47) compared to countries in the less developed regions excluding the least developed countries, where only 18 out of 107 provided similar data. Reporting was lowest among the least developed countries where only 3 out of 50 counties or areas reported census data on school attendance by sex and age (table 3.A).

Although the worldwide availability of school attendance data by sex and age from censuses is low in general, similar information on this topic can be obtained from national household surveys. For example, data on school attendance by sex and age collected through Multiple Indicator Cluster Surveys (MICS) or Demographic and Health Surveys (DHS) is available for 74 of the 164 countries that did not report such information from censuses (see chapter 2, box 2.4 for a description of DHS and MICS). Considering school attendance data from those surveys brings the total number of countries with such data broken down by sex and age to 114.

Multiple Indicator Cluster Surveys or Demographic and Health Surveys are a particularly important source of school attendance data in the least developed countries. Of the 50 least developed countries, 36 have data on school attendance disaggregated by sex and age through either MICS or DHS. This brings the total number of least

developed countries with such data from 3 to 39.

Teachers

The Beijing Platform for Action calls on Governments to "take actions to ensure that female teachers and professors have the same opportunities as and equal status with male teachers and professors".[11] It also calls for the promotion of non-stereotyped images of women and men through education. In this respect, women teachers are important, serving as role models and helping to attract and retain girls in school. It is therefore important to monitor the prevalence of women teachers at all levels of education. The primary source of information on the number of teachers and proportion of women teachers is the administrative data collected by ministries of education for all three levels of education.[12]

As with the reporting of enrolment, more countries or areas were able to provide data on teachers in primary education than for higher levels of education. For the six academic years considered between 1995/1996 and 2001/2002, 176 countries or areas provided the total number of teachers in primary education at least once, compared to 149 countries or areas providing the number of teachers for tertiary education (chart 3.3).

The number of countries or areas reporting total number of teachers without breaking down the data by sex ranges from 8 for primary education to 23 for tertiary education. In a greater number of cases, data on numbers of female and male teachers is missing for the analysed time period because the countries or areas did not report any data at all: these range from 28 not reporting the number of teachers in primary education to 55 not reporting on tertiary education.

Multiple Indicator Cluster Surveys or Demographic and Health Surveys are a particularly important source of school attendance data in the least developed countries

More countries or areas were able to provide data on teachers in primary education than for higher levels of education

Chart 3.3

Number of countries or areas that reported the number of teachers, by level of education, for the academic years 1995/1996 – 2001/2002[a]

	Primary	Secondary	Tertiary
All countries or areas	204	204	204
Teachers			
Total, at least once	176	144	149
By sex, at least once	168	136	126
Total, at least three years	136	75	87
By sex, at least three years	119	64	60

Source:
Prepared by the United Nations Statistics Division, Department of Economic and Social Affairs, based on data provided by the UNESCO Institute for Statistics excluding UIS estimates (November 2004).

[a] The academic year 1997/1998 was excluded from analysis owing to a lack of data.

Particularly limited is the capacity of countries or areas to report teacher data frequently (chart 3.3). In general, of the countries that reported teacher data by level of education at least once, a much smaller number were able to provide such data frequently. That is the case especially for reports of teachers in secondary and tertiary education. Compared to 119 countries or areas that frequently reported the numbers of female and male teachers in primary education, only 64 and 60 countries or areas respectively provided this data frequently for secondary and tertiary education.

Education outcomes: literacy and educational attainment

Statistics on literacy and educational attainment by sex and age are reflections of the outcome of the educational process for each generation of women and men. Such information may be used to assess the quality of the labour force, to adjust the national school systems and to evaluate and reformulate policies on lifelong learning for women and men who are in or out of the school system.

According to the Beijing Platform for Action, more than two thirds of the world's 960 million illiterate adults in 1995 were women, and eradicating illiteracy is one of its strategic objectives. Moreover, the outcome document of the twenty-third special session of the General Assembly, entitled "Women 2000: gender equality, development and peace for the twenty-first century", stated that little progress had been made in eradicating illiteracy and called for a 50 per cent improvement in the levels of adult literacy by 2015, especially for women. In order to assess whether a 50 per cent improvement in the levels has taken place, it is necessary to know past national levels of literacy and to monitor them on an ongoing basis.

It is important to note that not all the countries or areas that collected statistics on literacy and educational attainment in the 2000 census round have as yet reported them to the United Nations Statistics Division. So far, out of the 178 countries or areas that conducted a census, 77, comprising 64 per cent of the world's population, have reported literacy by sex and age. For educational attainment, only 71 countries or areas, comprising 48 per cent of the world population, have reported the data by sex and age (chart 3.4 and table 3.B). It is, however, expected that more data will come in from the 2000 round of censuses as time goes on.

As in the case of school attendance, comparable data on literacy and educational attainment by

sex and age is available from MICS and DHS for a number of countries that have not reported such data from censuses. For example, 38 countries or areas, comprising 14 per cent of the world population, have survey data on literacy by sex and age, while 60 countries or areas, comprising 38 per cent of the world population have survey data on educational attainment by sex and age. Taking into consideration the availability of literacy and educational attainment data from those surveys, the total number of countries with literacy data by sex and age is 115 and the total with educational attainment data by sex and age is 131 (chart 3.4).

Chart 3.4

Number of countries or areas for which data on literacy and educational attainment by sex and age are available, by source of data, 1995 – 2003

Source	Literacy	Educational attainment
Total	115	131
Population census	77	71
DHS or MICS	38[a]	60[a]

Source:
Prepared by the United Nations Statistics Division, Department of Economic and Social Affairs, based on data from the United Nations *Demographic Yearbook* system (November 2004); data provided by the UNESCO Institute for Statistics excluding UIS estimates (April 2005); data from the Demographic and Health Surveys website http://www.measuredhs.com (March 2005); and data from Multiple Indicator Cluster Surveys website http://www.childinfo.org (June 2005).

[a] Considers only countries that did not report the data from censuses to the international statistical system for the period 1995-2003.

As is the case with other education statistics, there are notable differences between geographic regions in the reporting of census data on literacy and educational attainment (chart 3.5). The relative number of countries or areas reporting is highest in Europe and Asia and lowest in Africa and Oceania.

In Africa, 39 out of the 55 countries or areas conducted a census between 1995 and 2004, but so far only 14 have reported data by sex and age on literacy and 9 on educational attainment. Most of the existing data on literacy and educational attainment in this region is available from household and other sample surveys: for example, an additional 26 countries or areas in Africa have data by sex and age on literacy and 36 on educational attainment from MICS or DHS.

There are also differences in the reporting of data on literacy and educational attainment among development groups. Most countries in the more

Statistics on literacy and educational attainment by sex and age are reflections of the outcome of the educational process for each generation of women and men

In Africa, 39 out of the 55 countries or areas conducted a census between 1995 and 2004, but so far only 14 have reported data by sex and age on literacy and 9 on educational attainment

Table 3.B
Percentage of the world and regional populations in countries or areas that reported selected education statistics, 1995 – 2003

| | World | Geographic region | | | | | | Development group | | |
		Africa	North America	South America	Asia	Europe	Oceania	More developed regions	Less developed regions [a]	Least developed countries
All countries or areas	100	100	100	100	100	100	100	100	100	100
Access to educational services										
Enrolment in primary education [b]										
Total, at least once	99	99	99	100	99	99	94	100	99	99
By sex, at least once	99	99	99	100	99	99	94	100	99	99
By sex and age, at least once [c]	61	61	97	77	53	71	93	82	52	78
By sex, for at least three years	92	66	94	98	96	99	93	100	92	83
Enrolment in secondary education [b]										
Total, at least once	96	78	98	100	99	99	94	100	96	91
By sex, at least once	96	78	98	100	98	99	94	100	96	91
By sex and age, at least once [c]	30	28	66	85	13	66	31	64	16	58
By sex, for at least three years	85	59	94	100	90	79	93	87	86	77
Vocational, by sex, for at least three years	48	32	29	28	49	78	92	60	44	53
Enrolment in tertiary education [b]										
Total, at least once	93	78	97	100	94	99	94	100	92	86
By sex, at least once	69	71	94	87	58	99	93	100	59	78
By sex, for at least three years	59	36	90	69	55	79	92	87	52	51
By sex and field of study, for at least three years	37	22	27	12	39	60	74	52	32	42
School attendance [d]										
Total	14	4	86	22	4	25	0	42	8	5
By sex	14	4	85	22	4	25	0	42	7	5
By sex and age	14	2	85	22	4	25	0	42	7	3
Outcomes of educational experience										
Literacy [d]										
Total	65	34	27	78	80	40	22	24	83	22
By sex	65	34	27	78	80	40	21	24	83	22
By sex and age	64	32	26	78	80	40	21	24	82	22
Educational attainment [d]										
Total	51	31	91	9	54	53	75	61	54	19
By sex	50	31	70	9	54	53	75	61	51	19
By sex and age	48	23	69	9	53	53	75	61	49	17

Sources:
Prepared by the United Nations Statistics Division, Department of Economic and Social Affairs, based on enrolment data (November 2004) and literacy data (April 2005) provided by the UNESCO Institute for Statistics excluding UIS estimates; and on data from the United Nations *Demographic Yearbook* system (November 2004).

a   Excluding the least developed countries.
b   Reported data for the academic years 1995/1996 to 2001/2002 (excluding the academic year 1997/1998).
c   Reported data at least once for the academic years 1998/1999 to 2001/2002.
d   From population censuses only.

Notes

1   See *Report of the Fourth World Conference on Women, Beijing, 4-15 September 1995* (United Nations publication, Sales No. E.96.IV.13), chap. I, resolution 1, annex II, paras. 69, 80(a) and 81(a).

2   Ibid., para. 71.

3   The ISCED levels were developed by UNESCO in order to define levels of education uniformly across countries and enable the compilation of internationally comparable statistics. ICSED 1997 is available from: http://www.uis.unesco.org/TEMPLATE/pdf/isced/ISCED_A.pdf.

4   Analysis of enrolment data for the present report includes data available as of November 2004.

5   Where feasible, the UNESCO Institute for Statistics (UIS) publishes estimates of enrolment data when countries do not report the requisite data; when countries report only totals but not data disaggregated by sex, age or level of education; or when data adjustments are necessary to account for issues such as undercoverage and, occasionally, overcoverage. Although not included in the present analysis, UIS estimates are included in annex table A8 and indicated by the footnote "UIS estimate."

6   Countries or areas reporting at least the number of students in general education programmes were counted as being able to provide data.

7   Countries or areas reporting at least the number of students enrolled in ISCED level 5A of tertiary education for the academic years 1998/1999 to 2001/2002 as well as countries reporting at least the number of students enrolled in universities or equivalent institutions for the academic years before 1998 were counted as being able to provide data. See also note 8.

8   At the time of the preparation of the present report at least 11 countries or areas did not provide tertiary education within their territory: Antigua and Barbuda, Dominica, Grenada, Maldives, Monaco, Nauru, Saint Kitts and Nevis, Saint Vincent and the Grenadines, Seychelles, Solomon Islands and Tuvalu.

9   See *Report of the Fourth World Conference on Women, Beijing, 4-15 September 1995* (United Nations publication, Sales No. E.96.IV.13), chap. I, resolution 1, annex II, para. 82.

10   It should be noted that not all countries provide vocational education at the secondary level. At the time of preparation of the present report the following countries did not provide such education: Bahamas, Ireland, Malawi, Marshall Islands, Nauru, Oman, Palau, Philippines, Qatar, Samoa, United Arab Emirates, United States, Saint Kitts and Nevis, and Zimbabwe.

11   See *Report of the Fourth World Conference on Women, Beijing, 4-15 September 1995* (United Nations publication, Sales No. E.96.IV.13), chap. I, resolution 1, annex II, para. 83(d).

12   Additional data can be found in population censuses and labour force surveys using information on occupations.

13   See the definition of "functional literacy" available from: http://www.uis.unesco.org (April 2005). Links: Literacy/Technical guides/Glossary

Chapter 4
Work

"Women contribute to development not only through remunerated work but also through a great deal of unremunerated work."
Beijing Platform for Action

All over the world, women and men spend the major portion of their lives working. Some of the work may be paid and some may be unpaid. The conditions under which women work, and women's access to employment and productive resources, can differ considerably from those of men. As observed in the Beijing Platform for Action, almost everywhere, women are now working more outside the home, but there has not been a parallel lightening of their responsibility for unremunerated work in the household and community. For women in paid work, obstacles remain that hinder them from achieving their potential, and women are poorly represented in economic decision-making, as well as in certain occupations and sectors. Unemployment and underemployment[1] are serious problems in many countries, especially for women. Where formal employment opportunities are not accessible, women often seek livelihoods for themselves and their dependants in the informal sector, some becoming self-employed or owners of small-scale enterprises.[2]

According to the Millennium Development Goals, strategies to achieve gender equality and the empowerment of women include advocating women's empowerment in employment. Countries are also called on to develop and implement strategies for decent and productive work for youth and to ensure that girls are given the same opportunities as boys.[3]

To address those concerns, Governments require information on the economically active population, employment, unemployment, occupations, status in employment, wages and related statistics. For effective gender-sensitive planning and evaluation, the data should be generated and disseminated by sex, age and other socio-economic variables as needed. Statistics on the economically active, employed and unemployed populations, and on the distribution of those populations by occupation and by status in employment (i.e. whether employers, own-account workers, employees or contributing family workers), are already collected regularly in many countries, mainly through labour force surveys. These data are also collected in population censuses.

Data on the earnings of women and men are routinely collected in many countries from payroll figures through establishment censuses or surveys,[4] and in some cases from labour force surveys or administrative records.

Official statistics on the labour force and its characteristics are typically collected in a country by the ministry of labour or the national statistical office. At the international level, the International Labour Office is generally responsible for collecting those statistics from national authorities. The United Nations Statistics Division is responsible for collecting from national authorities those statistics on economic characteristics that are derived from population censuses.

On the basis of what has been reported to the international organizations, it is apparent that the worldwide availability of statistics on economic activity, employment and unemployment is far from satisfactory, with slightly more than half of all countries providing data by sex and only roughly a third of all countries doing so with fair regularity. The lack of data has received particular attention in recent years as a result of the monitoring and reporting requirements of the Millennium Development Goals. One positive aspect is that when economically active population, employment and unemployment data are provided, they are almost always disaggregated by sex.

In general, labour force surveys and establishment surveys capture the more formal types of economic activity better than the non-formal types of economic activity. As a result, the economic activities of women are often under-reported. The production of goods and services for household consumption is done by women more than by men. Although included in the United Nations System of National Accounts (SNA),[5] work of this nature is often under-recorded. It is believed that women also perform most of the unremunerated domestic and community work that are not part of the SNA and a significant part of the activities in the informal sector of the economy, which tend to be underreported in official statistics. In that light, the Beijing Platform for

The worldwide availability of statistics on economic activity, employment and unemployment is far from satisfactory...

...with slightly more than half of all countries providing data by sex and only roughly a third doing so with fair regularity

Action called on countries to improve data collection on the full contribution of women and men to the economy, including their participation in the informal sector, and to conduct regular time-use surveys to measure unremunerated work in quantitative terms.[6]

Current state of statistics 1995-2003

The labour force, the unemployed and the employed

The labour force

Most Governments attach a high priority to up-to-date information on the labour force (see box 4.1 for concepts related to the labour force) and the employment and unemployment situation, given the importance of the information in economic planning and monitoring. For many countries, that emphasis is reflected in the breadth and regularity of available statistics on the labour force. For other countries, however, it is a challenge to produce even the most basic of these important statistics. The result is that for the world, for the period 1995 to 2003, a total of 127 out of 204 countries or areas, comprising about 50 per cent of the world population, reported the numbers of the economically active population[7] at least once to the international statistical system. The count includes only countries or areas that provided data on the economically active population from either a survey or a population census.[8] All but two

Box 4.1

Concepts related to the labour force

The **economically active population** comprises all persons of either sex who furnish or are available to furnish the supply of labour for the production of goods and services, during a specified reference period; that is, it comprises all persons above a specified minimum age who were either employed or unemployed during that time. If the reference period used to define this population is short, for example one week or one day, the term **labour force or currently active population** is used to denote the group. If the reference period is long, for example a year, the term **usually active population** is used.

As defined by the System of National Accounts, the concept of economic activity covers (i) all production oriented to the market; (ii) some types of non-market production, including production and processing of primary products for own consumption; (iii) own-account construction; and (iv) other production of fixed assets for own use. It excludes some unpaid activities, such as unpaid domestic activities and certain types of volunteer community services.[a]

The **employed** population comprises all persons above a specified age who during a specified brief period, either one week or one day, worked for pay or profit, or contributed to a family business (or farm) without receiving any remuneration (i.e. were unpaid).

The **unemployed** population comprises all persons above a specified age who during the reference period were:

- "without work", that is, were not employed;
- "currently available for work", that is, were available for paid employment or self-employment; and

- "seeking work", that is, had taken specific steps in a specified reference period to seek paid employment or self-employment (this condition is relaxed in situations where the conventional means of seeking employment are of limited relevance, where the labour market is largely unorganized or of limited scope, where labour absorption is, at the time, inadequate, or where the labour force is largely self-employed).

Persons **not in the labour force** (or population **not currently active**) comprise all persons who were not classified as employed or unemployed during the brief reference period and hence not currently active, because of any of the following reasons:

- attendance at educational institutions
- engagement in household duties
- retirement or old age
- other reasons such as infirmity, disability or being below a specified age

Source:
Yearbook of Labour Statistics, 2004 (Geneva, International Labour Office, 2004); and Commission of the European Communities and others, *System of National Accounts, 1993* (United Nations publication, Sales No. E.94.XVII.4).

a Under the Resolution of the thirteenth International Conference of Labour Statisticians, it was recommended that all volunteers be classified as not economically active. However, as a result of changes to the SNA in 1993, the treatment of unpaid volunteer community services is no longer as simple; some volunteer activities are included in the concept of economic activity while others are not.

Share of women in wage employment in the non-agricultural sector

For the indicator on the share of women in wage employment in the non-agricultural sector, the required statistics are the number of employees among employed persons, broken down by sex and major industry group. The number of countries or areas reporting that data at least once increased substantially from the first period to the third: from 20 in 1975-84 to 74 in 1995-2003 (chart 4.16). The number able to report the data frequently also increased considerably, from 16 in the first period (1975-84) to 61 in the most recent period. In spite of the improvement, however, that number represents less than a third of all countries.

Unemployment rate of young people aged 15-24 years, by sex

For the youth unemployment indicator, the data required are the total numbers unemployed by sex and age. The number of countries reporting that data has increased substantially during the last three periods but remains low. From 22 countries reporting the data at least once in the period 1975-1984, there are now 96 able to do so; however, of those, only 72 report data frequently (chart 4.17).

Chart 4.15

Number of countries or areas that reported data on wages at least once, for three periods

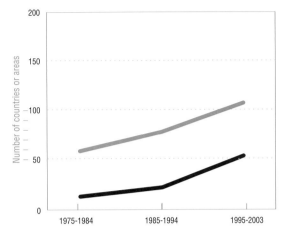

By major industry group

By major industry group and sex

Source:
Prepared by the United Nations Statistics Division, Department of Economic and Social Affairs, based on data from the International Labour Office, LABORSTA database (March 2005).

Chart 4.16

Number of countries or areas that reported wage employment by sex and major industry group, for three periods

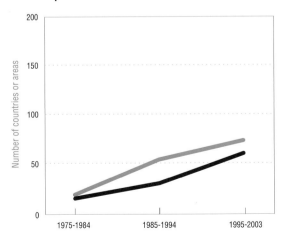

Source:
Prepared by the United Nations Statistics Division, Department of Economic and Social Affairs, based on data from the International Labour Office, LABORSTA database (July 2005).

Chart 4.17

Number of countries or areas that reported unemployment by sex and age, for three periods

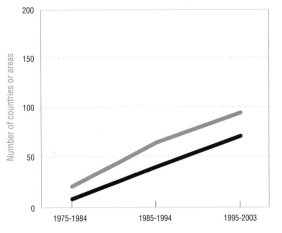

At least once

For at least five years

Source:
Prepared by the United Nations Statistics Division, Department of Economic and Social Affairs, based on data from the International Labour Office, LABORSTA database (March 2005).

Challenges

Strengthening statistical capacity

The findings reported in the present chapter point to the need for a concerted effort and commitment by Governments to collecting basic labour statistics in countries or areas where the statistics are deficient. In most countries in Africa, Asia and Oceania, no survey programme is in place to furnish data regularly on the labour force and its characteristics (such as employment status, occupations, unemployment and wages) to guide policy. Some countries in Africa and Asia that do conduct labour force or other sample surveys to collect the data still do so irregularly, occasionally or at long intervals, in some cases as far apart as every 10 years.

Thus, in a number of countries, the census is the only source of statistics on the characteristics of the labour force. In those statistically less developed and resource-poor countries, it takes a long time to process the large amount of data that censuses produce. Consequently, the results are often disseminated partially or late, thereby reducing their usefulness for policy and decision-making. For the concerned countries, efforts should be made to improve the availability and timeliness of census results.

At the same time, however, the rapidity of changes in the labour force, employment and unemployment situations point to the need for regular sources of timely data on those topics. More importantly, the complex task of measuring women's work and its associated problems is better addressed by labour force or related household surveys. The existence of a regular and integrated survey programme is imperative for informing policy and addressing gender issues in employment.

The main challenge for the less developed countries is to strengthen their capacity to produce statistics within the limits of their resources. In many cases, international, regional or bilateral donors have stepped in to help countries implement a population census or labour force survey, but their efforts rarely produced long-term results. The focus should be on making a sustainable improvement in the recipient countries' statistical capacity, keeping in mind that capacity building can be a lengthy process and that national resources are limited and Government commitment may fluctuate.

Mainstreaming gender in labour statistics

A separate but related issue in strengthening statistics is mainstreaming gender in the collection, analysis and dissemination of statistics on work. Whether obtained through administrative records, household or establishment-based surveys or censuses, most data on the labour force and its characteristics are collected on individuals. Each individual's sex, age and other personal and contextual factors are usually recorded. However, in the processing, analysis or presentation of data, sex and age—not to mention the more detailed characteristics—are often dropped. In order to better reflect gender concerns, countries should ensure that this information is collected and compiled and that the resulting statistics are disaggregated by sex and age as a minimum and, if possible, by the worker's personal and family characteristics (such as marital status, number of children or other family members requiring care) and work environment (such as the existence of childcare facilities) as well. Detailed cross-tabulations, however, will require a large sample size, which many countries may find difficult to implement owing to the significant resources needed.

Of the statistics reviewed in the present chapter, those on wages stand out as being most deficient in terms of availability of sex-disaggregated data. Many countries that produce those statistics from establishment censuses and surveys have not been able to report the data by sex. This is in part due to payrolls of establishments not having recorded the sex of the employee. To improve the situation, all data collection entities, including those that do not produce statistics but have administrative information that can be used by statistical agencies, should be encouraged to record their data in a way that will allow the reporting of wage statistics by sex.

There is a need to ensure that definitions and measurement methods cover and adequately describe all workers and work situations in sufficient detail to allow gender comparisons to be made. In most countries, women are the majority of workers in non-standard work, such as temporary, casual, part-time, contract and home-based work. The methods of measuring those varied types of employment need to be improved and effectively mainstreamed into the regular data collection system.

A critical area that needs improved mainstreaming in the regular data collection system is women's and men's work activities in agriculture. Population censuses and labour force surveys largely overlook and thus under-report women's work in agriculture since it is usually unpaid and often includes activities such as food processing and providing water and fuel that are easily considered part of housework. Improved methods for measuring the

---

In most countries in Africa, Asia and Oceania, no survey programme is in place to furnish data regularly on the labour force and its characteristics

In a number of countries, the census is the only source of statistics on the characteristics of the labour force

Of the statistics reviewed, those on wages stand out as being most deficient in terms of availability of sex-disaggregated data

There is a need to ensure that definitions and measurement methods cover and adequately describe all workers and work situations

wide range of agricultural activities are needed to better reflect both women's and men's roles in agricultural production and participation in the economy.

Unemployment as currently measured in official statistics often underestimates the actual level of unemployment of women, especially rural women. Unemployment is particularly difficult to define and measure in populations largely dependent on subsistence agriculture, such as in the poorer countries of Asia and sub-Saharan Africa. Attention is drawn to the need to improve the measurement of women's unemployment, especially in rural areas.

Improving knowledge and measurement of women's work

Many aspects of women's work are not measured well by mainstream employment statistics as they currently stand. Developing a more comprehensive knowledge of all forms of work and employment through the improvement of data collection on the unremunerated work that is already included in the System of National Accounts (SNA) was stipulated in the Beijing Platform for Action,[32] and should continue to be a priority for national, regional and international statistical services. In addition, more knowledge is needed on non-SNA work, employment in the informal economy and income from paid and self-employment, among other topics.

Since the adoption of the Platform for Action, significant methodological work has been undertaken to improve the measurement of employment in the informal sector. However, more needs to be done. Many countries do not collect the data necessary for producing statistics on employment in the informal sector. In others, statistics on the informal sector are collected on an ad hoc basis and survey methodologies change over time so that statistics often cannot be fully compared even within the same country. Countries that do not currently have statistics on informal employment will need technical assistance and training to develop those statistics, while countries that already have statistics on informal employment will need assistance to improve the quality of those statistics, including their international comparability.

A data source that is essential in understanding the various forms of women's and men's work is time-use surveys, which capture both paid and unpaid work. However, such surveys are still not widely conducted in the less developed regions. In addition, methods for conducting time-use surveys need to be further developed and elaborated to suit different situations and contexts. As stated above, the United Nations Statistics Division has developed the trial International Classification of Activities for Time-Use Statistics, but it needs refinement and has yet to be adopted.

A recent initiative to better cover the various types of economic work that women engage in, especially in the less developed regions, is evidenced in the work of the United Nations Millennium Project Task Force on Education and Gender Equality. The Task Force recommended the production of indicators that would reflect women's status in employment, while at the same time distinguishing agricultural from non-agricultural employment, and formal and informal employment in the case of employment in the non-agricultural sector.[33]

To derive the recommended indicators requires the total number of employed women and men to be broken down along three dimensions: status in employment, sector (agricultural, non-agricultural) and formal/informal employment in the case of the non-agricultural sector. The task poses a great challenge for developing countries, the majority of which do not currently have the capacity to produce data regularly on informal employment or even on status in employment. At present, less than 40 countries are able to provide such detailed data. Detailed guidelines on how to collect the required data and produce the indicators are needed.

Developing a more comprehensive knowledge of all forms of work and employment should continue to be a priority for national, regional and international statistical services

Methods for conducting time-use surveys need to be further developed and elaborated to suit different situations and contexts

Table 4.A

Number of countries or areas that reported data[a] on selected economic characteristics, 1995 – 2003

| | World | Geographic region | | | | | | Development group | | |
		Africa	North America	South America	Asia	Europe	Oceania	More developed regions	Less developed regions [b]	Least developed countries
All countries or areas	204	55	27	13	50	42	17	47	107	50
Economically active population										
Total, at least once	127	19	17	11	34	38	8	43	70	14
By sex, at least once	125	18	17	11	34	37	8	42	70	13
By sex and age, at least once	123	18	17	11	34	37	6	42	69	12
By sex and age, for at least five years	59	1	10	6	12	28	2	33	26	0
Unemployed population										
Total, at least once	115	13	19	12	31	35	5	40	66	9
By sex, at least once	114	12	19	12	31	35	5	40	65	9
By sex and age, at least once	96	8	15	9	27	34	3	39	51	6
By sex and age, for at least five years	72	2	14	9	14	31	2	36	36	0
Employed population by occupation										
Total, at least once	108	10	16	10	32	33	7	38	60	10
By sex, at least once	105	9	15	10	32	33	6	38	58	9
By sex, for at least five years	68	1	13	8	15	29	2	34	34	0
Employed population by status in employment										
Total, at least once	106	15	16	9	28	33	5	38	59	9
By sex, at least once	104	13	16	9	28	33	5	38	57	9
By sex, for at least five years	64	1	12	6	14	29	2	34	30	0

Sources:

Prepared by the United Nations Statistics Division, Department of Economic and Social Affairs, based on data from the International Labour Office, LABORSTA database (March 2005) and from the United Nations *Demographic Yearbook* system (November 2004).

a　From labour force surveys, household surveys, population censuses or labour-related establishment surveys.
b　Excluding the least developed countries.

Table 4.B
Percentage of the world and regional populations in countries or areas that reported data[a] on selected economic characteristics, 1995 – 2003

| | World | Geographic region | | | | | | Development group | | |
		Africa	North America	South America	Asia	Europe	Oceania	More developed regions	Less developed regions[b]	Least developed countries
All countries or areas	100	100	100	100	100	100	100	100	100	100
Economically active population										
Total, at least once	50	47	94	98	31	99	96	100	36	50
By sex, at least once	50	47	94	98	31	98	96	99	36	50
By sex and age, at least once	50	47	94	98	31	98	95	99	36	50
By sex and age, for at least five years	32	4	90	78	15	85	74	91	20	0
Unemployed population										
Total, at least once	66	33	93	100	60	98	92	99	61	36
By sex, at least once	66	32	93	100	60	98	92	99	61	36
By sex and age, at least once	45	22	91	91	30	97	75	98	33	27
By sex and age, for at least five years	36	12	91	91	16	96	74	97	24	0
Employed population by occupation										
Total, at least once	42	24	91	98	25	88	92	93	29	36
By sex, at least once	42	23	90	98	25	88	75	93	29	35
By sex, for at least five years	34	8	89	95	16	87	74	92	23	0
Employed population by status in employment										
Total, at least once	46	32	93	91	29	88	76	93	34	38
By sex, at least once	45	27	93	91	29	88	76	93	34	33
By sex, for at least five years	30	8	89	40	16	85	74	91	18	0

Sources:

Prepared by the United Nations Statistics Division, Department of Economic and Social Affairs, based on data from the International Labour Office, LABORSTA database (March 2005) and from the United Nations *Demographic Yearbook* system (November 2004).

a   From labour force surveys, household surveys, population censuses or labour-related establishment surveys.
b   Excluding the least developed countries.

Notes

1   Individuals are considered underemployed in any of the follow-ing situations, which may coexist: (a) they are working fewer hours than they are able or want to (referred to as "time-related unemployment"); (b) they are earning less than they are willing or able to; (c) their work does not match or make full use of their occupational skills; and/or (d) their working hours are excessive (situations [c] and [d] are described as "inadequate employment"). Source: see International Labour Organization, *Report of the Conference*, Sixteenth International Conference of Labour Statisticians, held at Geneva from 6-15 October 1998 (Geneva, International Labour Office, 1998), appendix I, resolution 1.

2   *Report of the Fourth World Conference on Women, Beijing, 4-15 September 1995* (United Nations publication, Sales No. E.96.IV.13), chap. I, resolution 1, annex II, paras. 150, 153, 156, 158 and 161.

3   See "Road map towards the implementation of the United Nations Millennium Declaration", Report of the Secretary-General (A/56/326), paras. 125 and 128.

4   Establishment censuses and surveys provide data on the number of workers on establishment payrolls for a specified payroll period or working day in the period; on average earnings from establishment payrolls; on hours of work; and on employment. Statistics derived from establishment surveys do not always distinguish between women and men because such distinction may not be made in the payrolls of the establishments surveyed.

5   Commission of the European Communities, *System of National Accounts*, 1993 (United Nations publication, Sales No. E.94.XVII.4).

6   *Report of the Fourth World Conference on Women, Beijing, 4-15 September 1995* (United Nations publication, Sales No. E.96.IV.13), chap. I, resolution 1, annex II, paras. 206 (e), (g)(i) and (g)(ii).

7   In the present report, the terms "economically active population" and "labour force" are used interchangeably. For a fuller explanation of the concepts, see box 4.1.

8   Two countries provided only "official estimates" of the economically active population. They are excluded from the count of 127 countries or areas presented here. Official estimates provided by national authorities are based on combined information drawn from one or more sources.

9   Labour force surveys in general provide more accurate and detailed data than population censuses owing to the limitations on the number of questions and extent of probing possible in a population census. The census, as a result of its universal coverage, has the advantage of being able to provide statistics for small administrative areas or population subgroups not normally possible in surveys but, as stated, the disadvantage of being conducted in general only once every 10 years.

10   For unemployment statistics, employment office records provide an alternative data source. The extent to which statistics from that source represent the general level of unemployment is, however, difficult to ascertain. The statistics typically include persons who register at an employment office, and the reasons for and extent of registration vary within and across countries; in some cases, they are limited to work applicants. Still other countries report "official estimates", which are usually based on combined information drawn from one or more of the other sources already mentioned. For the period 1995-2003, 16 countries provided unemployment statistics from employ-ment office statistics (eight that covered registered unemploy-ment and eight that covered work applicants) and another nine provided "official estimates". The 115 countries or areas reported to have unemployment data do not include those 25 countries.

11   *Report of the Fourth World Conference on Women, Beijing, 4-15 September 1995* (United Nations publication, Sales No. E.96.IV.13), chap. I, resolution 1, annex II, para. 206 (f).

12   *Ibid.*, para. 178 (g).

13   See, for example, Richard Anker, "Women's access to occupa-tions with authority, influence and decision-making power: women as legislators, senior officials and managers", working paper (Geneva, International Labour Office, forthcoming).

14   SEGREGAT database can be accessed through www.ilo.laborsta.

15   The term "decent work" refers to opportunities for "work that is productive and delivers a fair income, security in the workplace and social protection for families, better prospects for personal development and social integration, freedom for people to express their concerns, organize and participate in the decisions that affect their lives and equality of opportunity and treatment for all women and men". See http://www.ilo.org/public/english/decent.htm (Geneva, International Labour Office) (4 August 2005).

16   "Road map towards the implementation of the United Nations Millennium Declaration", Report of the Secretary-General (A/56/326).

17   Information on the number of female and male employees in the non-agricultural sector is obtained mainly from labour force surveys or labour-related establishment surveys. Population censuses or establishment censuses may also provide the information. The indicator is calculated from labour force surveys or population censuses using data on the employed population of each sex, cross-classified by status in employment and type of industry. The status in employment category of interest would be "employees", and the relevant industry groups are all groups other than agriculture, hunting, forestry and fishing. If the indicator is calculated from labour force establishment surveys or censuses, the data required are the total number of female and male employees, cross-classified by type of industry. At a minimum, the agricultural and non-agricultural sectors must be separable.

18   Based on material provided by the International Labour Office.

19   *Report of the Fourth World Conference on Women, Beijing,
      4-15 September 1995* (United Nations publication, Sales No.
      E.96.IV.13), chap. I, resolution 1, annex II, para. 162.

20   Some results have been reported in *The World's Women 1995:
      Trends in Statistics* and *The World's Women 2000: Trends in
      Statistics* (United Nations publications, Sales Nos. E.95.XVII.2
      and E.00.XVII.14).

21   Barbados (1998), Ethiopia (1999), Georgia (1999), India (2000),
      Latvia (1999), Peru (1999), Russian Federation (1999) and
      Turkey (2000).

22   The informal sector defined as private unincorporated
      enterprises (excluding quasi-corporations) that produce at least
      some of their goods and services for sale or barter, have less
      than five paid employees, are not registered and are engaged in
      non-agricultural activities (including professional or technical
      activities).

23   Argentina (1998), Bolivia (1997), Brazil (1999), Chile (2000),
      Colombia (2000), Costa Rica (2000), Ecuador (2000), Honduras
      (1999), Mexico (2000), Panama (2000), Paraguay (1996), Peru
      (2000), Uruguay (1999) and Venezuela (2000).

24   Defined as all own-account workers (excluding professionals
      and technicians) and unpaid family workers, and employers and
      employees working in establishments with less than 5 or 10
      persons engaged, depending on the available information. Paid
      domestic workers are excluded. Agriculture is excluded.

25   For more information, see Ralf Hussmanns and B. du Jeu,
      "The ILO Compendium of official statistics on employment in
      the informal sector", STAT working paper No. 1-2002
      (Geneva, International Labour Office, 2002).

26   See *Report of the Fourth World Conference on Women, Beijing,
      4-15 September 1995* (United Nations publication, Sales No.
      E.96.IV.13), chap. I, resolution 1, annex II, para. 68 (b).

27   *The World's Women 1990: Trends in Statistics* (United Nations
      publication, Sales No. E.90.XVII.3); *The World's Women 1995:
      Trends in Statistics* (United Nations publication, Sales No.
      E.95.XVII.2); and *The World's Women 2000: Trends in Statistics*
      (United Nations publication, Sales No. E.00.XVII.14).

28   The trial International Classification of Activities for Time-Use
      Statistics (ICATUS), which is published as an annex in the
      *Guide to Producing Statistics on Time Use: Measuring Paid and
      Unpaid Work* (United Nations publication, Sales No. E.04.XVII.7)
      and available from the United Nations Statistics Division website
      "Allocation of time and time use",
      http://unstats.un.org/unsd/demographic/sconcerns/tuse/tu3.aspx.

29   *Guide to Producing Statistics on Time Use: Measuring Paid and
      Unpaid Work* (United Nations publication, Sales No. E.04.XVII.7).

30   National authorities sometimes provide "official estimates" to
      the international statistical system. These estimates are usually
      based on combined information drawn from one or more
      sources.

31   Suriname and Venezuela (Bolivarian Republic of) reported data
      at least five times in 1985-1994 but provided data for only two
      and four years respectively in the most recent period.

32   *Report of the Fourth World Conference on Women, Beijing,
      4-15 September 1995* (United Nations publication, Sales No.
      E.96.IV.13), chap. I, resolution 1, annex II, para. 206 (f).

33   Millennium Project, *Taking Action: Achieving Gender Equality
      and Empowering Women*, Task Force on Education and Gender
      Equality (London, Earthscan, 2005).

Whereas the criminal and civil justice systems may be obligated to record, classify and report statistics of violence against women, it is often not mandatory for the health-care system to record and report cases of violence. Moreover, the types of information kept by health providers are very diverse and often not comparable across institutions or over time owing to the lack of a standardized system for recording and processing the information. However, efforts to improve injury surveillance are underway in some countries, including documenting the relationship between the victim and the perpetrator.

As with the police and legal systems, the cases that become known to health services are but a fraction of all cases of violence against women, in all likelihood limited to violence that resulted in serious physical injuries. In addition, health services are not accessible in many developing countries, especially in rural areas.

One source that can potentially be tapped for some information on violence against women is statistics on deaths by sex, age and cause. Those statistics are already produced by countries as vital statistics and are based on information from death certificates.[20] Where death registration is complete and reliable, statistics on deaths by sex, age and cause (in particular, external causes), or even just deaths by sex and age, can potentially provide information on certain forms of violence against women and girls.

For example, infant deaths or infant mortality rates broken down by sex from vital statistics systems or derived from other sources may be examined to detect evidence of the practice of female infanticide or discrimination against girls. In general, male babies are more susceptible to death than female babies. Thus, when statistics show more baby girls than boys dying in a population or subpopulation, there is reason to suspect that female infanticide, or at least son preference manifesting itself in the neglect, deprivation and discriminatory treatment of infant girls, is being practised. Based on the number of countries that have reported infant mortality by sex, it is possible to examine the statistics for 114 countries of the world (see chapter 2).

Where death statistics by sex, age and cause are reliable, they can also provide an indication of the presence of dowry deaths or so-called "honour" killings, although those events are known to be grossly underreported.[21] Deaths of women in the age groups most susceptible to such deaths can be examined, focusing on deaths reported as caused by homicide, suicides, accidents and the like. However, several problems present themselves with the use of this source. First, the cause of such deaths may be recorded as something entirely different. Second, in countries where such forms of violence are more likely to be practised, vital statistics on deaths are often inadequate.

Administrative records from other types of service providers

Public and private agencies, including non-governmental organizations, provide a wide range of support services to women victims of violence, including emergency shelters or refuges, crisis centres, sexual assault phone lines, and legal counsel and legal aid services. As in the case of the police and health-care providers, the persons seeking support services are likely to be a tiny fraction of all women who have experienced violence.

Although providers of the services collect information about the women they assist and, to various degrees, their clients' experience of violence, the type of information collected is very diverse. Provision of statistics is generally not a priority of service providers, so information is seldom systematically collated, processed or reported. In the absence of a mechanism to consolidate information from the various organizations in a meaningful way over time and across type of service provided, the information often remains fragmented and accessible only within the confines of the individual organizations.

Grappling with statistics on trafficking in women and girls [22]

The wide range of activities and the multiplicity of actors involved in the process of human trafficking, coupled with the clandestine and undercover nature of the activities and their possible links to organized crime and corruption, make the measurement of trafficking complex and problematic. At present, comprehensive and reliable statistics on trafficking in women and girls are not available.

Estimates on the volume of trafficking may be derived by combining information from several sources, or may be based solely on statistics pertaining to a particular stage in the trafficking process that is the area of responsibility of the organization or programme producing them. Data on trafficking in women may be collected by organizations with responsibility for crime prevention, prosecution and law enforcement or by those providing protection and assistance to victims, among others. The quality and focus of the data vary according to the financial resources and priorities of the organizations producing them and the concepts, definitions and methods

The multiplicity of actors involved in the process of human trafficking makes the measurement of trafficking complex and problematic

At present, comprehensive and reliable statistics on trafficking in women and girls are not available

employed. In short, statistics are being produced by numerous agencies with an interest in the area of human trafficking, but there is no single body to systematically gather, harmonize and effectively utilize them.

The adoption by the General Assembly in November 2000 of the Protocol to Prevent, Suppress and Punish Trafficking in Persons, Especially Women and Children, supplementing the United Nations Convention against Transnational Organized Crime, provided the international community with an agreed definition of human trafficking. The definition, given below, provides a broad and inclusive framework for studying trafficking in women and girls.

> Trafficking in persons means "the recruitment, transportation, transfer, harbouring or receipt of persons, by means of threat or use of force or other forms of coercion, of abduction, of fraud, of deception, of the abuse of power or of a position of vulnerability or of the giving or receiving of payments or benefits to achieve the consent of a person having control over another person, for the purpose of exploitation".[23]

However, using the definition for the purpose of data collection is still a problem. Thus far, only a few countries have begun to systematically collect data on trafficking, and it is still common in many countries to mingle data relating to trafficking, smuggling and irregular migration.

In general, data on human trafficking can originate from (a) source or origin areas, where data on missing people can be used; (b) different stages of the process of movement, where for example border crossing statistics and border apprehension data provide a basis for estimates; and (c) the destination, where law enforcement agencies, health professionals, researchers or intergovernmental and non-governmental organizations assisting victims may collect and provide useful data.

Some source, transit and destination countries collect some of the types of data listed above; however, data collection is seldom systematic. The lack of adequate and specific legislation on trafficking in women results in the absence of official criminal justice statistics on trafficking cases, in terms of both the number of crimes recorded by the police and the number of persons prosecuted or convicted. Registers kept by authorities and organizations of the victims that they assist tend to be fragmentary and not coordinated. Given the fragmentary and non-repre-

sentative nature of the available data, researchers and trafficking experts find it difficult to provide reliable national, regional or global estimates of the number of women and girls trafficked.

There are, however, several initiatives to gather global data on human trafficking, of both women and men, and they are described below. Among the most frequently quoted global numbers of human trafficking are those published by official United States sources. Since 2001, the Office to Monitor and Combat Trafficking in Persons has published annual reports providing country narratives that describe the scope and nature of the trafficking problem in the respective countries, as well as government efforts to combat trafficking. The Protection Project at the Johns Hopkins School of Advanced International Studies also collects and disseminates information about trafficking, especially of women and children.

A global database on trafficking trends, established under the Global Programme against Trafficking in Human Beings of the United Nations Office on Drugs and Crime, systematically collects and collates information on trafficking in persons. A broad range of sources is scrutinized for information on trafficking trends and routes, characteristics of victims and offenders, and criminal justice responses. The main sources include official reports from Governments, information disseminated by intergovernmental and non-governmental organizations, research reports, conference material and media reports.

The International Organization for Migration's *Counter-Trafficking Module* database is a compilation of information from the Organization's counter-trafficking programmes. The database draws on detailed interviews of victims who were assisted through the Organization's counter-trafficking activities worldwide. The quantitative and qualitative data collected contribute to a better understanding of the socio-economic profile and background of victims, their recruitment and trafficking process and their exploitation in the destination countries.

Progress in statistics

Considerable progress has been made in the past ten years in the development of methodology and procedures for data collection on violence against women, particularly on intimate partner violence. While comparing data across countries and regions is still a problem, the situation is also improving. The years following the Fourth World Conference on Women, held in Beijing in 1995, have witnessed multiple initiatives to develop and collect internationally com-

Statistics on human trafficking are being produced by numerous agencies, but there is no single body to gather, harmonize and effectively utilize them

The lack of adequate and specific legislation on trafficking in women results in the absence of official criminal justice statistics on trafficking

parable statistics on violence against women through standardized survey methods.

The World Health Organization (WHO) spearheaded the effort through its Multi-Country Study on Women's Health and Domestic Violence (see box 5.1). Launched in 1998, the study has been implemented in at least 10 countries.

Another international initiative is the International Violence against Women Survey (IVAWS), coordinated by the European Institute for Crime

Box 5.1

WHO Multi-Country Study on Women's Health and Domestic Violence

The World Health Organization launched the Multi-Country Study on Women's Health and Domestic Violence in 1998. The study aims (a) to obtain reliable estimates of the prevalence of different forms of violence, particularly those inflicted by intimate partners; (b) to document the association of intimate partner violence with health outcomes and other aspects of women's lives; (c) to examine factors that may protect women from or make them vulnerable to intimate partner violence; and (d) to document the strategies and services that women use to deal with such violence. In carrying out the study, WHO made use of both qualitative and quantitative research methodologies, allowing the qualitative findings to inform the development of the core questionnaire for the study's quantitative component. In most countries, the quantitative component consists of a cross-sectional, population-based household survey conducted in two sites: the capital or other large city and a province with rural and urban populations.

The WHO Multi-Country Study has been implemented in at least 10 culturally diverse countries in Africa, Asia, Oceania and South America. Domestic violence research projects based on the WHO study methodology have also been conducted in several other countries.

Box 5.2

The International Violence against Women Survey (IVAWS)

The European Institute for Crime Prevention and Control affiliated with the United Nations, with inputs from the United Nations Office on Drugs and Crime, the United Nations Interregional Crime and Justice Research Institute and Statistics Canada, initiated the International Violence against Women Survey project in 2001. IVAWS is an international comparative survey specifically designed to study men's violence against women, especially intimate partner violence and sexual assault. It aims to promote and implement research on violence against women in countries around the world and to assess the level of victimization of women in those countries using a standardized methodology and questionnaire, making possible cross-cultural comparisons on the subject.

The IVAWS is conducted within a crime victimization framework and has relied largely on the network, infrastructure and methodology of the International Crime Victim Survey.[a] The information it provides is expected to provide inputs for the development of specific criminal justice approaches.

a The International Crime Victim Surveys (ICVS) provide information on crime and victimization through a standard questionnaire, the results of which are internationally comparable. To ensure this, all aspects of the methodology have been standardized to the maximum possible extent (See http://www.unodc.org/unodc/en/research_icvs.html).

Prevention and Control, affiliated with the United Nations (HEUNI) (see box 5.2). So far, IVAWS has been administered in 11 countries, both developed and developing, and funding assistance is being sought to ensure the participation of additional developing countries and countries in transition.

The Demographic and Health Surveys, supported by Macro International Inc., collect data on violence against women through a domestic violence module. The module includes in-depth questions

to enable the assessment of the prevalence and intergenerational consequences of domestic and other violence against women in the household context. Since 1995, at least 11 countries implementing the Demographic and Health Surveys have included the domestic violence module.

Both the WHO Multi-Country Study and the International Violence against Women Survey brought together international agencies, national researchers and statistical offices experienced in conducting surveys on violence against women to develop and design the study protocol and questionnaire, to support the country teams and to facilitate the analysis. Carrying out the research in culturally diverse countries gave the World Health Organization and the European Institute for Crime Prevention and Control a better understanding of the realities of conducting surveys on violence against women in various contexts. By participating in research on violence against women under the

An important develop-
ment in recent years is the
increased attention paid
to ethical and safety
issues associated with
research on intimate
partner violence

Efforts should be made
to promote the imple-
mentation of surveys on
violence against women
within the framework of
official statistics

Researchers need to find
methods to improve the
disclosure of violence in
generalized surveys

umbrella of an internationally coordinated study, countries gained valuable experience in all aspects of survey planning and operations on this sensitive subject and improved their technical capacity for collecting internationally comparable data on the subject.

An important development in recent years relating to surveys on violence against women is the increased attention paid to ethical and safety issues associated with research on intimate partner violence. The World Health Organization emphasizes the importance of ensuring the safety of both respondents and field staff and has developed safety and ethical guidelines for conducting research on domestic violence.[24] The guidelines have been adopted by other organizations carrying out surveys in this area. The World Health Organization has also produced ethical and safety recommendations for interviewing trafficked women.[25]

A positive trend that has emerged in relation to research on violence against women is the building of partnerships and strong consultation processes among policy-setting institutions, service providers and development cooperation entities. For example, in the case of the WHO Multi-Country Study, country research teams included national organizations that have been addressing violence against women, as well as a multi-stakeholder consultative committee to guide the study's implementation. The committees comprise individuals from key government departments and from non-governmental organizations. The ongoing process of consultation created a sense of commitment among the participants and contributed to the data being linked to advocacy and policy making. In Latin America, dialogue between the users and producers of information was instrumental to the success of various studies on violence against women in the region, and to the effective use of the study results.[26]

Challenges

Strengthening statistical capacity

Countries need to develop their capacity to collect, process and disseminate quality data on violence against women. Many countries that lack knowledge of the scope and extent of domestic and other violence against women do not have the capacity to carry out a specialized national survey on the issue. For those countries, the possibility of collecting data on violence against women through an existing multi-purpose survey can be considered. However, where international support can be secured, it is desirable to implement a baseline specialized survey with technical assistance provided by external sources. The WHO Multi-Country Study and the International Violence against Women Survey present good opportunities for such collaboration.

More importantly, efforts should be made to promote the implementation of surveys on violence against women within the framework of official statistics: in other words, to mainstream them into the country's regular statistics programme.

For many countries, records kept by the police and the courts are often weak and uneven. There is a need to strengthen their recording and processing systems to enable them to produce reliable statistics with comprehensive national coverage. However, in many countries, the required financial and human resources may not be available.

Improving survey methods

The relatively lower cost of collecting data on violence against women through existing multi-purpose national surveys has made that approach an attractive option for many countries, and it will no doubt continue to be used. Its main disadvantage is that the disclosure of violence is not as high as in the case of specialized surveys. One of the ways to improve disclosure is to include a separate module—with an adequate number of well-tested questions—rather than just to add a few questions. Another is to provide additional training to the interviewers normally engaged in large-scale surveys, including training on ethical and safety issues related to this type of research. Such training can be very costly, however, and not always practical owing to the large number of interviewers involved. Researchers need to find other innovative methods to improve the disclosure of violence in generalized surveys.

In general, research is also needed on how other factors, such as the approach used for administering the survey, the order and wording of questions, the number and type of questions asked, interviewer characteristics and the like affect disclosure or otherwise have an impact on the survey findings.

Improving administrative data

As mentioned above, police and court data collection systems in many countries do not always record the sex and age of the victim or the relationship of the perpetrator to the victim, making it impossible to identify cases of intimate partner violence or other violence against women or girls within the family. Attention has to be paid to the collection of information so that the records include all information necessary to identify the various types of violence against women. That, however, can be accomplished only if legislation exists that clearly specifies violence against women as a crime and that punishes and redresses the wrongs done to women and girls who are subjected to any form of violence, whether in the home, the workplace, the community or society.

Administrative records kept by other types of organizations (for example, non-governmental organizations) providing victim assistance are particularly problematic. In most cases, information is dispersed and is not subject to standardized collection procedures or inter-institutional cross-checking. Furthermore, there is no single institution to consolidate the information. The lack of an integrated information system makes it difficult to know, for instance, how many times the same woman has sought care, what kind of care was received, who provided it, where and when it was provided and whether such visits were associated with the same act of violence or the same aggressor. As a result, it is impossible to trace either the history of violence affecting each woman who seeks help or the assistance that was actually received.

For the information to be useful for statistical purposes, an integrated database or information system linking data from the various organizations has to be in place. Information from the organizations must be systematically and consistently transferred to the database and periodically processed and disseminated. This is easier said than done, however, as there is no institution that governs all of the different types of service providers. Moreover, the types of data collected are very diverse.

To improve the coverage of administrative data on violence against women, there has to be an enabling environment for victims of violence to seek help. This includes creating or strengthening institutional mechanisms so that women and girls can report acts of violence, file charges or seek refuge in a safe, confidential and supportive environment that is easily accessible. Women victims of violence will also be encouraged to seek help if they know that they will have access to the mechanisms of justice and to just and effective remedies as provided by law for the harm they have suffered. In that connection, law enforcement officers, police personnel and judicial, medical and social workers need to be given training to increase their understanding and knowledge of the causes, consequences and mechanisms of violence against women so that fair treatment of female victims can be assured.

Complementary use of data sources

Surveys and a variety of administrative data together can provide a more complete picture of violence against women. Surveys provide comprehensive information on various aspects of such violence, while administrative statistics from the criminal justice system can be regularly produced and disseminated at the national level. Other administrative statistics produced by various organizations shed light on women's use of their services and the response of those organizations to specific aspects of violence against women. The main challenge to the complementary use of survey data and administrative records is the absence of a common language among different sources. Concepts, classifications, time frames and many other aspects of the data gathered differ across sources. Finding a way of harmonizing concepts used in specialized surveys, criminal justice statistics and other administrative records requires time and innovation, but it is not impossible.

A holistic and multisectoral response to the problem of violence against women at the State level is the best route to the integration, harmonization and utilization of data sources. Such an approach would bring together the various actors—in law enforcement, the judiciary, education, health and social services, and community and women's organizations—to design and implement a holistic response that addresses both the prevention and treatment of violence from the perspective of the victim, including addressing information needs in an integrated way. Such response is particularly urgent in the case of trafficking in women and girls owing to the multiplicity of actors involved.

Areas requiring more attention

Statistics on most types of violence specified under the three general classes of violence against women (see definition at the beginning of the chapter) are still either not available or inadequate. In the first class, violence occurring in the family, areas for which reliable statistics are not available or are limited in coverage include sexual abuse of female children in the household, dowry-related violence, "honour" killings, female genital cutting and other traditional practices harmful to women, non-spousal violence and violence related to exploitation. There is a need to find effective methods of collecting those data, for example through population-based surveys. For dowry-related violence and "honour" killings, other methods have to be explored because the relatively rare occurrences of those forms of violence among

The main challenge to the complementary use of survey data and administrative records is the absence of a common language among different sources

A holistic and multisectoral response to the problem of violence against women at the State level is the best route to the integration, harmonization and utilization of data sources

Statistics on most types of violence against women are still either not available or inadequate

the general population may not be captured in a sample; in addition, many of the victims would no longer be alive to be sampled. Methods that might be explored include the analysis of police records or homicide reports, if available.

Population-based surveys on violence against women may not adequately cover women belonging to minority groups, indigenous women, refugee women, women migrants, elderly women or other groups of women who are particularly vulnerable to violence. Since they are a relatively small proportion of the population and tend to be harder to reach, those groups of women are often not present in big enough numbers in the sample to allow separate analysis to be made of them. In some surveys, the specification of the target population intentionally excludes certain groups. For example, many surveys of intimate partner violence have focused on women of reproductive age (15-49) because they are the group most likely to be exposed to violence and are most frequently the targets of ongoing surveys such as the DHS. Such surveys, therefore, do not capture the experience of older women who also experience violence, including from intimate partners. In order to study violence against the above-mentioned groups of women, researchers have to ensure that those groups are included in adequate numbers in the sample.

For the second general class, violence occurring within the general community, statistics on certain areas are still scarce. Sexual harassment and intimidation at work, in educational institutions, in prisons and in other institutions are forms of violence that have existed for a long time but are only beginning to be publicly or seriously addressed. Statistics on those issues therefore tend to be scarce and limited in scope. Methods for collecting comprehensive data on sexual harassment need to be developed.

Much more also has to be done to find better methods of data collection related to trafficking in women and girls for sexual exploitation, forced marriage and forced labour. Integrating data on human trafficking produced by various organizations presents a huge challenge, as by definition those sources of data often include different subsets of trafficked women. The introduction of national rapporteurs on trafficking, a measure that has been taken in several countries in the European Union, may help in coordinating data collection on trafficking and in integrating and utilizing the information from the various sectors.

With respect to the last class of violence against women, that perpetrated or condoned by the State, reliable statistics on the extent of violence are particularly difficult to obtain. This is especially true where armed conflict, foreign occupation, wars of aggression and civil wars are present. Obtaining statistics on those forms of violence continues to be a major challenge.

Methods for collecting comprehensive data on sexual harassment need to be developed

Integrating data on human trafficking produced by various organizations presents a huge challenge, as by definition those sources of data often include different subsets of trafficked women

Notes

1 See *Report of the Fourth World Conference on Women, Beijing, 4-15 September 1995* (United Nations publication, Sales No. E.96.IV.13), chap. I, resolution 1, annex II, paras. 112 and 117.

2 Ibid., paras. 116 and 121.

3 General Assembly resolution 48/104 of 20 December 1993, article 1.

4 *Report of the World Conference to Review and Appraise the Achievements of the United Nations Decade for Women: Equality, Development and Peace, Nairobi, 15-26 July 1985* (United Nations publication, Sales No. E.85.IV.10), paras. 231, 245, 258, 271 and 287-291.

5 Vienna Declaration and Programme of Action, World Conference on Human Rights, Vienna, 14-25 June 1993 (A/CONF.157/23), para. 18.

6 *Report of the Fourth World Conference on Women, Beijing, 4-15 September 1995* (United Nations publication, Sales No. E.96.IV.13), chap. I, resolution 1, annex II, sect. D, "Violence against women".

7 See General Assembly resolution 55/2 of 8 September 2000, para. 25.

8 *See Report of the Fourth World Conference on Women, Beijing, 4-15 September 1995* (United Nations publication, Sales No. E.96.IV.13), chap. I, resolution 1, annex II, paras. 206(j) and 129(a).

9 Millennium Project, *Taking Action: Achieving Gender Equality and Empowering Women,* Task Force on Education and Gender Equality (London, Earthscan, 2005).

10 For example, Statistics Canada included this feature in its Violence against Women Survey, 1993, and its General Social Survey on Victimization, 1999.

11 "Report of the expert group meeting on violence against women: a statistical overview, challenges and gaps in data collection and methodology and approaches to overcoming them" (Geneva, 11-14 April 2005, Department of Economic and Social Affairs, Division for the Advancement of Women, in collaboration with the Economic Commission for Europe and the World Health Organization). The report elaborates on the characteristics of population-based surveys carried out to date.

12 Ibid.

13 Female genital cutting or female genital mutilation refers to all procedures involving partial or total removal of the external female genitalia or other injury to the female genital organs for cultural or other non-medical reasons (from Female Genital Mutilation. A Joint WHO/UNICEF/UNFPA Statement, Geneva, World Health Organization, 1997).

14 See "Integration of the Human Rights of Women and the Gender Perspective: Violence against Women", Report of the Special Rapporteur on violence against women, its causes and consequences (E/CN.4/2002/83), para. 15.

15 P. Stanley Yoder, Noureddine Abderrahim and Arlinda Zhuzhuni, "Female genital cutting in the Demographic and Health Surveys: a critical and comparative analysis", DHS Comparative Reports No. 7 (Calverton, Maryland, ORC Macro, 2004).

16 See *Report of the Fourth World Conference on Women, Beijing, 4-15 September 1995* (United Nations publication, Sales No. E.96.IV.13), chap. I, resolution 1, annex II, para. 117.

17 In her 1994-2003 review (E/CN.4/2003/75.Add.1), the Special Rapporteur on violence against women, its causes and consequences, highlighted some problems of law enforcement in almost all of the reviewed States, citing a total of 79 countries that have no (or unknown) legislation against domestic violence. Marital rape is recognized specifically as a crime in only 51 countries in so far as information is available (see "Violence against women: new challenges – Beijing at 10: putting policy into practice", International Research and Training Institute for the Advancement of Women, INSTRAW progress report, available from http://www.un-instraw.org/en/images/stories/Beijing/violenceagainstwomen.pdf).

18 In some countries, civil injunctions – also known as peace bonds, restraining orders or domestic violence orders – bar partners from coming into contact with the victim. They can include other conditions such as drug and alcohol or weapons prohibitions. Other types of injunctions can have the violent partner removed from the home.

19 See "Report of the expert group meeting on violence against women: a statistical overview, challenges and gaps in data collection and methodology and approaches to overcoming them" (Geneva, 11-14 April 2005, Department of Economic and Social Affairs, Division for the Advancement of Women, in collaboration with the Economic Commission for Europe and the World Health Organization).

20 See remarks on national data sources in the Introduction to the report and box 1.3 "Civil registration and vital statistics" in chapter 1.

21 See "Integration of the Human Rights of Women and the Gender Perspective: Violence against Women", Report of the Special Rapporteur on violence against women, its causes and consequences (E/CN.4/2002/83), para. 23.

22 This section is based largely on the following three papers: "Human trafficking and statistics: the state of the art", paper prepared by Nicole Suter, Heikki Mattila and Frank Laczko, International Organization for Migration, Economic Commission for Europe Work Session on Gender Statistics, Geneva, 18-20 October 2004, Working Paper No. 15; Frank Laczko and Marco Gramegna, "Developing better indicators of human trafficking", *Brown Journal of World Affairs,* vol. X, No. 1 (Summer/Fall 2003); and Kristina Kangaspunta, "Collecting data on human trafficking", paper prepared for the panel on remaining challenges in relation to statistics and indicators, forty-ninth session of the Commission on the Status of Women, New York, 28 February-11 March 2005 (Geneva, United Nations Office on Drugs and Crime).

23 General Assembly resolution 55/25 of 15 November 2000, annex II, article 3(a).

24 See, for example, World Health Organization, "Putting women first: ethical and safety recommendations for research on domestic violence against women" (WHO/FCH/GWH/01.1).

25 Cathy Zimmerman and Charlotte Watts, *WHO Ethical and Safety Recommendations for Interviewing Trafficked Women* (Geneva, World Health Organization, 2003). The recommendations have been translated into Armenian, Bosnian, Croatian, Japanese, Serbian, Romanian and Russian.

26 See, for example, Diane Almeras and others, *Violence against Women in Couples: Latin America and the Caribbean - A Proposal for Measuring its Incidence and Trends,* Mujer y Desarrollo Series, No. 40 (United Nations publication, Sales No. E.02.II.G.56).

Chapter 6
Poverty, decision-making and human rights

"The empowerment of women is a critical factor in the eradication of poverty."
"Equality in decision-making is essential to the empowerment of women."
"Women's rights are human rights."
Beijing Platform for Action

Chapter 6 reviews deficiencies and gaps in the collection, dissemination, presentation and use of data in the following three areas of concern highlighted in the Beijing Platform for Action:

- Women and poverty
- Women in power and decision-making
- Human rights of women

Women and poverty. The Beijing Platform for Action calls on Governments to ensure equal access of women and men to resources, opportunities and public services as a strategy for the eradication of poverty.[1] To support that strategic objective, the Platform for Action stresses the need to collect sex and age-disaggregated data on poverty and all aspects of economic activity. It also underscores the need to develop qualitative and quantitative statistical indicators to facilitate the assessment of economic performance from a gender perspective.[2] At the same time, the Platform calls for the improvement of the concepts and methods of data collection on the measurement of poverty among women and men.[3] The United Nations Millennium Declaration places a priority on the eradication of poverty. Governments have agreed that the promotion of gender equality and women's empowerment is an effective strategy to achieve that goal.[4]

Women in power and decision-making. The Beijing Platform for Action emphasizes the goal of equal participation by women and men in political decision-making. It calls on Governments to monitor and evaluate progress in the representation of women at all levels in the public and private sectors through the collection, analysis and dissemination of quantitative and qualitative data.[5] Increasing women's representation in political office is now a widely held development goal. It is an indicator for tracking progress towards the Millennium Development Goal 3 (promote gender equality and empower women).

Human rights of women. In the Beijing Declaration, Governments affirmed their commitment to promote and protect the human rights of women through the full implementation of all human rights instruments, especially the Convention on the Elimination of All Forms of Discrimination against Women.[6] The need for better methods to collect, collate and analyse data related to women's human rights was underlined in the Platform for Action.[7] Similarly, the United Nations Millennium Declaration emphasized the need to respect and fully uphold the Universal Declaration of Human Rights and reminded Governments that economic, social and cultural rights were at the heart of all the Millennium Development Goals, including that of promoting gender equality and empowering women (Goal 3).[8] More recently, the Declaration adopted by the Commission on the Status of Women at its forty-ninth session recognized that the implementation of the Beijing Declaration and Platform for Action and the fulfilment of obligations under the Convention were mutually reinforcing and essential to achieving the internationally agreed development goals.[9]

Various sources can be used to obtain information on the three areas of concern examined in the present chapter. Some gender-sensitive poverty statistics have been derived from household surveys. Data on women in power and decision-making and human rights can be derived from administrative records, censuses or surveys.

Current state of statistics

In many countries, mainstream statistical agencies and programmes do not routinely collect, present and disseminate statistics on women and poverty, women in power and decision-making and the human rights of women. Regular and sustained collection and reporting of data in the above-mentioned areas has been constrained by a lack of statistical capacity. Poorly developed methodologies have also limited the use of existing data to examine gender-based differences in these critical areas of concern.

The Platform for Action stresses the need to collect sex and age-disaggregated data on poverty and all aspects of economic activity

The need for better methods to collect, collate and analyse data related to women's human rights was underlined in the Platform for Action

Mainstream statistical agencies and programmes do not routinely collect, present and disseminate statistics on women and poverty, women in power and decision-making and the human rights of women

Women and poverty

It is generally recognized
that poverty is a multi-
dimensional phenomena.
Nevertheless, in the
measurement of poverty,
priority is given to its
economic dimension

It is generally recognized that poverty is a multidi-mensional phenomena. Nevertheless, in the measure-ment of poverty, priority is given to its economic dimension. The primary sources of national poverty statistics are, consequently, income and expenditure data collected through household surveys; those data are used as indirect measures of access to opportuni-ties and resources by household members. Reliance on such data, however, has proved inadequate for capturing differences in poverty among women and men since it focuses on poverty estimates for house-holds rather than on those for individuals. Such estimates do not readily show sex differences in pat-terns of distribution of food, income and the like, nor do they reveal the experience of poverty by individual women and men within households.

In addition, poverty statistics based on income and expenditure data do not assign an economic value to unpaid domestic work or to caregiving activ-ities that are most often performed by women. Failure to value those unremunerated activities intro-duces a significant bias in poverty statistics and may lead to underestimating the level of poverty experi-enced by women and by single-parent households, especially those headed by women. The underestima-tion can occur for two key reasons: first, unpaid domestic work and caregiving activities performed by women in dual parent households are an economic asset not readily available to single parent households who may instead need to purchase those services from the market. Second, the unremunerated activi-ties also have a direct effect on women's time, limit-ing their ability to participate in other activities, including wage employment, education and training, and leisure.[10]

Data collected through
household surveys
can be used to provide
evidence of the extent to
which women may be
at a greater risk of poverty
as compared with men

However, despite the limitations, data collect-ed through household surveys can be and have been used to provide preliminary evidence of the extent to which women may be at a greater risk of experi-encing poverty as compared with men. Examples include the work carried out by the Women and Development Unit of the Economic Commission for Latin America and the Caribbean (see box 6.1) and by the International Food Policy Research Institute (IFPRI), which analysed survey data from countries in Asia and sub-Saharan Africa.[11]

The Millennium Project has also contributed to improvements in the use of existing data on women and poverty, as reflected in the United Nations Development Programme (UNDP) 2005 review of gender in national reports on the

Millennium Development Goals.[12] The review found that 22 per cent of the reports included indicators for poverty by sex.

Although differences in poverty among women and men can at times be demonstrated using information available through standard household surveys, there is a need for new concepts, instruments and methodologies designed specifically to measure those differences. For instance, the concept of "time poverty" has been advanced as an alternative approach that captures both the social and economic dimensions of poverty. It can be analysed on the basis of data from time-use surveys that show how women and men apportion their time between various income-earning and other tasks (see also chapter 4). Since 1995, at least 67 countries or areas have conducted a time-use survey. However, time-use surveys are not yet widely conducted by countries around the world.

Women's participation in the informal sector is an important coping strategy for households in poverty, and in that regard the work of the Delhi Group on Informal Sector Statistics is of particular interest. At its sixth meeting, the Group specifically considered the linkages of informal sector statistics with income and expenditure and poverty statistics. The Group's 2004-2005 work programme included identification, definition and development of a core set of indicators on informal sector and informal employment in line with the importance placed on informal employment by the Task Force on Education and Gender Equality of the United Nations Millennium Project.[13]

Women in power and decision-making

The major source of statistics concerning women in power and decision-making is personnel data from administrative records. However, most of the avail-able data, particularly from the private sector, are nei-ther collated nor disseminated owing to the absence of official reporting requirements. The collection and dissemination of statistics by Governments on women's participation in decision-making tends to be ad hoc and in response to specific demands such as the preparation of national reports for the Committee on the Elimination of All Forms of Discrimination against Women or the response to the Secretary-General's questionnaire on the imple-mentation of the Beijing Platform for Action.

Monitoring and analysis of
women's participation in
decision-making has been
largely focused on the
most visible senior levels
in the public sector and
in national politics

As a result, monitoring and analysis of women's participation in decision-making has been largely focused on the most visible senior levels in the

Box 6.1

Assessing gender differences in poverty through existing household surveys

Although data from standard household surveys are, for the most part, inadequate for examining gender differences in poverty, novel approaches have been developed that show various ways in which existing data can be used to document disparities in poverty between women and men. An example is the recent work by the Women and Development Unit of the Economic Commission for Latin America and the Caribbean (ECLAC).[a]

Based mainly on existing data from Demographic and Health Surveys, the analysis carried out by the Commission shows how household income and expenditure data can be combined with various kinds of information to address three main questions regarding women and poverty: first, whether women are at a greater risk of living in poor households as compared with men; second, whether female-headed households are more vulnerable to poverty than those headed by men; and third, whether women are, in general, more vulnerable to poverty than men.

To address the first question, the ECLAC study combined household income and expenditure data with information on household size and composition to reveal differences in the proportion of women and men living in poor households versus those living in non-poor households. Through this type of analysis the study was able to document that, throughout the region, women are at a greater risk of living in poor households than men. Further analysis by age and place of residence revealed that this is particularly the case for women in the economically active years (aged 20 to 59) in both urban and rural areas.

To address the second question, the ECLAC study disaggregated information on household headship by sex to compare the proportion of women-headed and men-headed households that are poor. Results showed that female headship was more common among extremely poor households than among non-poor households in most countries of the region.

Finally, to address the third question, information about own income was introduced into the analysis as a measure of economic dependency that can place women and men at greater risk of becoming poor. This type of analysis revealed that a greater proportion of women over the age of 15 did not have their own income compared to men and that a greater proportion of the women with no income lived in poor rather than in non-poor households.

Overall, the study by the Commission illustrates the ways in which basic data routinely collected through household surveys—the age, sex and economic status of household members combined with information on household size, composition and headship—can be used to gauge gender differences in poverty.

a "Poverty and inequality from a gender perspective", in *Social Panorama of Latin America, 2002-2003* (United Nations Publication, Sales No. E.03.II.G.185).

public sector and in national politics. For example, the Inter-Parliamentary Union (IPU) compiles information on the participation of women in national parliaments through surveys and studies conducted among its member parliaments. Topics covered include the distribution of seats between women and men in national parliaments, women's suffrage and women's exercise of the right to vote. The statistics on women's participation in national parliaments are updated regularly and disseminated through the Union's website (see box 6.2).

Some data on women's participation in local government have also been collected by United Cities and Local Governments (UCLG), an international organization whose membership comprises individual cities and national associations of local governments from 112 countries. Data on the proportion of women serving as elected representatives, councillors and mayors in more than 70 countries was collected through a survey conducted by the organization in 2003. The data collection effort is part of the organization's Global Programme on Women in Local Decision-Making and is currently being disseminated through its website.[14]

In addition to information from administrative records, occupation data from labour force surveys have also been used to analyse gender disparities in access to decision-making positions. The proportion of women in occupations that usually involve decision-making, such as legislators, senior officials and managers, can provide an indication of gender differentials in access to decision-making (see also chapter 4). For example, the International Labour Office publication, *Breaking through the Glass Ceiling - Women in Management: Update 2004,* makes extensive use of statistics on occupations from the Office's Yearbook of Labour Statistics to explore women's access to decision-making in the public and private sectors through employment in managerial jobs.[15]

Box 6.2

Data on women in political decision-making from the Inter-Parliamentary Union

On the occasion of the forty-ninth session of the Commission on the Status of Women (March 2005), the Inter-Parliamentary Union (IPU), in collaboration with the Division for the Advancement of Women, published an informational poster entitled *Women in Politics: 2005*. The poster provides data on the proportion of women in ministerial ranks, in parliaments and in the highest decision-making bodies (women who are Heads of State or Government and women who are presiding officers of parliamentary bodies). The Union has also published historical information in "Women in politics: 1945-2005", an information kit that presents data on women's participation in politics over the past 60 years, including the following:

1. A historical table on the presence of women in national parliaments;

2. Progress and setbacks of women in national parliaments between 1995 and 2005;

3. Women in the two parliamentary regional assemblies elected by direct suffrage: the Central American Parliament and the European Parliament;

4. A chronology of women Heads of State or Government between 1945 and 2005;

5. An overview of women in the executive and legislative branches;

6. Ten years in review: trends of women in parliaments worldwide.

Source:
http://www.ipu.org/english/home.htm (8 August 2005).

Human rights of women

Monitoring the full implementation of all human rights instruments, especially the Convention on the Elimination of All Forms of Discrimination against Women, requires the collection of data, broken down by sex, age and other key characteristics, on many aspects of every day life. The Convention is a comprehensive treaty on women's human rights, calling for equality between women and men in the enjoyment of civil, political, economic, social and cultural rights. As of 18 March 2005, the Convention had

been ratified or acceded to by 180 countries—over 90 per cent of the member States of the United Nations. Governments that ratify the convention agree to take all appropriate measures to modify the social and cultural patterns of conduct of women and men that lead to discrimination or exclusion on the basis of sex.

Even though many countries have taken steps to incorporate the rights covered under the Convention and other human rights treaties in their Constitutions and legislations, the realization of these rights can be guaranteed only when discrimination and exclusion on the basis of sex are made evident through monitoring and are removed through policies and programmes (box 6.3). Key sources of evidence on discrimination and exclusion are process-oriented data from administrative records collected by government and private agencies. Additional sources of information include population and housing censuses and sample surveys.

Previous chapters in the present report review the availability of data broken down by sex and age that can be used to document, in four key areas, inequalities in the enjoyment of basic human rights and freedoms between women and men. For example, data on deaths and diseases (chapter 2) can reveal inequalities between women and men in the effective enjoyment of the right to health; data on enrolment and literacy (chapter 3) can provide evidence concerning the effective enjoyment of the right to education; and data on the economically active population and on earnings can shed light on the effective enjoyment of the rights to employment and equal remuneration (chapter 4). The data reviewed in previous chapters are used primarily to monitor inequalities in outcomes between women and men. To implement all human rights effectively, additional information is needed to identify the discriminatory practices that lead to such inequalities. This could be best accomplished with the use of process data from administrative records.

However, efforts to use administrative data to monitor human rights have been constrained in a number of ways. Only a few countries have established official reporting requirements to integrate such data collection into national statistical systems. The lack of reporting requirements has limited the dissemination of existing administrative data. Even when data is disseminated, data by sex are either not collected or, although sex is included in the primary record, omitted from the tabulations. For

Human rights of women

A major challenge to improve the monitoring of human rights is that of collecting, processing and disseminating gender-sensitive process-oriented data. One way to address this challenge is to demand accountability and transparency of government and private agencies by requiring them to produce and publicly disseminate relevant statistics from administrative records generated as part of the routine performance of their functions. The statistics should be disaggregated by sex and by other key characteristics.

A related challenge is that of improving the availability of information on women who are particularly vulnerable to human rights violations such as those who are members of ethnic minorities and indigenous groups, those living in poverty and those living in rural areas. This requires a concerted effort by Governments to ensure that existing data collection systems properly cover the above-mentioned groups. At the same time there is a need to ensure that information about membership in a disadvantaged group, such as one defined by race, ethnicity, caste or indigenous group affiliation, place of residence and socio-economic status, are also collected and disseminated.

Similarly, there is a dire need to improve the availability of information on the women and men who are internally displaced or who are stateless. Although significant improvements have been made in the availability of sex-disaggregated data on refugee populations, most of the available information refers to officially recognized refugees in countries where the Office of the United Nations High Commissioner for Refugees plays an operational role. Women and men who live in their own country of birth but who are considered to be stateless, who have been internally displaced or who were refugees but have recently returned as part of a resettlement programme are often not properly registered and are therefore underrepresented in existing data from UNHCR and other sources. Improving the registration of those groups requires a concerted effort between Governments and national and international non-governmental agencies to establish a registration system that complies with international standards, particularly that of confidentiality of data.

General outlook

Overall, improving the availability of the statistics needed for monitoring gender inequalities in poverty, decision-making and human rights depends primarily on activities at the national level. In the face of resource constraints and the limitations of conventional statistics, countries need to maximize the use of a wider range of existing data sources.

In particular, administrative statistics based on data collected outside national statistics offices by government agencies, including the criminal justice system, and by the private sector, including banks, could expand the limited availability of information in the three critical areas of concern. Sex-disaggregated administrative statistics are already used extensively in the education sector; they are used to a lesser extent in the health sector, by gender budgeting initiatives and by women's groups promoting greater participation in politics and governance among women. To expand the use of administrative data for monitoring and planning in the areas of poverty, power and decision-making, and human rights, formal requirements to collect and report data by sex and age have to be institutionalized. Increasing the use of such data may also create incentives for those responsible for their collection, quality and presentation, with consequent benefits to other potential users and to the overall quality of governance.

In the face of resource constraints and the limitations of conventional statistics, countries need to maximize the use of a wider range of existing data sources

To expand the use of administrative data, formal requirements to collect and report data by sex and age have to be institutionalized

Notes

1   See *Report of the Fourth World Conference on Women, Beijing, 4-15 September 1995* (United Nations publication, Sales No. E.96.IV.13), chap. I, resolution 1, annex II, para. 47.

2   Ibid., para. 68(a).

3   Ibid., para. 206(h).

4   See General Assembly resolution 55/2 of 8 September 2000.

5   See *Report of the Fourth World Conference on Women, Beijing, 4-15 September 1995* (United Nations publication, Sales No. E.96.IV.13), chap. I, resolution 1, annex II, para. 190(e).

6   Ibid., annex I, item 8, and annex II, strategic objective I.1.

7   Ibid., chap. I, resolution 1, annex II, para. 208(a).

8   "Road map towards the implementation of the United Nations Millennium Declaration", report of the Secretary-General (A/56/326), paras. 196-202 and annex.

9   *Official Records of the Economic and Social Council, 2005, Supplement No. 7* (E/2005/27 and Corr.1), chap. I, section A, para. 4.

10   Vivian Milosavljevic, "El enfoque de género y la medición de la pobreza", paper presented at the expert meeting on poverty and gender, Santiago, Chile, 12-13 August 2003, Economic Commission for Latin America and the Caribbean/International Labour Organization.

11   "Women and poverty", in *The World's Women 1995: Trends and Statistics* (United Nations publication, Sales No. E.95.XVII.2), chap. 5, box.

12   "Looking for equality: a gender review of national MDG reports, 2005", report prepared for the United Nations Development Programme, Bureau of Development Policy.

13   See "Report of the Delhi Group on Informal Sector Statistics", note by the Secretary-General (E/CN.3/2005/10).

14   See http://www.cities-localgovernments.org/uclg/ (18 August 2005).

15   http://www.ilo.org/dyn/gender/docs/RES/292/F267981337/ (18 August 2005).

16   See United Nations Millennium Project, "Guarantee women's property and inheritance rights", in *Taking Action: Achieving Gender Equality and Empowering Women,* Task Force on Education and Gender Equality (London, Earthscan, 2005).

17   http://www.unhcr.ch/cgi-bin/texis/vtx/statistics (2 September 2005).

18   Information provided to the United Nations Statistics Division by the Office of the United Nations High Commissioner for Refugees (January 2005).

19   See *Report of the Fourth World Conference on Women, Beijing, 4-15 September 1995* (United Nations publication, Sales No. E.96.IV.13), chap. I, resolution 1, annex II, para. 112.

20   Commission of the European Communities, System of National Accounts, 1993 (United Nations publication, Sales No. E.94.XVII.4).

21   "Indicators for monitoring the Millennium Development Goals and for follow-up to the outcomes of the major United Nations conferences and summits in the economic and social fields", report of the Secretary-General (E/CN.3/2005/20), annex, para. 4.

22   *A learning programme in action: UNIFEM gender responsive budgeting programme. Mid-term review summary report* (New York, United Nations Development Fund for Women, 2004).

23   Information provided to the United Nations Statistics Division by the Office of the United Nations High Commissioner for Refugees (January 2005).

24   United Kingdom, Equal Opportunities Commission, "Gender statistics for the 21st century: challenges and priorities", Economic Commission for Europe Work Session on Gender Statistics, Geneva, 18-20 October 2004, Working Paper No. 2, para. 9.

Chapter 7
Conclusion

The statistical review presented in the preceding chapters points to mixed progress in the capacity of countries to produce and report sex-disaggregated data and data on key gender issues of concern to women and men. Similarly, progress on statistical methodology has been mixed: there have been encouraging developments in statistical methodology in certain areas of concern but not in others.

As a result, there is a lack of sex-disaggregated data on many of the topics covered by the present report. The extent of data reporting varies by geographic region. In general, Europe reports the most data and Africa reports the least. The other regions—Asia, North America, South America and Oceania—fall between the two extremes. The differences in reporting are even more pronounced when regions and countries are categorized as "more developed regions", "less developed regions excluding the least developed countries" and "least developed countries", with the more developed regions providing the most data and the least developed countries the least.

In addition to varying by region, the extent of data reporting varies by topic. The same region (or country) may have relatively comprehensive data on certain topics but not on others, with more countries usually reporting on the more basic topics as compared with the number reporting on new and emerging issues. Furthermore, data availability decreases as more detail is called for, such as disaggregation by sex, age and other social characteristics.

The general lack of data necessary to address gender issues and the differences in availability of such data across regions and across topics is a reflection of three factors:

- Inadequate statistical capacity
- Lack of gender mainstreaming
- Inadequate concepts and methods

To improve gender statistics, it is crucial that all three factors be addressed. The actions proposed to address those factors can thus be categorized as follows:

- Strengthening national statistical systems
- Mainstreaming gender in all aspects of the production of statistics
- Developing and improving concepts and methods

Many strategies exist to improve statistics on the world's women and men. The list below is not exhaustive but represents the basic strategies that should be considered for each action. Gender mainstreaming necessarily cuts across all activities: both the strengthening of statistical systems and the development of concepts and methods need to be designed and implemented from a gender perspective.

Strengthening national statistical systems

In order to develop and improve gender statistics at the national level, the capacity to produce reliable and timely basic statistics must be present. For many countries in the less developed regions, this is not the case. The situation calls for strengthening the national statistical systems, starting with the national statistics office.

Strategy 1. Secure sustained commitment at the highest level of Government to strengthen the national statistical system

Governments should strive to the extent possible to support the programmes listed below, adopting a coordinated approach to produce a core set of socio-economic statistics required for policy formulation and planning. The priorities would vary according to national circumstances.

a. Implement at least one population and housing census every 10 years and disseminate the results widely and in a timely manner;

b. Establish, strengthen and maintain civil registration and vital statistics systems, strengthen other administrative recording systems and make statistics easily accessible to policy makers and other users;

c. Ensure the sustainability of an integrated national survey programme that produces regular and timely statistics to guide policy and that allows population surveys addressing new research topics to be conducted as the need arises.

Strategy 2. Maximize the use of official statistics

National statistics offices and line ministries should widely disseminate and promote the use of all statistics that they produce. Both producers and users of statistics should strive to consider all available sources of data and use them complementarily as appropriate for their purposes. Since data from different sources are typically collected using different approaches and time frames, they are not expected to replicate each other. Rather, they collectively provide a more complete picture of the topic under study. In addition, evaluation of a data source can be, and often is, carried out using other relevant sources of data. Such complementary use of diverse sources of data leads to a better understanding of their various advantages and disadvantages and opens the way to improving or strengthening each source.

Strategy 3. Build capacity among producers of statistics in data presentation

Although it is Governments that ultimately provide resources, national statistics offices can do much to increase the willingness of Governments to support statistical systems. Producers of statistics need to be more proactive in making the value of gender statistics visible to Governments, the public and other stakeholders. Innovative and more user-friendly ways of presenting and disseminating data need to be developed for Government and civil society, in forms that are appropriate for a wide range of purposes, including policy-making, planning and programming, and monitoring and evaluation, as well as public education, advocacy and lobbying. Taking such steps would help widen the use of the data and in the process create a demand for statistics that would strengthen the claim of the statistics office on the national budget.

Strategy 4. Develop human resources at all levels in national statistics offices

The success of a national statistics office depends not only on commitments at the highest level but also on the commitment and skills of women and men in the organization. Continuous staff training and skill upgrading is crucial to this success. Women and men should be given the same opportunities for training and advancement. In national statistics offices where women are underrepresented at decision-making levels, increasing their representation should also be an explicit goal.

Mainstreaming gender in all aspects of the production of statistics

Mainstreaming a gender perspective into national statistical systems has to be systematic: it must be implemented in all aspects of the production of statistics, from the development of concepts and methods for collecting data to the presentation of results. This endeavour requires political will at all levels, not only in national statistics offices but also in the statistical services of other government agencies and in all institutions that provide administrative data. Gender mainstreaming includes ensuring that the following occur:[1]

- Population statistics are systematically collected, collated, analysed and presented by sex and age

- Other relevant characteristics that define potential forms of discrimination, such as race, ethnicity, disability status, place of residence and socio-economic status, are likewise collected, collated, analysed and presented

- Concepts, definitions and methods used in the collection, production and analysis of data are developed to reflect gender issues and gender disparities in society

- Statistics are produced with the full participation of women and men

- Information is disseminated and presented in ways that are easily accessible to users

- Producers and users of statistics, including women's groups, work together to review regularly the adequacy of the official statistical system and its coverage of gender issues

Some strategies for mainstreaming gender in statistics are presented below.

Strategy 5. Specify the development of gender statistics within the legal framework of official statistics

Of crucial importance to improving the availability of gender statistics is the specification of formal requirements for sex-disaggregation and the incorporation of a gender perspective within national statistical legislation that regulates the production and dissemination of official statistics.

To expand the range of information available for gender analysis, the requirements need to be established not only for statistics already officially collected by the national statistics office but also for other sources of data, particularly administrative data being collected and disseminated by other government agencies and organizations in the public and private sectors.

In addition, legislation can be especially important in establishing standards for transparency in data systems. Freedom-of-information legislation can empower civil society groups, including women's groups, to gain access to administrative data, within the principles and rules of privacy and confidentiality.

Strategy 6. Support and strengthen gender statistics units

National statistics offices can benefit from setting up a gender statistics unit within their organizations. Such a unit can play a catalytic role in initiating and monitoring the process of mainstreaming a gender perspective into national statistical systems, especially at the early stages. Through their contacts with national machineries for women and non-governmental organizations, gender statistics units facilitate communication between the producers and end users of gender statistics. The units provide information to users and help them understand the uses of existing statistics. At the same time, they can increase the awareness among statisticians of the need to produce or disseminate statistics that address gender concerns and to develop gender statistics in new areas such as violence against women, the informal sector and unpaid work.

National statistics offices should strengthen the technical capacity of gender statistics units and as much as possible integrate their activities into the regular statistical work programme.

Strategy 7. Foster dialogue between statistics offices and interested stakeholders, including women's groups

Dialogue between national statistics offices and interested stakeholders can enable women's groups and gender advocates to understand, gain access to and use gender statistics more effectively. Women's groups need statistics to monitor, advocate and lobby for gender-sensitive policies and to hold Governments accountable to commitments they have made, both nationally and as signatories to such international agreements as the Beijing Platform for Action and the Convention on the Elimination of All Forms of Discrimination against Women. At the

same time, the dialogue can help to increase the capacity of statisticians to identify and understand gender issues and to present data in formats that better address the needs of users.

National machineries for women and other user groups, including NGOs, can also be effective in gathering support for collecting statistics in new areas and in raising awareness of the need for revision of concepts, definitions and methods of data collection. Indeed, in many cases involving gender mainstreaming of statistics, the need for change has first been voiced by women's groups, who may continue to play an important role in the actual mainstreaming activities. The experiences of India and Nepal in incorporating gender concerns into the conduct of their 2001 censuses are examples of how women's groups and the national statistics office can work together. The 2010 round of the population and housing censuses creates a significant opportunity for dialogue between statistics offices and interested stakeholders to improve the overall statistical base on women and men through activities at the national level.

Strategy 8. Train producers of statistics to incorporate a gender perspective into their work

One way to achieve gender-mainstreamed statistics is through the provision of regular training courses on gender statistics for general statisticians, either within tertiary training institutions or in national statistics offices.

The training should be extended to field personnel and other staff members involved in the production of statistics. Gender statistics units can also participate in the training.

Strategy 9. Tap existing sources of data and enhance their usefulness for producing gender statistics

Administrative data, much of which is currently underutilized, represent a potential source of gender statistics. Using administrative data to produce needed statistics is a cost-effective approach since these data are already routinely collected by organizations as part of regular administrative processes. National statistical systems may already include a wide range of such data collected by the Government and other agencies for various purposes. With the introduction of appropriate changes in the methods of collecting and processing information, the resulting data can be compiled into statistics for addressing gender issues. For example, police and court records can be used to understand the criminal justice system's response to domestic violence, but this is possible only if information on the victim's sex and relationship to offender is collected in the primary record.

Other potential sources of administrative data are personnel records, credit and banking records, and land and housing registers. For some of those sources, statistics may have been produced but not disseminated separately by sex; for others, statistics may not have been produced at all from the primary records. Information on sex is often available in the primary records, allowing the production of sex-disaggregated statistics for monitoring gender equality in access to resources and opportunities, such as access to decision-making positions, access to and utilization of commercial services and credit, and access to land and housing.

For all of the above administrative data, the collection of additional information on the primary record and the production and dissemination of statistics from those records may require legislation. These activities would in all cases have to be governed by the rules and principles of privacy and confidentiality.

Statistics on agriculture, industry, business, the environment, finance, trade and transport represent additional potential sources of gender statistics. Although women and men often have different interests in and access to resources in those areas, the differences are not readily obvious because the individual is typically not the unit of data collection. However, in some cases, sex can be recorded as a characteristic of the primary unit of data collection, thereby increasing the value of the data for gender analysis. For example, in transport surveys information on the sex of the traveller can be included to enable analysis of gender differences in travel patterns.[2]

Strategy 10. Make official national statistics a required component of international reporting mechanisms

The periodic country reports on the implementation of the Convention on the Elimination of All Forms of Discrimination against Women and of the Beijing Platform for Action provide opportunities to promote the production and reporting of more standardized and harmonized gender statistics. Utilization of statistics in the country reports has been limited to date. Consideration should be given to establishing formal requirements for the inclusion of official national statistics on gender issues in a standardized format in those reports.

Developing and improving concepts and methods

Strategy 11. Promote collaboration between international and regional organizations and agencies, national statistics offices and academic and research institutions

International and regional organizations and agencies, national statistics offices and academic and research institutions need to work together to mainstream gender in the development and revision of concepts, definitions and methods of collecting data on topics where methods are inadequate. The collaboration extends to all methodological issues, including the design of survey questionnaires or modules within questionnaires, the revision of international classifications and standards and the development of analytical methods and appropriate indicators, among others.

Some of the areas identified in the present report as requiring further development of concepts and methods are statistics on migration, poverty, human rights, violence against women, trafficking in women and girls, time use, informal employment, unpaid work, morbidity, disability, access to health services and access to positions of power and decision-making.

Concluding remarks

Ten years after the Fourth World Conference on Women in Beijing, limited progress has been made in producing the statistics needed to monitor implementation of the Platform for Action and of the goals of other international conferences and summits, including the Millennium Development Goals. Consequently, a more comprehensive approach to improving gender statistics is required. Gender-sensitive concepts, definitions and methods of data collection, presentation and dissemination are necessary not only in demographic and social statistics but also throughout entire statistical systems. New data sources must be developed and existing sources adapted in order to provide comprehensive statistics that reflect the situation and concerns of women and men equally.

At the national level, increasing the coverage of statistics on gender issues and ensuring that concepts and methods incorporate a gender perspective is particularly challenging in view of the human and financial resource constraints faced by most national statistical systems. Resource constraints are particularly severe in the least developed countries, where the most pressing need is to strengthen national statistical systems to produce the most basic statistics in a timely manner.

In the long term, to improve the lives of women and men, statistical systems and budgets at the national as well as international level must bring about the sustained and institutionalized change needed to ensure the availability of quality gender statistics.

Notes

1   *Report of the Fourth World Conference on Women, Beijing, 4-15 September 1995* (United Nations publication, Sales No. E.96.IV.13), chap. I, resolution 1, annex II, para 206; and *Gender Mainstreaming: An Overview*, Office of the Special Adviser on Gender Issues and Advancement of Women (United Nations, New York, 2002), available from http://www.un.org/womenwatch/osagi/pdf/e65237.pdf.

2   See United Kingdom, Equal Opportunities Commission, "Gender statistics for the 21st century: challenges and priorities", Economic Commission for Europe Work Session on Gender Statistics, Geneva, 18-20 October 2004, Working Paper No. 2, para. 10.

Table A1 (continued)
National reporting of selected demographic statistics, 1995 – 2003

| Country or area | Conducted a census (1995/2004) | Ever reported Households | | | Frequency of annual reporting Population | | | Marriages | | Divorces | |
		Total	By sex and age of head [a]	By sex and age of head and size of household	Total	By sex	By sex and age	Total	First, by age of bride and groom	Total	By number of dependent children
Asia (continued)											
Japan	✓	✓	✓	✓	●	●	●	●	●	●	●
Jordan	✓	·	·	·	●	●	●	●	◐	●	●
Kazakhstan	✓	✓	·	·	●	●	●	●	●	●	●
Kuwait	✓	✓	·	·	●	●	◐	●	◐	●	○
Kyrgyzstan	✓	✓	✓	✓	●	●	●	●	●	●	●
Lao People's Dem. Rep.	✓	✓	·	·	●	◐	◐	○	○	○	○
Lebanon	·	·	·	·	○	○	○	●	○	●	○
Malaysia	✓	✓	·	·	●	●	●	○	○	○	○
Maldives	✓	✓	·	·	●	●	◐	◐	○	◐	○
Mongolia	✓	✓	·	·	●	●	●	●	○	●	○
Myanmar	·	·	·	·	◐	◐	◐	○	○	○	○
Nepal	✓	✓	✓	·	●	◐	◐	○	○	○	○
Occupied Palestinian Territory	✓	✓	✓	✓	●	●	◐	●	●	●	◐
Oman	✓	✓	·	·	●	●	◐	○	○	○	○
Pakistan	✓	·	·	·	●	◐	◐	○	○	○	○
Philippines	✓	✓	✓	✓	●	●	◐	●	◐	○	○
Qatar	✓	✓	·	·	◐	◐	◐	●	◐	●	○
Republic of Korea	✓	✓	✓	✓	●	●	●	●	●	●	●
Saudi Arabia	✓	·	·	·	●	◐	◐	●	○	●	○
Singapore	✓	·	·	·	●	●	●	●	●	●	●
Sri lanka	✓	·	·	·	●	●	◐	●	○	○	○
Syrian Arab Republic	✓	·	·	·	●	●	●	●	○	●	○
Tajikistan	✓	·	·	·	●	◐	○	◐	○	○	○
Thailand	✓	·	·	·	●	●	●	◐	○	◐	○
Timor-Leste	✓	·	·	·	○	○	○	○	○	○	○
Turkey	✓	·	·	·	●	●	●	●	●	●	●
Turkmenistan	✓	·	·	·	◐	◐	◐	◐	○	◐	○
United Arab Emirates	✓	·	·	·	●	●	◐	◐	○	◐	○
Uzbekistan	·	·	·	·	●	●	◐	●	●	●	●
Viet Nam	✓	·	·	·	●	●	○	◐	○	◐	○
Yemen	✓	·	·	·	●	●	◐	○	○	○	○
Europe											
Albania	✓	✓	✓	✓	●	◐	○	◐	○	○	○
Andorra	✓ [b]	·	·	·	●	●	○	●	○	○	○
Austria	✓	✓	✓	✓	●	●	●	●	●	●	●
Belarus	✓	✓	·	·	●	●	●	●	●	●	●
Belgium	✓	✓	✓	✓	●	●	◐	●	◐	●	◐
Bosnia and Herzegovina	·	·	·	·	●	○	○	◐	◐	◐	○
Bulgaria	✓	·	·	·	●	●	●	●	●	●	●

Legend

✓ Yes
· No
○ Did not report data for any of the nine years considered (1995 - 2003).
◐ Reported data for one to four out of nine years.
● Reported data for at least five out of nine years.

Table A1 (continued)
National reporting of selected demographic statistics, 1995 – 2003

Country or area	Conducted a census (1995/2004)	Ever reported – Households			Frequency of annual reporting – Population			Marriages		Divorces	
		Total	By sex and age of head[a]	By sex and age of head and size of household	Total	By sex	By sex and age	Total	First, by age of bride and groom	Total	By number of dependent children
Europe (continued)											
Croatia	✓	·	·	·	●	●	●	●	●	●	●
Czech Republic	✓	✓	✓	✓	●	●	●	●	●	●	●
Denmark	✓ c	·	·	·	●	●	●	●	●	●	○
Estonia	✓	✓	✓	✓	●	●	●	●	●	●	●
Finland	✓ c	✓	✓	✓	●	●	●	●	●	●	●
France	✓	·	·	·	●	●	●	●	◐	●	○
Germany	✓ b	·	·	·	●	●	●	●	◐	●	◐
Greece	✓	✓	✓	✓	●	●	◐	●	◐	●	◐
Hungary	✓	✓	✓	✓	●	●	●	●	●	●	●
Iceland	✓ b	·	·	·	●	●	●	●	●	●	●
Ireland	✓	✓	✓	✓	●	●	●	●	◐	◐	○
Italy	✓	✓	✓	✓	●	●	●	●	◐	●	●
Latvia	✓	✓	✓	✓	●	●	●	●	●	●	●
Liechtenstein	✓	·	·	·	●	●	◐	◐	○	◐	○
Lithuania	✓	✓	✓	✓	●	●	●	●	●	●	●
Luxembourg	✓	✓	✓	✓	●	●	●	●	●	●	●
Malta	✓	·	·	·	●	●	●	●	●	○	○
Monaco	✓	·	·	·	◐	◐	◐	●	○	●	○
Netherlands	✓ c	✓	✓	✓	●	●	●	●	●	●	●
Norway	✓ c	✓	✓	✓	●	●	●	●	◐	●	●
Poland	— ✓	✓	✓	✓	●	●	●	●	●	●	●
Portugal	✓	·	·	·	●	●	●	●	●	●	●
Republic of Moldova	✓	·	·	·	●	●	●	●	●	●	●
Romania	✓	✓	✓	✓	●	●	●	●	●	●	●
Russian Federation	✓	·	·	·	●	●	◐	●	◐	●	◐
San Marino	✓ b	·	·	·	●	◐	◐	●	◐	●	◐
Serbia and Montenegro d	✓	✓	·	·	●	●	●	●	◐	●	●
Slovakia	✓	✓	✓	✓	●	●	●	●	●	●	●
Slovenia	✓	✓	✓	✓	●	●	●	●	●	●	●
Spain	✓	·	·	·	●	●	●	●	◐	●	○
Sweden	✓ b	·	·	·	●	●	●	●	●	●	●
Switzerland	✓	✓	✓	✓	●	●	●	●	◐	●	●
TFYR Macedonia e	✓	✓	✓	✓	●	●	◐	●	●	●	●
Ukraine	✓	·	·	·	●	●	●	●	◐	●	◐
United Kingdom	✓	·	·	·	●	●	●	●	●	●	●
Oceania											
Australia	✓	·	·	·	●	●	●	●	●	●	●
Fiji	✓	·	·	·	◐	◐	◐	◐	○	○	○
French Polynesia	✓	·	·	·	●	●	●	◐	○	○	○

Legend

✓	Yes
·	No
○	Did not report data for any of the nine years considered (1995 - 2003).
◐	Reported data for one to four out of nine years.
●	Reported data for at least five out of nine years.

Table A1 (continued)
National reporting of selected demographic statistics, 1995 – 2003

Country or area	Conducted a census (1995/2004)	Ever reported			Frequency of annual reporting						
		Households			Population			Marriages		Divorces	
		Total	By sex and age of head [a]	By sex and age of head and size of household	Total	By sex	By sex and age	Total	First, by age of bride and groom	Total	By number of dependent children
Oceania (continued)											
Guam	✓	·	·	·	●	◐	◐	●	O	◐	O
Kiribati	✓	·	·	·	◐	◐	O	O	O	O	O
Marshall Islands	✓	·	·	·	●	●	◐	O	O	O	O
Micronesia (Fed. States of)	✓	·	·	·	●	◐	O	O	O	O	O
Nauru	✓	·	·	·	●	O	O	◐	O	O	O
New Caledonia	✓	·	·	·	●	●	◐	●	O	●	O
New Zealand	✓	✓	✓	✓	●	●	●	●	●	●	●
Palau	✓	·	·	·	●	●	◐	O	O	O	O
Papua New Guinea	✓	·	·	·	●	◐	O	O	O	O	O
Samoa	✓	·	·	·	◐	◐	O	◐	O	O	O
Solomon Islands	✓	·	·	·	◐	◐	O	O	O	O	O
Tonga	✓	·	·	·	●	●	●	●	◐	●	O
Tuvalu	✓	·	·	·	◐	◐	O	O	O	O	O
Vanuatu	✓	·	·	·	◐	◐	O	O	O	O	O

Legend

✓	Yes
·	No
O	Did not report data for any of the nine years considered (1995 - 2003).
◐	Reported data for one to four out of nine years.
●	Reported data for at least five out of nine years.

Source:
Prepared by the United Nations Statistics Division, Department of Economic and Social Affairs based on data from the United Nations *Demographic Yearbook* system (November 2004).

Notes:
a   All countries that reported households by sex of head also reported by age.
b   Detailed population statistics provided by continuous population registers.
c   Census taken from administrative registers.
d   As of 4 February 2003, the official name of the "Federal Republic of Yugoslavia" has been changed to "Serbia and Montenegro".
e   The former Yugoslav Republic of Macedonia.

Table A2
National reporting of statistics on births and deaths, 1995 – 2003

Country or area	Births[a]				Deaths[a]			Infant deaths[a]		Deaths by cause				
	Total	By age of mother	By sex of child	Civil registration at least 90% complete	Total	By sex	By sex and age	Total	By sex	Total	By sex	By sex and age	Estimated coverage[b] (%)	Percentage of deaths attributed to ill-defined diseases[c]
Africa														
Algeria	●	○	●	✓	●	●	◐	●	●	○	○	○	–	–
Angola	○	○	○	∗	○	○	○	○	○	○	○	○	–	–
Benin	●	○	●	∗	●	●	○	◐	◐	○	○	○	–	–
Botswana	●	○	◐	∗	●	◐	◐	◐	○	○	○	○	–	–
Burkina Faso	○	○	○	∗	○	○	○	○	○	○	○	○	–	–
Burundi	◐	○	◐	∗	◐	◐	○	◐	○	○	○	○	–	–
Cameroon	○	○	○	∗	○	○	○	○	○	○	○	○	–	–
Cape Verde	●	○	◐	✓	◐	◐	○	◐	◐	○	○	○	–	–
Central African Republic	○	○	○	∗	○	○	○	○	○	○	○	○	–	–
Chad	◐	○	○	∗	◐	○	○	○	○	○	○	○	–	–
Comoros	○	○	○	∗	○	○	○	○	○	○	○	○	–	–
Congo	○	○	○	∗	○	○	○	○	○	○	○	○	–	–
Côte d'Ivoire	◐	○	○	∗	◐	○	○	◐	○	○	○	○	–	–
Dem. Rep. of the Congo	○	○	○	∗	○	○	○	○	○	○	○	○	–	–
Djibouti	○	○	○	∗	○	○	○	○	○	○	○	○	–	–
Egypt	●	●	●	✓	●	●	●	●	●	●	●	●	80	21
Equatorial Guinea	○	○	○	∗	○	○	○	○	○	○	○	○	–	–
Eritrea	○	○	○	∗	○	○	○	○	○	○	○	○	–	–
Ethiopia	◐	○	○	∗	◐	○	○	◐	◐	○	○	○	–	–
Gabon	○	○	○	∗	○	○	○	○	○	○	○	○	–	–
Gambia	○	○	○	∗	○	○	○	○	○	○	○	○	–	–
Ghana	○	○	○	∗	○	○	○	○	○	○	○	○	–	–
Guinea	○	○	○	∗	○	○	○	○	○	○	○	○	–	–
Guinea-Bissau	○	○	○	∗	○	○	○	○	○	○	○	○	–	–
Kenya	○	○	○	∗	○	○	○	○	○	○	○	○	–	–
Lesotho	◐	○	○	∗	○	○	○	○	○	○	○	○	–	–
Liberia	○	○	○	∗	○	○	○	○	○	○	○	○	–	–
Libyan Arab Jamahiriya	●	◐	◐	✓	●	◐	◐	◐	◐	○	○	○	–	–
Madagascar	○	○	○	∗	○	○	○	○	○	○	○	○	–	–
Malawi	●	○	○	∗	●	◐	◐	◐	○	○	○	○	–	–
Mali	◐	○	○	∗	○	○	○	○	○	○	○	○	–	–
Mauritania	◐	○	○	∗	◐	○	○	◐	○	○	○	○	–	–
Mauritius	●	●	●	✓	●	●	●	●	●	●	●	●	100	4
Morocco	●	●	●	✓	●	●	●	●	●	○	○	○	–	–
Mozambique	◐	○	◐	∗	◐	◐	◐	◐	◐	○	○	○	–	–
Namibia	○	○	○	∗	○	○	○	○	○	○	○	○	–	–
Niger	○	○	○	∗	○	○	○	○	○	○	○	○	–	–
Nigeria	○	○	○	∗	○	○	○	○	○	○	○	○	–	–
Réunion	●	●	◐	✓	●	●	◐	●	●	○	○	○	–	–
Rwanda	○	○	○	∗	○	○	○	○	○	○	○	○	–	–

Legend

✓   Yes
∗   No
○   Did not report data for any of the nine years considered (1995 - 2003).
◐   Reported data for one to four out of nine years.
●   Reported data for at least five out of nine years.

Table A2 (continued)
National reporting of statistics on births and deaths, 1995 – 2003

Country or area	Births[a] Total	By age of mother	By sex of child	Civil registration at least 90% complete	Deaths[a] Total	By sex	By sex and age	Infant deaths[a] Total	By sex	Deaths by cause Total	By sex	By sex and age	Estimated coverage[b] (%)	Percentage of deaths attributed to ill-defined diseases[c]
Africa (continued)														
Sao Tome and Principe	O	O	O	·	O	O	O	O	O	O	O	O	–	–
Senegal	O	O	O	·	O	O	O	O	O	O	O	O	–	–
Seychelles	●	O	●	✓	●	●	●	●	O	◐	◐	◐	..	–
Sierra Leone	O	O	O	·	O	O	O	O	O	O	O	O	–	–
Somalia	O	O	O	·	O	O	O	O	O	O	O	O	–	–
South Africa	●	◐	◐	·	◐	◐	◐	◐	◐	◐	◐	◐	< 50	–
Sudan	O	O	O	·	◐	◐	◐	O	O	O	O	O	–	–
Swaziland	◐	◐	O	·	◐	◐	◐	◐	O	O	O	O	–	–
Togo	O	O	O	·	O	O	O	O	O	O	O	O	–	–
Tunisia	●	◐	◐	✓	●	◐	◐	●	◐	O	O	O	–	–
Uganda	O	O	O	·	O	O	O	O	O	O	O	O	–	–
United Rep. of Tanzania	O	O	O	·	O	O	O	O	O	O	O	O	–	–
Western Sahara	O	O	O	·	O	O	O	O	O	O	O	O	–	–
Zambia	O	O	O	·	O	O	O	O	O	O	O	O	–	–
Zimbabwe	O	O	O	·	◐	◐	◐	O	O	●	●	●	< 50	–
North America														
Antigua and Barbuda	●	◐	◐	✓	●	◐	◐	◐	◐	◐	◐	◐	..	–
Bahamas	●	●	●	·	●	●	●	●	◐	●	●	●	88	1
Barbados	◐	O	◐	·	◐	◐	O	◐	◐	◐	◐	◐	100	3
Belize	●	●	◐	·	●	●	●	●	◐	●	●	●	100	2
Canada	●	●	●	✓	●	●	●	●	●	●	●	●	100	1
Costa Rica	●	●	●	✓	●	●	●	●	●	●	●	●	79	3
Cuba	●	●	●	✓	●	●	●	●	●	●	●	●	100	1
Dominica	●	O	O	✓	●	O	O	◐	O	●	●	●	..	–
Dominican Republic	◐	◐	◐	·	◐	◐	◐	◐	◐	●	●	●	< 50	–
El Salvador	●	●	●	✓	●	●	●	●	●	●	●	●	73	12
Grenada	●	◐	●	✓	●	●	◐	●	●	◐	◐	◐	..	–
Guadeloupe	●	◐	●	✓	●	◐	◐	●	O	O	O	O	–	–
Guatemala	●	●	●	✓	●	●	●	●	●	●	●	●	86	9
Haiti	O	O	O	·	O	O	O	O	O	◐	◐	◐	< 10	–
Honduras	O	O	O	·	O	O	O	O	O	O	O	O	–	–
Jamaica	●	◐	O	✓	●	O	O	◐	O	O	O	O	–	–
Martinique	●	◐	O	✓	●	◐	◐	●	O	O	O	O	–	–
Mexico	●	●	●	·	●	●	●	●	●	●	●	●	96	2
Netherlands Antilles	●	O	O	✓	●	O	O	O	O	O	O	O	–	–
Nicaragua	●	●	●	·	●	●	●	●	●	●	●	●	55	4
Panama	●	●	●	✓	●	●	●	●	●	●	●	●	86	9
Puerto Rico	●	●	●	✓	●	●	●	●	●	●	●	●	..	1
Saint Kitts and Nevis	●	●	●	✓	●	●	●	◐	◐	◐	◐	◐	..	–

Legend

✓	Yes
·	No
O	Did not report data for any of the nine years considered (1995 - 2003).
◐	Reported data for one to four out of nine years.
●	Reported data for at least five out of nine years.

Table A2 (continued)
National reporting of statistics on births and deaths, 1995 – 2003

Country or area	Births[a]				Deaths[a]			Infant deaths[a]		Deaths by cause				
	Total	By age of mother	By sex of child	Civil registration at least 90% complete	Total	By sex	By sex and age	Total	By sex	Total	By sex	By sex and age	Estimated coverage[b] (%)	Percentage of deaths attributed to ill-defined diseases[c]
North America (continued)														
Saint Lucia	●	●	●	✓	●	●	●	●	●	●	●	●	..	–
St. Vincent/Grenadines	●	●	●	✓	●	●	●	●	●	●	●	●	..	–
Trinidad and Tobago	◐	◐	◐	✓	◐	◐	◐	◐	◐	◐	◐	◐	92	2
United States	●	●	●	✓	●	●	●	●	●	●	●	●	100	1
South America														
Argentina	●	●	●	✓	●	●	●	●	◐	●	●	●	100	7
Bolivia	◐	○	○	·	●	○	○	●	○	○	○	○	–	–
Brazil	●	◐	●	·	●	●	●	●	●	●	●	●	79	10
Chile	●	●	●	✓	●	●	●	●	●	●	●	●	100	4
Colombia	●	●	●	·	●	●	●	●	●	●	◐	●	79	2
Ecuador	●	●	●	·	●	●	●	●	●	●	●	●	76	13
French Guiana	●	●	●	✓	●	●	◐	●	◐	○	○	○	–	–
Guyana	○	○	○	·	◐	◐	○	○	○	◐	◐	◐	74	2
Paraguay	○	○	○	·	◐	◐	◐	○	○	●	●	●	74	12
Peru	●	◐	○	·	●	◐	◐	●	○	●	●	●	51	12
Suriname	●	●	◐	✓	●	●	●	●	◐	○	○	○	–	–
Uruguay	●	●	●	✓	●	●	●	●	●	●	●	●	100	7
Venezuela (Bolivarian Rep. of)	●	●	●	✓	●	●	●	●	●	●	●	●	97	1
Asia														
Afghanistan	○	○	○	·	○	○	○	○	○	○	○	○	–	–
Armenia	●	●	●	✓	●	●	●	●	●	●	●	●	98	3
Azerbaijan	●	●	●	✓	●	●	●	●	●	●	●	●	72	3
Bahrain	●	●	●	·	●	●	●	●	●	●	●	●	93	16
Bangladesh	◐	○	○	·	◐	○	○	◐	○	○	○	○	–	–
Bhutan	○	○	○	·	○	○	○	○	○	○	○	○	–	–
Brunei Darussalam	●	●	●	✓	●	●	●	●	●	●	●	●	100	7
Cambodia	○	○	○	·	○	○	○	○	○	○	○	○	–	–
China	●	○	○	·	●	◐	◐	○	○	●	●	●	< 10	–
Hong Kong SAR	●	●	●	✓	●	●	●	●	●	●	●	●	..	1
Macao SAR	●	●	●	✓	●	●	●	●	●	○	○	○	–	–
Cyprus	●	●	●	✓	●	●	●	●	●	◐	◐	○	70	44
Dem. People's Rep. of Korea	○	○	○	·	○	○	○	○	○	○	○	○	–	–
Georgia	●	●	●	✓	●	●	●	●	●	●	●	●	64	3
India	○	○	○	·	○	○	○	○	○	○	○	○	–	–
Indonesia	○	○	○	·	○	○	○	○	○	○	○	○	–	–
Iran (Islamic Rep. of)	●	○	●	✓	●	●	○	◐	○	◐	◐	◐	< 50	–
Iraq	●	●	○	·	●	○	○	○	○	○	○	○	–	–
Israel	●	●	●	✓	●	●	●	●	●	●	●	●	100	4

Legend

✓	Yes
·	No
○	Did not report data for any of the nine years considered (1995 - 2003).
◐	Reported data for one to four out of nine years.
●	Reported data for at least five out of nine years.

Table A2 (continued)
National reporting of statistics on births and deaths, 1995 – 2003

Country or area	Births[a]				Deaths[a]			Infant deaths[a]		Deaths by cause				
	Total	By age of mother	By sex of child	Civil registration at least 90% complete	Total	By sex	By sex and age	Total	By sex	Total	By sex	By sex and age	Estimated coverage[b] (%)	Percentage of deaths attributed to ill-defined diseases[c]
Asia (continued)														
Japan	●	●	●	✓	●	●	●	●	●	●	●	●	97	3
Jordan	●	○	●	✓	●	●	○	○	○	○	○	○	–	–
Kazakhstan	●	●	●	✓	●	●	●	●	●	●	●	●	81	3
Kuwait	●	●	●	✓	●	●	●	●	●	●	●	●	90	3
Kyrgyzstan	●	●	●	✓	●	●	●	●	●	●	●	●	78	3
Lao People's Dem. Rep.	◐	○	◐	·	◐	◐	○	◐	◐	○	○	○	–	–
Lebanon	●	○	○	·	●	○	○	○	○	○	○	○	–	–
Malaysia	●	○	●	✓	●	●	●	●	●	◐	◐	◐	< 50	–
Maldives	●	◐	●	✓	●	●	●	●	●	○	○	○	–	–
Mongolia	●	●	●	✓	●	●	●	●	●	●	●	●	76	1
Myanmar	○	○	○	·	○	○	○	○	○	○	○	○	–	–
Nepal	○	○	○	·	◐	◐	◐	◐	◐	○	○	○	–	–
Occupied Palestinian Territory	●	○	●	·	●	●	◐	●	●	○	○	○	–	–
Oman	●	◐	○	·	●	○	○	●	○	○	○	○	–	–
Pakistan	◐	◐	◐	·	◐	◐	◐	◐	◐	○	○	○	–	–
Philippines	●	●	●	✓	●	●	●	●	●	◐	◐	◐	85	5
Qatar	●	●	●	✓	●	●	◐	●	●	◐	◐	◐	77	9
Republic of Korea	●	●	●	✓	●	●	●	●	●	●	●	●	88	10
Saudi Arabia	◐	◐	◐	·	◐	◐	◐	◐	◐	○	○	○	–	–
Singapore	●	●	●	✓	●	●	●	●	●	●	●	●	81	0
Sri Lanka	●	◐	◐	✓	●	◐	◐	◐	◐	◐	◐	◐	77	34
Syrian Arab Republic	●	○	●	✓	●	●	○	○	○	◐	◐	◐	100	21
Tajikistan	◐	○	○	✓	●	◐	○	◐	○	●	●	●	50	7
Thailand	●	◐	◐	·	●	◐	◐	●	◐	●	●	●	89	38
Timor-Leste	○	○	○	·	○	○	○	○	○	○	○	○	–	–
Turkey	●	◐	○	·	●	○	○	●	○	◐	◐	◐	< 50	–
Turkmenistan	◐	○	○	✓	◐	○	○	◐	○	◐	◐	◐	76	2
United Arab Emirates	◐	○	○	·	◐	○	○	◐	○	○	○	○	–	–
Uzbekistan	●	●	●	✓	●	●	●	●	●	●	●	●	82	2
Viet Nam	○	○	○	·	○	○	○	○	○	○	○	○	–	–
Yemen	○	○	○	·	○	○	○	○	○	○	○	○	–	–
Europe														
Albania	◐	○	○	✓	●	◐	◐	◐	○	●	●	●	69	9
Andorra	●	○	●	✓	●	●	○	●	◐	○	○	○	–	–
Austria	●	●	●	✓	●	●	●	●	●	●	●	●	100	1
Belarus	●	●	●	✓	●	●	●	●	●	●	●	●	98	9
Belgium	●	○	●	✓	●	●	◐	●	●	◐	◐	◐	100	3
Bosnia and Herzegovina	◐	◐	○	✓	◐	◐	◐	◐	○	◐	◐	◐	88	12
Bulgaria	●	●	●	✓	●	●	●	●	●	●	●	●	100	4

Legend

✓	Yes
·	No
○	Did not report data for any of the nine years considered (1995 - 2003).
◐	Reported data for one to four out of nine years.
●	Reported data for at least five out of nine years.

Table A2 (continued)
National reporting of statistics on births and deaths, 1995 – 2003

Country or area	Births[a] Total	By age of mother	By sex of child	Civil registration at least 90% complete	Deaths[a] Total	By sex	By sex and age	Infant deaths[a] Total	By sex	Deaths by cause Total	By sex	By sex and age	Estimated coverage[b] (%)	Percentage of deaths attributed to ill-defined diseases[c]
Europe (continued)														
Croatia	●	●	●	✓	●	●	●	●	●	●	●	●	100	2
Czech Republic	●	●	●	✓	●	●	●	●	●	●	●	●	100	1
Denmark	●	●	●	✓	●	●	●	●	●	●	●	●	100	4
Estonia	●	●	●	✓	●	●	●	●	●	●	●	●	100	4
Finland	●	●	●	✓	●	●	●	●	●	●	●	●	100	1
France	●	●	●	✓	●	●	●	●	●	●	●	●	100	6
Germany	●	●	●	✓	●	●	●	●	◐	●	●	●	100	3
Greece	●	●	◐	✓	●	●	●	●	◐	●	●	●	90	7
Hungary	●	●	●	✓	●	●	●	●	●	●	●	●	100	0
Iceland	●	●	●	✓	●	●	●	●	●	●	●	●	91	1
Ireland	●	●	●	✓	●	●	●	●	●	●	●	●	98	1
Italy	●	◐	●	✓	●	●	●	●	●	●	●	●	98	1
Latvia	●	●	●	✓	●	●	●	●	●	●	●	●	99	4
Liechtenstein	◐	◐	◐	✓	◐	◐	◐	◐	◐	○	○	○	–	–
Lithuania	●	●	●	✓	●	●	●	●	●	●	●	●	99	1
Luxembourg	●	●	●	✓	●	●	●	●	◐	●	●	●	100	4
Malta	●	●	●	✓	●	●	●	●	●	●	●	●	95	1
Monaco	●	○	◐	✓	●	◐	○	○	○	○	○	○	–	–
Netherlands	●	●	●	✓	●	●	●	●	●	●	●	●	100	5
Norway	●	●	●	✓	●	●	●	●	●	●	●	●	98	5
Poland	●	●	●	✓	●	●	●	●	●	●	●	●	100	7
Portugal	●	●	●	✓	●	●	●	●	●	●	●	●	100	9
Republic of Moldova	●	●	●	✓	●	●	●	●	●	●	●	●	87	1
Romania	●	●	●	✓	●	●	●	●	●	●	●	●	100	0
Russian Federation	●	●	◐	✓	●	●	●	●	◐	●	●	●	100	5
San Marino	●	●	●	✓	●	●	●	●	◐	●	●	●	..	–
Serbia and Montenegro[d]	●	●	●	✓	●	●	●	●	●	●	●	●	97	8
Slovakia	●	●	●	✓	●	●	●	●	●	●	●	●	100	1
Slovenia	●	●	●	✓	●	●	●	●	●	●	●	●	100	4
Spain	●	◐	●	✓	●	●	●	●	◐	●	●	●	100	4
Sweden	●	●	●	✓	●	●	●	●	●	●	●	●	100	3
Switzerland	●	●	●	✓	●	●	●	●	●	●	●	●	100	3
TFYR Macedonia[e]	●	●	●	✓	●	●	●	●	●	●	●	●	92	8
Ukraine	●	◐	●	✓	●	●	●	●	●	●	●	●	96	4
United Kingdom	●	●	●	✓	●	●	●	●	●	●	●	●	100	2
Oceania														
Australia	●	●	●	✓	●	●	●	●	●	●	●	●	100	0
Fiji	◐	○	○	✓	◐	○	○	◐	○	●	●	●	66	25
French Polynesia	●	○	○	✓	●	○	○	●	○	○	○	○	–	–

Legend
✓ Yes
· No
○ Did not report data for any of the nine years considered (1995 - 2003).
◐ Reported data for one to four out of nine years.
● Reported data for at least five out of nine years.

Table A2 (continued)
National reporting of statistics on births and deaths, 1995 – 2003

Country or area	Births [a]				Deaths [a]			Infant deaths [a]		Deaths by cause				
	Total	By age of mother	By sex of child	Civil registra-tion at least 90% complete	Total	By sex	By sex and age	Total	By sex	Total	By sex	By sex and age	Estimated coverage [b] (%)	Percentage of deaths attributed to ill-defined diseases [c]
Oceania (continued)														
Guam	●	◐	◐	✓	●	◐	○	●	◐	○	○	○	–	–
Kiribati	◐	◐	○	·	○	○	○	○	○	◐	◐	◐	..	–
Marshall Islands	●	●	◐	·	◐	◐	◐	◐	◐	○	○	○	–	–
Micronesia (Fed. States of)	◐	○	○	·	◐	○	○	◐	○	○	○	○	–	–
Nauru	◐	○	○	✓	◐	○	○	◐	○	◐	◐	◐	..	–
New Caledonia	●	●	●	✓	●	●	●	●	●	○	○	○	–	–
New Zealand	●	●	●	✓	●	●	●	●	●	●	●	●	99	0
Palau	●	●	○	✓	●	●	●	●	○	○	○	○	–	–
Papua New Guinea	◐	○	○	·	◐	○	○	◐	○	○	○	○	–	–
Samoa	◐	○	○	·	◐	○	○	◐	○	○	○	○	–	–
Solomon Islands	○	○	○	·	○	○	○	○	○	○	○	○	–	–
Tonga	●	●	●	✓	●	●	●	●	●	◐	◐	◐	..	–
Tuvalu	○	○	○	·	○	○	○	○	○	●	●	●	..	–
Vanuatu	○	○	○	·	○	○	○	○	○	○	○	○	–	–

Legend

✓	Yes
·	No
○	Did not report data for any of the nine years considered (1995 - 2003).
◐	Reported data for one to four out of nine years.
●	Reported data for at least five out of nine years.

Sources:
Prepared by the United Nations Statistics Division, Department of Economic and Social Affairs: for deaths and infant deaths, based on data from the United Nations *Demographic Yearbook* system (November 2004); for deaths by cause, based on data from World Health Organization, *WHO Mortality Database* (December 2004).

Notes:
Two dots (..) indicate that data are not available.
A hyphen (−) indicates that data are not applicable.

a   In general, data come from the civil registration system of a country or area; however, for some countries, data may be derived from a survey or a census.
b   Refers to data for latest available year. Coverage is estimated by dividing the total number of deaths reported for a given country and year from the civil registration system by the total number of deaths estimated by WHO for that year for the national population.
c   Refers to data for latest available year. Calculated only for countries with estimated coverage of at least 50 per cent. Ill-defined diseases include data coded to the International Classification of Diseases (ICD-10) chapter "symptoms, signs and abnormal clinical and laboratory findings, not elsewhere classified".
d   As of 4 February 2003, the official name of the "Federal Republic of Yugoslavia" has been changed to "Serbia and Montenegro".
e   The former Yugoslav Republic of Macedonia.

Table A3
National reporting of selected education statistics, 1995 – 2003

Country or area	Access to educational services [a]									Outcomes of educational experience [b]					
	Enrolment in primary education		Enrolment in secondary education		Enrolment in tertiary education		School attendance			Literacy			Educational attainment		
	Total	By sex	Total	By sex	Total	By sex	Total	By sex	By sex and age	Total	By sex	By sex and age	Total	By sex	By sex and age
Africa															
Algeria	●	●	●	●	◐	○	·	·	·	✓	✓	✓	✓	✓	·
Angola	◐	◐	●	●	◐	◐	·	·	·	·	·	·	·	·	·
Benin	●	●	●	●	●	●	·	·	·	✓	✓	✓	✓	✓	✓
Botswana	●	●	●	●	●	●	·	·	·	·	·	·	·	·	·
Burkina Faso	●	●	●	●	●	●	·	·	·	✓	✓	✓	✓	✓	✓
Burundi	●	●	●	●	●	●	·	·	·	·	·	·	·	·	·
Cameroon	●	●	◐	◐	●	○	·	·	·	·	·	·	·	·	·
Cape Verde	●	●	◐	◐	◐	◐	·	·	·	·	·	·	·	·	·
Central African Republic	◐	◐	◐	◐	◐	◐	·	·	·	·	·	·	·	·	·
Chad	●	●	●	●	●	●	·	·	·	·	·	·	·	·	·
Comoros	●	◐	●	◐	●	◐	·	·	·	·	·	·	·	·	·
Congo	●	●	●	●	●	◐	·	·	·	·	·	·	·	·	·
Côte d'Ivoire	●	●	●	●	◐	◐	·	·	·	·	·	·	·	·	·
Dem. Rep. of the Congo	◐	◐	○	○	○	○	·	·	·	·	·	·	·	·	·
Djibouti	●	●	●	●	●	●	·	·	·	·	·	·	·	·	·
Egypt	◐	◐	◐	◐	◐	◐	·	·	·	✓	✓	✓	✓	✓	✓
Equatorial Guinea	●	◐	◐	◐	◐	◐	·	·	·	·	·	·	·	·	·
Eritrea	●	●	●	●	●	●	·	·	·	·	·	·	·	·	·
Ethiopia	●	●	●	●	●	●	·	·	·	·	·	·	·	·	·
Gabon	●	●	●	◐	◐	◐	·	·	·	·	·	·	·	·	·
Gambia	●	●	●	●	○	○	·	·	·	·	·	·	·	·	·
Ghana	●	●	●	●	●	●	·	·	·	✓	✓	·	✓	✓	·
Guinea	●	●	●	●	◐	◐	·	·	·	·	·	·	·	·	·
Guinea-Bissau	◐	◐	◐	◐	◐	◐	·	·	·	·	·	·	·	·	·
Kenya	●	●	●	●	◐	◐	·	·	·	·	·	·	·	·	·
Lesotho	●	●	●	●	●	●	·	·	·	·	·	·	·	·	·
Liberia	◐	◐	◐	◐	◐	◐	·	·	·	·	·	·	·	·	·
Libyan Arab Jamahiriya	●	●	◐	◐	●	◐	·	·	·	·	·	·	·	·	·
Madagascar	●	●	●	●	●	●	·	·	·	·	·	·	·	·	·
Malawi	●	●	●	●	◐	◐	✓	✓	·	✓	✓	✓	✓	✓	·
Mali	●	●	●	●	●	◐	·	·	·	✓	✓	✓	·	·	·
Mauritania	●	●	●	●	●	●	·	·	·	✓	✓	✓	·	·	·
Mauritius	●	●	●	●	●	●	✓	✓	✓	✓	✓	✓	✓	✓	✓
Morocco	●	●	●	●	●	●	·	·	·	·	·	·	·	·	·
Mozambique	●	●	●	●	◐	◐	✓	✓	✓	✓	✓	✓	✓	✓	✓
Namibia	●	●	●	●	●	●	·	·	·	✓	✓	✓	✓	✓	✓
Niger	●	●	●	●	◐	◐	·	·	·	✓	✓	✓	·	·	·
Nigeria	◐	◐	○	○	○	○	·	·	·	·	·	·	·	·	·
Réunion	◐	○	◐	◐	○	○	·	·	·	·	·	·	·	·	·
Rwanda	●	●	◐	◐	◐	◐	·	·	·	·	·	·	·	·	·

Legend

✓	Yes
·	No
○	Did not report data for any of the six academic years considered.
◐	Reported data for one or two academic years out of a possible total of six years.
●	Reported data for at least three years out of a possible total of six academic years.

Table A3 (continued)
National reporting of selected education statistics, 1995 – 2003

Country or area	Enrolment in primary education Total	By sex	Enrolment in secondary education Total	By sex	Enrolment in tertiary education Total	By sex	School attendance Total	By sex	By sex and age	Literacy Total	By sex	By sex and age	Educational attainment Total	By sex	By sex and age
Africa (continued)															
Sao Tome and Principe	◐	◐	○	○	◐	◐	·	·	·	·	·	·	·	·	·
Senegal	●	●	●	●	●	○	·	·	·	·	·	·	·	·	·
Seychelles	●	●	●	●	○	○	✓	✓	✓	✓	✓	✓	✓	✓	✓
Sierra Leone	◐	◐	◐	◐	◐	◐	·	·	·	·	·	·	·	·	·
Somalia	○	○	○	○	○	○	·	·	·	·	·	·	·	·	·
South Africa	●	●	●	●	●	●	·	·	·	✓	✓	✓	✓	✓	✓
Sudan	●	●	●	◐	◐	◐	·	·	·	·	·	·	·	·	·
Swaziland	●	●	●	●	●	●	·	·	·	·	·	·	·	·	·
Togo	●	●	●	●	●	●	·	·	·	·	·	·	·	·	·
Tunisia	●	●	●	●	●	◐	·	·	·	·	·	·	·	·	·
Uganda	●	●	●	●	●	●	·	·	·	·	·	·	·	·	·
United Rep. of Tanzania	●	●	●	●	●	●	·	·	·	✓	✓	✓	✓	✓	✓
Western Sahara	○	○	○	○	○	○	·	·	·	·	·	·	·	·	·
Zambia	●	●	●	◐	◐	◐	·	·	·	·	·	·	·	·	·
Zimbabwe	●	●	●	●	◐	◐	·	·	·	·	·	·	·	·	·
North America															
Antigua and Barbuda	◐	◐	◐	◐	○	○	·	·	·	·	·	·	·	·	·
Bahamas	◐	◐	◐	◐	○	○	·	·	·	·	·	·	·	·	·
Barbados	●	●	●	●	●	●	·	·	·	·	·	·	·	·	·
Belize	●	●	●	●	○	○	·	·	·	✓	✓	✓	✓	✓	✓
Canada	●	●	●	●	●	●	✓	✓	✓	·	·	·	✓	✓	✓
Costa Rica	●	●	●	●	●	●	✓	·	·	✓	·	·	·	·	·
Cuba	●	●	●	●	●	●	·	·	·	·	·	·	·	·	·
Dominica	●	●	●	●	○	○	·	·	·	·	·	·	·	·	·
Dominican Republic	●	◐	◐	◐	◐	◐	·	·	·	✓	✓	✓	✓	✓	✓
El Salvador	●	●	●	●	●	●	·	·	·	·	·	·	·	·	·
Grenada	◐	◐	◐	◐	○	○	·	·	·	·	·	·	·	·	·
Guadeloupe	○	○	○	○	○	○	·	·	·	·	·	·	·	·	·
Guatemala	●	●	●	●	◐	●	·	·	·	✓	✓	✓	✓	✓	✓
Haiti	◐	◐	◐	◐	○	○	·	·	·	·	·	·	·	·	·
Honduras	◐	◐	○	○	◐	◐	·	·	·	✓	✓	✓	·	·	·
Jamaica	●	●	●	◐	●	●	✓	·	·	·	·	·	✓	✓	·
Martinique	◐	◐	◐	◐	○	○	·	·	·	·	·	·	·	·	·
Mexico	●	●	●	●	●	●	✓	✓	✓	✓	✓	✓	✓	·	·
Netherlands Antilles	●	●	●	●	●	●	✓	·	·	·	·	·	·	·	·
Nicaragua	●	●	●	●	◐	◐	·	·	·	·	·	·	·	·	·
Panama	●	●	●	●	◐	○	·	·	·	✓	✓	✓	✓	·	·
Puerto Rico	○	○	○	○	○	○	·	·	·	·	·	·	✓	✓	·
Saint Kitts and Nevis	◐	◐	◐	◐	○	○	·	·	·	·	·	·	·	·	·

Legend
✓ Yes
· No
○ Did not report data for any of the six academic years considered.
◐ Reported data for one or two academic years out of a possible total of six years.
● Reported data for at least three years out of a possible total of six academic years.

Table A3 (continued)
National reporting of selected education statistics, 1995 – 2003

Country or area	Access to educational services [a]									Outcomes of educational experience [b]					
	Enrolment in primary education		Enrolment in secondary education		Enrolment in tertiary education		School attendance			Literacy			Educational attainment		
	Total	By sex	Total	By sex	Total	By sex	Total	By sex	By sex and age	Total	By sex	By sex and age	Total	By sex	By sex and age
North America (continued)															
Saint Lucia	●	●	●	●	◑	◑	✓	✓	✓	✓	✓	✓	✓	✓	✓
St. Vincent/Grenadines	●	●	◑	◑	○	○	·	·	·	·	·	·	·	·	·
Trinidad and Tobago	●	●	●	●	●	●	·	·	·	·	·	·	·	·	·
United States	●	●	●	●	●	●	✓	✓	✓	·	·	·	✓	✓	✓
South America															
Argentina	●	●	●	●	●	◑	✓	✓	✓	✓	✓	✓	·	·	·
Bolivia	●	●	●	●	●	○	·	·	·	✓	✓	✓	·	·	·
Brazil	●	●	●	●	●	●	·	·	·	✓	✓	✓	·	·	·
Chile	●	●	●	●	●	●	·	·	·	✓	✓	✓	✓	✓	✓
Colombia	●	●	●	●	●	●	·	·	·	·	·	·	·	·	·
Ecuador	●	●	●	●	◑	○	✓	✓	✓	✓	✓	✓	✓	✓	✓
French Guiana	◑	◑	◑	◑	○	○	·	·	·	·	·	·	·	·	·
Guyana	●	●	●	●	◑	◑	·	·	·	·	·	·	·	·	·
Paraguay	◑	◑	●	●	●	●	·	·	·	·	·	·	·	·	·
Peru	●	●	●	●	◑	○	·	·	·	·	·	·	·	·	·
Suriname	◑	◑	◑	◑	◑	◑	·	·	·	·	·	·	·	·	·
Uruguay	●	●	●	●	●	●	✓	✓	✓	✓	✓	✓	✓	✓	✓
Venezuela (Bolivarian Rep. of)	●	●	●	●	◑	◑	✓	✓	✓	✓	✓	✓	·	·	·
Asia															
Afghanistan	●	◑	◑	◑	○	○	·	·	·	·	·	·	·	·	·
Armenia	●	◑	●	◑	●	●	✓	✓	✓	✓	✓	✓	✓	✓	✓
Azerbaijan	●	●	●	●	●	●	✓	✓	✓	✓	✓	✓	✓	✓	✓
Bahrain	●	●	●	●	◑	◑	·	·	·	✓	✓	✓	✓	✓	✓
Bangladesh	●	●	●	●	●	●	·	·	·	·	·	·	·	·	·
Bhutan	●	●	●	●	○	○	·	·	·	·	·	·	·	·	·
Brunei Darussalam	●	●	●	●	●	●	·	·	·	✓	✓	✓	·	·	·
Cambodia	●	●	●	●	●	●	·	·	·	✓	✓	✓	✓	✓	✓
China	●	●	●	●	●	○	·	·	·	✓	✓	✓	·	·	·
Hong Kong SAR	◑	◑	◑	◑	◑	◑	✓	✓	✓	·	·	·	✓	✓	✓
Macao SAR	●	●	●	●	●	●	✓	✓	✓	✓	✓	✓	✓	✓	✓
Cyprus	●	●	●	●	●	●	·	·	·	✓	✓	✓	✓	✓	✓
Dem. People's Rep. of Korea	○	○	○	○	○	○	·	·	·	·	·	·	·	·	·
Georgia	●	●	●	●	●	●	·	·	·	·	·	·	·	·	·
India	●	●	●	●	●	●	·	·	·	✓	✓	✓	·	·	·
Indonesia	●	●	●	●	●	●	·	·	·	·	·	·	✓	✓	✓
Iran (Islamic Rep. of)	●	●	●	●	●	●	·	·	·	✓	✓	✓	✓	✓	✓
Iraq	●	●	●	●	◑	◑	·	·	·	✓	✓	·	✓	✓	·
Israel	●	●	●	●	●	●	·	·	·	✓	✓	✓	·	·	·

Legend

✓	Yes
·	No
○	Did not report data for any of the six academic years considered.
◑	Reported data for one or two academic years out of a possible total of six years.
●	Reported data for at least three years out of a possible total of six academic years.

Table A3 (continued)
National reporting of selected education statistics, 1995 – 2003

Country or area	Access to educational services [a]									Outcomes of educational experience [b]					
	Enrolment in primary education		Enrolment in secondary education		Enrolment in tertiary education		School attendance			Literacy			Educational attainment		
	Total	By sex	Total	By sex	Total	By sex	Total	By sex	By sex and age	Total	By sex	By sex and age	Total	By sex	By sex and age
Asia (continued)															
Japan	●	●	●	●	●	●	·	·	·	·	·	·	·	·	·
Jordan	●	●	●	●	◐	●	·	·	·	·	·	·	·	·	·
Kazakhstan	●	●	●	●	●	●	·	·	·	✓	✓	✓	✓	✓	✓
Kuwait	●	●	●	●	◐	◐	·	·	·	·	·	·	·	·	·
Kyrgyzstan	●	●	●	●	●	●	✓	✓	✓	✓	✓	✓	✓	✓	✓
Lao People's Dem. Rep.	●	●	●	●	●	●	✓	✓	✓	✓	✓	✓	✓	✓	✓
Lebanon	●	●	●	●	●	●	·	·	·	·	·	·	·	·	·
Malaysia	●	●	●	●	●	●	·	·	·	✓	✓	✓	✓	✓	✓
Maldives	●	●	●	●	○	○	✓	✓	✓	✓	✓	✓	✓	✓	✓
Mongolia	●	●	●	●	●	●	✓	✓	✓	✓	✓	✓	✓	✓	✓
Myanmar	●	●	●	●	◐	○	·	·	·	·	·	·	·	·	·
Nepal	●	●	●	●	●	◐	·	·	·	✓	✓	✓	✓	✓	✓
Occupied Palestinian Territory	●	●	●	●	●	●	✓	✓	✓	✓	✓	✓	✓	✓	✓
Oman	●	●	●	●	●	●	·	·	·	·	·	·	·	·	·
Pakistan	●	●	◐	◐	○	○	·	·	·	✓	✓	✓	✓	✓	✓
Philippines	●	●	●	●	●	●	·	·	·	✓	✓	✓	·	·	·
Qatar	●	●	●	●	●	●	·	·	·	✓	✓	✓	·	·	·
Republic of Korea	●	●	●	●	●	●	✓	✓	✓	·	·	·	✓	✓	✓
Saudi Arabia	●	●	●	●	●	●	·	·	·	·	·	·	·	·	·
Singapore	◐	◐	◐	○	◐	◐	·	·	·	✓	✓	✓	✓	✓	✓
Sri Lanka	●	●	◐	◐	◐	◐	·	·	·	✓	✓	✓	✓	✓	✓
Syrian Arab Republic	●	●	●	●	○	○	·	·	·	·	·	·	·	·	·
Tajikistan	●	●	●	●	●	●	·	·	·	✓	✓	✓	·	·	·
Thailand	●	●	●	◐	●	●	✓	✓	✓	✓	✓	✓	·	·	·
Timor-Leste	◐	○	◐	○	◐	◐	·	·	·	·	·	·	·	·	·
Turkey	◐	◐	◐	◐	●	●	·	·	·	✓	✓	✓	·	·	·
Turkmenistan	○	○	○	○	○	○	·	·	·	✓	✓	✓	·	·	·
United Arab Emirates	●	●	●	●	◐	◐	·	·	·	·	·	·	·	·	·
Uzbekistan	○	○	○	○	○	○	·	·	·	·	·	·	·	·	·
Viet Nam	●	●	●	●	●	●	·	·	·	✓	✓	✓	·	·	·
Yemen	●	●	●	●	◐	◐	·	·	·	·	·	·	·	·	·
Europe															
Albania	●	●	●	●	●	●	·	·	·	✓	✓	✓	·	·	·
Andorra	◐	◐	◐	◐	◐	◐	·	·	·	·	·	·	·	·	·
Austria	●	●	●	●	●	●	✓	✓	✓	·	·	·	·	·	·
Belarus	●	●	●	●	●	●	✓	✓	✓	✓	✓	✓	✓	✓	✓
Belgium	●	●	●	●	●	●	·	·	·	·	·	·	·	·	·
Bosnia and Herzegovina	○	○	○	○	○	○	·	·	·	·	·	·	·	·	·
Bulgaria	●	●	●	●	●	●	✓	✓	✓	✓	✓	✓	✓	✓	✓

Legend

✓ Yes

· No

○ Did not report data for any of the six academic years considered.

◐ Reported data for one or two academic years out of a possible total of six years.

● Reported data for at least three years out of a possible total of six academic years.

Table A3 (continued)
National reporting of selected education statistics, 1995 – 2003

Country or area	Enrolment in primary education — Total	By sex	Enrolment in secondary education — Total	By sex	Enrolment in tertiary education — Total	By sex	School attendance — Total	By sex	By sex and age	Literacy — Total	By sex	By sex and age	Educational attainment — Total	By sex	By sex and age
Europe (continued)															
Croatia	●	●	●	●	●	●	✓	✓	✓	✓	✓	✓	✓	✓	✓
Czech Republic	●	●	●	●	●	●	·	·	·	·	·	·	✓	✓	✓
Denmark	●	●	●	●	●	●	·	·	·	·	·	·	✓	✓	✓
Estonia	●	●	●	●	●	●	✓	✓	✓	✓	✓	✓	✓	✓	✓
Finland	●	●	●	●	●	●	✓	✓	✓	·	·	·	✓	✓	✓
France	●	●	●	●	●	●	·	·	·	·	·	·	·	·	·
Germany	●	●	●	●	●	●	·	·	·	·	·	·	·	·	·
Greece	●	●	●	●	●	●	·	·	·	·	·	·	·	·	·
Hungary	●	●	●	●	●	●	·	·	·	✓	✓	✓	✓	✓	✓
Iceland	●	●	●	●	●	●	·	·	·	·	·	·	·	·	·
Ireland	●	●	●	●	●	●	✓	✓	✓	·	·	·	✓	✓	✓
Italy	●	●	●	●	●	●	·	·	·	·	·	·	·	·	·
Latvia	●	●	●	●	●	●	·	·	·	✓	✓	✓	✓	✓	✓
Liechtenstein	○	○	○	○	○	○	·	·	·	·	·	·	·	·	·
Lithuania	●	●	●	●	●	●	✓	✓	✓	✓	✓	✓	✓	✓	✓
Luxembourg	●	●	●	●	●	◐	✓	✓	✓	·	·	·	✓	✓	✓
Malta	●	●	●	●	●	●	·	·	·	✓	✓	✓	·	·	·
Monaco	●	●	●	●	○	○	·	·	·	·	·	·	·	·	·
Netherlands	●	●	●	●	●	●	·	·	·	·	·	·	✓	✓	✓
Norway	●	●	●	●	●	●	✓	✓	✓	·	·	·	✓	✓	✓
Poland	●	●	●	●	●	●	✓	✓	✓	·	·	·	✓	✓	✓
Portugal	●	●	●	●	●	●	·	·	·	✓	✓	✓	✓	✓	✓
Republic of Moldova	●	●	●	●	●	●	·	·	·	·	·	·	·	·	·
Romania	●	●	●	●	●	●	✓	✓	✓	✓	✓	✓	✓	✓	✓
Russian Federation	●	●	●	◐	◐	◐	·	·	·	✓	✓	✓	✓	✓	✓
San Marino	●	●	●	●	◐	◐	·	·	·	·	·	·	·	·	·
Serbia and Montenegro [c]	●	●	●	●	●	●	✓	✓	✓	✓	✓	✓	✓	✓	✓
Slovakia	●	●	●	●	●	●	✓	✓	✓	✓	✓	✓	✓	✓	✓
Slovenia	●	●	●	●	●	●	✓	✓	✓	·	·	·	✓	✓	✓
Spain	●	●	●	●	●	●	·	·	·	·	·	·	·	·	·
Sweden	●	●	●	●	●	●	·	·	·	·	·	·	✓	✓	✓
Switzerland	●	●	●	●	●	●	✓	✓	✓	·	·	·	✓	✓	✓
TFYR Macedonia [d]	●	●	●	●	●	●	·	·	·	✓	✓	✓	✓	✓	✓
Ukraine	●	●	●	●	●	●	✓	✓	✓	✓	✓	✓	✓	✓	✓
United Kingdom	●	●	●	●	●	●	·	·	·	·	·	·	·	·	·
Oceania															
Australia	●	●	●	●	●	●	·	·	·	·	·	·	✓	✓	✓
Fiji	○	○	○	○	○	○	·	·	·	✓	✓	✓	·	·	·
French Polynesia	◐	◐	○	○	○	○	·	·	·	·	·	·	✓	✓	✓

Legend
✓ Yes
· No
○ Did not report data for any of the six academic years considered.
◐ Reported data for one or two academic years out of a possible total of six years.
● Reported data for at least three years out of a possible total of six academic years.

Table A3 (continued)
National reporting of selected education statistics, 1995 – 2003

| Country or area | Access to educational services [a] | | | | | | | | | Outcomes of educational experience [b] | | | | | |
| | Enrolment in primary education | | Enrolment in secondary education | | Enrolment in tertiary education | | School attendance | | | Literacy | | | Educational attainment | | |
	Total	By sex	Total	By sex	Total	By sex	Total	By sex	By sex and age	Total	By sex	By sex and age	Total	By sex	By sex and age
Oceania (continued)															
Guam	O	O	O	O	O	O	·	·	·	·	·	·	·	·	·
Kiribati	●	●	◐	◐	O	O	·	·	·	·	·	·	·	·	·
Marshall Islands	◐	◐	◐	◐	◐	◐	·	·	·	✓	✓	·	✓	·	·
Micronesia (Fed. States of)	O	O	◐	O	◐	O	·	·	·	·	·	·	·	·	·
Nauru	O	O	O	O	O	O	·	·	·	·	·	·	·	·	·
New Caledonia	O	O	O	O	O	O	·	·	·	✓	✓	✓	·	·	·
New Zealand	●	●	●	●	●	●	·	·	·	·	·	·	✓	✓	✓
Palau	◐	◐	◐	◐	◐	◐	·	·	·	·	·	·	·	·	·
Papua New Guinea	●	●	●	●	●	●	·	·	·	✓	✓	✓	·	·	·
Samoa	●	●	●	●	●	●	·	·	·	·	·	·	·	·	·
Solomon Islands	O	O	O	O	O	O	·	·	·	·	·	·	·	·	·
Tonga	●	●	●	●	◐	◐	✓	✓	✓	✓	✓	✓	✓	✓	✓
Tuvalu	◐	◐	◐	◐	O	O	·	·	·	·	·	·	·	·	·
Vanuatu	●	●	●	●	◐	O	·	·	·	✓	·	·	·	·	·

Legend

✓	Yes
·	No
O	Did not report data for any of the six academic years considered.
◐	Reported data for one or two academic years out of a possible total of six years.
●	Reported data for at least three years out of a possible total of six academic years.

Sources:

Prepared by the United Nations Statistics Division, Department of Economic and Social Affairs, based on enrolment data (November 2004) and literacy data (April 2005) provided by the UNESCO Institute for Statistics excluding UIS estimates; and on data from the United Nations *Demographic Yearbook* system (November 2004).

Notes:

a   Primary, secondary and tertiary education data are obtained through administrative records and cover six academic years: 1995/1996, 1996/1997 and from 1998/1999 to 2001/2002. School attendance data are obtained through censuses.

b   Data from censuses.

c   As of 4 February 2003, the official name of the "Federal Republic of Yugoslavia" has been changed to "Serbia and Montenegro".

d   The former Yugoslav Republic of Macedonia.

Table A4
National reporting of statistics on selected economic characteristics, 1995 – 2003

Country or area	Economic activity						Unemployment			Occupation			Status in employment		
	Data reported from labour force surveys [a]			Census data reported			Data reported from labour force surveys [a]			Data reported from labour force surveys [a]		Census data reported	Data reported from labour force surveys [a]		Census data reported
	Total	By sex	By sex and age	Total	By sex	By sex and age	Total	By sex	By sex and age	Total	By sex	By sex	Total	By sex	By sex
Africa															
Algeria	◐	◐	◐	✓	✓	·	○	○	○	○	○	·	○	○	·
Angola	○	○	○	·	·	·	○	○	○	○	○	·	○	○	·
Benin	◐	◐	◐	·	·	·	○	○	○	○	○	·	○	○	·
Botswana	◐	◐	◐	✓	✓	✓	◐	◐	◐	◐	◐	·	◐	◐	·
Burkina Faso	○	○	○	·	·	·	○	○	○	○	○	·	○	○	·
Burundi	○	○	○	·	·	·	○	○	○	○	○	·	○	○	·
Cameroon	○	○	○	·	·	·	◐	◐	○	○	○	·	◐	◐	·
Cape Verde	○	○	○	·	·	·	○	○	○	○	○	·	○	○	·
Central African Republic	○	○	○	·	·	·	○	○	○	○	○	·	○	○	·
Chad	○	○	○	·	·	·	○	○	○	◐	○	·	○	○	·
Comoros	○	○	○	·	·	·	○	○	○	○	○	·	○	○	·
Congo	○	○	○	·	·	·	○	○	○	○	○	·	○	○	·
Côte d'Ivoire	○	○	○	·	·	·	○	○	○	○	○	·	○	○	·
Dem. Rep. of the Congo	○	○	○	·	·	·	○	○	○	○	○	·	○	○	·
Djibouti	○	○	○	·	·	·	○	○	○	○	○	·	○	○	·
Egypt	◐	◐	◐	·	·	·	●	●	●	●	●	·	●	●	·
Equatorial Guinea	○	○	○	·	·	·	○	○	○	○	○	·	○	○	·
Eritrea	○	○	○	·	·	·	○	○	○	○	○	·	○	○	·
Ethiopia	◐	◐	◐	·	·	·	○	○	○	○	○	·	○	○	·
Gabon	○	○	○	·	·	·	○	○	○	○	○	·	○	○	·
Gambia	○	○	○	·	·	·	○	○	○	○	○	·	○	○	·
Ghana	○	○	○	✓	✓	✓	○	○	○	○	○	✓	○	○	✓
Guinea	○	○	○	·	·	·	○	○	○	○	○	·	○	○	·
Guinea-Bissau	○	○	○	·	·	·	○	○	○	○	○	·	○	○	·
Kenya	○	○	○	·	·	·	○	○	○	○	○	·	○	○	·
Lesotho	○	○	○	✓	·	·	◐	◐	○	○	○	·	◐	◐	·
Liberia	○	○	○	·	·	·	○	○	○	○	○	·	○	○	·
Libyan Arab Jamahiriya	○	○	○	·	·	·	○	○	○	○	○	·	○	○	·
Madagascar	◐	◐	◐	·	·	·	◐	◐	◐	○	○	·	◐	◐	·
Malawi	○	○	○	✓	✓	✓	○	○	○	○	○	✓	○	○	✓
Mali	○	○	○	·	·	·	○	○	○	○	○	·	○	○	·
Mauritania	○	○	○	·	·	·	○	○	○	○	○	·	○	○	·
Mauritius	◐	◐	◐	✓	✓	✓	○	○	○	○	○	✓	○	○	✓
Morocco	●	●	●	·	·	·	●	●	●	○	○	·	◐	◐	·
Mozambique	○	○	○	✓	✓	✓	○	○	○	○	○	·	○	○	·
Namibia	○	○	○	·	·	·	◐	◐	◐	◐	◐	·	◐	◐	·
Niger	○	○	○	·	·	·	○	○	○	○	○	·	○	○	·
Nigeria	○	○	○	·	·	·	○	○	○	○	○	·	○	○	·
Réunion	○	○	○	✓	✓	✓	○	○	○	○	○	·	○	○	·
Rwanda	◐	◐	◐	·	·	·	◐	◐	◐	○	○	·	◐	◐	·

Legend

✓	Yes
·	No
○	Did not report data for any of the nine years considered (1995 - 2003).
◐	Reported data for one to four out of nine years.
●	Reported data for at least five out of nine years.

Table A4 (continued)
National reporting of statistics on selected economic characteristics, 1995 – 2003

Country or area	Economic activity						Unemployment			Occupation			Status in employment		
	Data reported from labour force surveys [a]			Census data reported			Data reported from labour force surveys [a]			Data reported from labour force surveys [a]		Census data reported	Data reported from labour force surveys [a]		Census data reported
	Total	By sex	By sex and age	Total	By sex	By sex and age	Total	By sex	By sex and age	Total	By sex	By sex	Total	By sex	By sex
Africa (continued)															
Sao Tome and Principe	○	○	○	·	·	·	○	○	○	○	○	·	○	○	·
Senegal	○	○	○	·	·	·	○	○	○	○	○	·	○	○	·
Seychelles	○	○	○	✓	✓	✓	○	○	○	○	○	·	○	○	✓
Sierra Leone	○	○	○	·	·	·	○	○	○	○	○	·	○	○	·
Somalia	○	○	○	·	·	·	○	○	○	○	○	·	○	○	·
South Africa	◐	◐	◐	✓	✓	·	●	●	◐	◐	○	✓	◐	◐	·
Sudan	○	○	○	·	·	·	○	○	○	○	○	·	○	○	·
Swaziland	○	○	○	·	·	·	○	○	○	◐	◐	·	○	○	·
Togo	○	○	○	·	·	·	○	○	○	○	○	·	○	○	·
Tunisia	◐	◐	◐	·	·	·	●	○	○	○	○	·	●	○	·
Uganda	○	○	○	·	·	·	◐	◐	○	○	○	·	○	○	·
United Rep. of Tanzania	◐	◐	◐	·	·	·	◐	◐	○	◐	◐	·	◐	○	·
Western Sahara	○	○	○	·	·	·	○	○	○	○	○	·	○	○	·
Zambia	○	○	○	·	·	·	○	○	○	○	○	·	○	○	·
Zimbabwe	◐	◐	◐	·	·	·	◐	◐	◐	○	○	·	○	○	·
North America															
Antigua and Barbuda	○	○	○	·	·	·	○	○	○	○	○	·	○	○	·
Bahamas	◐	◐	◐	·	·	·	●	●	●	●	●	·	○	○	·
Barbados	◐	◐	◐	·	·	·	●	●	●	●	●	·	●	◐	·
Belize	◐	◐	◐	·	·	·	●	●	○	●	●	·	●	●	·
Canada	●	●	●	✓	✓	✓	●	●	●	●	●	✓	●	●	✓
Costa Rica	●	●	●	·	·	·	●	●	●	●	●	·	●	●	·
Cuba	○	○	○	·	·	·	○	○	○	○	○	·	○	○	·
Dominica	○	○	○	·	·	·	◐	◐	◐	◐	◐	·	◐	◐	·
Dominican Republic	○	○	○	·	·	·	○	○	○	○	○	·	○	○	·
El Salvador	●	●	●	·	·	·	●	●	●	●	●	·	●	●	·
Grenada	○	○	○	·	·	·	○	○	○	○	○	·	○	○	·
Guadeloupe	○	○	○	·	·	·	◐	◐	○	○	○	·	○	○	·
Guatemala	◐	◐	◐	·	·	·	◐	◐	○	○	○	·	◐	◐	·
Haiti	○	○	○	·	·	·	○	○	○	○	○	·	○	○	·
Honduras	●	●	●	·	·	·	●	●	●	●	◐	·	◐	◐	·
Jamaica	◐	◐	◐	·	·	·	●	●	●	●	○	·	●	●	·
Martinique	○	○	○	·	·	·	◐	◐	○	○	○	·	○	○	·
Mexico	●	●	●	✓	✓	✓	●	●	●	●	●	✓	●	●	✓
Netherlands Antilles	●	●	●	✓	✓	✓	●	●	●	●	●	✓	●	●	✓
Nicaragua	○	○	○	✓	✓	✓	○	○	○	○	○	·	○	○	·
Panama	●	●	●	✓	✓	✓	●	●	●	●	●	✓	●	●	✓
Puerto Rico	●	●	●	✓	✓	·	●	●	●	●	●	·	●	●	·
Saint Kitts and Nevis	○	○	○	·	·	·	○	○	○	○	○	·	○	○	·

Legend

✓	Yes
·	No
○	Did not report data for any of the nine years considered (1995 - 2003).
◐	Reported data for one to four out of nine years.
●	Reported data for at least five out of nine years.

120   Annex 1 Statistical tables

Table A4 (continued)
National reporting of statistics on selected economic characteristics, 1995 – 2003

Country or area	Economic activity						Unemployment			Occupation			Status in employment		
	Data reported from labour force surveys[a]			Census data reported			Data reported from labour force surveys[a]			Data reported from labour force surveys[a]		Census data reported	Data reported from labour force surveys[a]		Census data reported
	Total	By sex	By sex and age	Total	By sex	By sex and age	Total	By sex	By sex and age	Total	By sex	By sex	Total	By sex	By sex
North America (continued)															
Saint Lucia	○	○	○	✓	✓	✓	●	●	●	●	●	✓	●	●	✓
St. Vincent/Grenadines	○	○	○	·	·	·	○	○	○	○	○	·	○	○	·
Trinidad and Tobago	●	●	●	·	·	·	●	●	●	●	●	·	●	●	·
United States	●	●	●	·	·	·	●	●	●	●	●	·	●	●	·
South America															
Argentina	◐	◐	◐	✓	✓	·	●	●	●	●	●	·	●	●	·
Bolivia	◐	◐	◐	·	·	·	●	●	●	●	●	·	●	●	·
Brazil	●	●	●	✓	✓	✓	●	●	●	●	●	✓	○	○	✓
Chile	●	●	●	·	·	·	●	●	●	●	●	·	●	●	·
Colombia	●	●	●	·	·	·	●	●	●	●	●	·	●	●	·
Ecuador	●	●	●	·	·	·	●	●	●	●	◐	·	●	●	·
French Guiana	○	○	○	✓	✓	✓	◐	◐	○	○	○	·	○	○	·
Guyana	○	○	○	·	·	·	○	○	○	○	○	·	○	○	·
Paraguay	○	○	○	·	·	·	◐	◐	○	○	○	·	○	○	·
Peru	●	●	●	·	·	·	●	●	●	●	●	·	●	●	·
Suriname	◐	◐	◐	·	·	·	●	●	●	◐	◐	·	◐	◐	·
Uruguay	●	●	●	✓	✓	✓	●	●	●	●	●	✓	◐	◐	✓
Venezuela (Bolivarian Rep. of)	◐	◐	◐	✓	✓	✓	●	●	○	●	●	·	○	○	·
Asia															
Afghanistan	○	○	○	·	·	·	○	○	○	○	○	·	○	○	·
Armenia	◐	◐	◐	✓	✓	✓	◐	◐	○	○	○	✓	○	○	✓
Azerbaijan	○	○	○	✓	✓	✓	○	○	○	○	○	·	○	○	·
Bahrain	○	○	○	✓	✓	✓	◐	◐	○	○	○	✓	○	○	·
Bangladesh	◐	◐	◐	·	·	·	◐	◐	◐	◐	◐	·	◐	◐	·
Bhutan	○	○	○	·	·	·	○	○	○	○	○	·	○	○	·
Brunei Darussalam	○	○	○	·	·	·	○	○	○	○	○	✓	○	○	·
Cambodia	●	●	◐	✓	✓	✓	◐	◐	◐	◐	◐	✓	◐	◐	✓
China	○	○	○	·	·	·	○	○	○	○	○	·	○	○	·
Hong Kong SAR	●	●	●	✓	✓	✓	●	●	●	●	●	·	●	●	✓
Macao SAR	●	●	●	✓	✓	✓	●	●	●	●	●	✓	●	●	✓
Cyprus	◐	◐	◐	✓	✓	✓	●	●	◐	●	●	✓	●	●	✓
Dem. People's Rep. of Korea	○	○	○	·	·	·	○	○	○	○	○	·	○	○	·
Georgia	●	●	●	·	·	·	●	●	●	●	●	·	●	●	·
India	○	○	○	·	·	·	●	●	●	●	●	·	●	●	·
Indonesia	◐	◐	◐	✓	✓	✓	●	◐	◐	○	○	·	○	○	✓
Iran (Islamic Rep. of)	○	○	○	✓	✓	✓	◐	◐	◐	○	○	✓	○	○	✓
Iraq	○	○	○	✓	✓	✓	○	○	○	○	○	✓	○	○	·
Israel	●	●	●	✓	✓	✓	●	●	●	●	●	·	●	●	·

Legend
✓ Yes
· No
○ Did not report data for any of the nine years considered (1995 - 2003).
◐ Reported data for one to four out of nine years.
● Reported data for at least five out of nine years.

Table A4 (continued)
National reporting of statistics on selected economic characteristics, 1995 – 2003

Country or area	Economic activity — Data reported from labour force surveys [a] — Total	By sex	By sex and age	Economic activity — Census data reported — Total	By sex	By sex and age	Unemployment — Data reported from labour force surveys [a] — Total	By sex	By sex and age	Occupation — Data reported from labour force surveys [a] — Total	By sex	Occupation — Census data reported — By sex	Status in employment — Data reported from labour force surveys [a] — Total	By sex	Status in employment — Census data reported — By sex
Asia (continued)															
Japan	●	●	●	✓	✓	✓	●	●	●	●	●	✓	●	●	✓
Jordan	○	○	○	·	·	·	○	○	○	○	○	·	○	○	·
Kazakhstan	◑	◑	◑	✓	✓	✓	◑	◑	◑	◑	◑	✓	◑	◑	·
Kuwait	○	○	○	✓	✓	✓	◑	◑	◑	○	○	·	○	○	·
Kyrgyzstan	◑	◑	◑	✓	✓	✓	◑	◑	◑	◑	◑	·	◑	◑	✓
Lao People's Dem. Rep.	○	○	○	✓	✓	✓	○	○	○	○	○	✓	○	○	·
Lebanon	○	○	○	·	·	·	○	○	○	○	○	·	○	○	·
Malaysia	◑	◑	◑	·	·	·	●	●	●	●	●	·	●	●	·
Maldives	○	○	○	✓	✓	✓	◑	◑	◑	○	○	✓	○	○	✓
Mongolia	○	○	○	✓	✓	✓	○	○	○	○	○	✓	○	○	✓
Myanmar	○	○	○	·	·	·	○	○	○	○	○	·	○	○	·
Nepal	○	○	○	✓	✓	✓	○	○	○	○	○	✓	○	○	✓
Occupied Palestinian Territory	◑	◑	◑	✓	✓	✓	●	●	●	●	●	✓	●	●	✓
Oman	◑	◑	◑	·	·	·	○	○	○	◑	◑	·	◑	◑	·
Pakistan	●	●	●	✓	✓	✓	●	●	●	●	●	·	●	●	·
Philippines	●	●	●	·	·	·	●	●	●	●	●	·	○	○	·
Qatar	○	○	○	✓	✓	✓	◑	◑	◑	◑	◑	·	○	○	·
Republic of Korea	●	●	●	✓	✓	✓	●	●	●	●	●	✓	●	●	✓
Saudi Arabia	○	○	○	·	·	·	◑	◑	◑	◑	◑	·	○	○	·
Singapore	●	●	●	✓	✓	·	●	●	●	●	●	·	●	●	·
Sri Lanka	●	●	●	✓	✓	✓	●	●	●	●	●	·	◑	◑	·
Syrian Arab Republic	◑	◑	◑	·	·	·	◑	◑	◑	○	○	·	○	○	·
Tajikistan	○	○	○	·	·	·	○	○	○	○	○	·	○	○	·
Thailand	●	●	●	✓	✓	✓	●	●	●	●	●	✓	●	●	✓
Timor-Leste	○	○	○	·	·	·	○	○	○	○	○	·	○	○	·
Turkey	●	●	●	✓	✓	✓	●	●	●	●	●	✓	●	●	✓
Turkmenistan	○	○	○	·	·	·	○	○	○	○	○	·	○	○	·
United Arab Emirates	○	○	○	✓	✓	✓	○	○	○	○	○	·	○	○	·
Uzbekistan	○	○	○	·	·	·	○	○	○	○	○	·	○	○	·
Viet Nam	○	○	○	·	·	·	●	●	○	○	○	·	●	●	·
Yemen	○	○	○	·	·	·	◑	◑	◑	◑	◑	·	◑	◑	·
Europe															
Albania	◑	◑	◑	✓	✓	✓	◑	◑	◑	○	○	·	○	○	·
Andorra	○	○	○	·	·	·	○	○	○	○	○	·	○	○	·
Austria	●	●	●	✓	✓	✓	●	●	●	●	●	✓	●	●	✓
Belarus	○	○	○	✓	✓	✓	○	○	○	○	○	·	○	○	✓
Belgium	●	●	●	·	·	·	●	●	●	●	●	·	○	○	·
Bosnia and Herzegovina	○	○	○	·	·	·	○	○	○	○	○	·	○	○	·
Bulgaria	◑	◑	◑	·	·	·	●	●	●	●	◑	·	◑	◑	·

Legend

✓	Yes
·	No
○	Did not report data for any of the nine years considered (1995 - 2003).
◑	Reported data for one to four out of nine years.
●	Reported data for at least five out of nine years.

Table A4 (continued)
National reporting of statistics on selected economic characteristics, 1995 – 2003

Country or area	Economic activity						Unemployment			Occupation			Status in employment		
	Data reported from labour force surveys [a]			Census data reported			Data reported from labour force surveys [a]			Data reported from labour force surveys [a]		Census data reported	Data reported from labour force surveys [a]		Census data reported
	Total	By sex	By sex and age	Total	By sex	By sex and age	Total	By sex	By sex and age	Total	By sex	By sex	Total	By sex	By sex
Europe (continued)															
Croatia	◐	◐	◐	✓	✓	✓	●	●	●	●	●	✓	●	●	✓
Czech Republic	●	●	●	✓	✓	·	●	●	●	●	●	✓	●	●	✓
Denmark	●	●	●	·	·	·	●	●	●	●	●	·	●	●	·
Estonia	●	●	●	✓	✓	✓	●	●	●	●	●	✓	●	●	✓
Finland	●	●	●	✓	✓	✓	●	●	●	●	●	✓	●	●	·
France	◐	◐	◐	·	·	·	●	●	●	○	○	·	○	○	·
Germany	●	●	●	·	·	·	●	●	●	●	●	·	●	●	·
Greece	●	●	●	✓	✓	✓	●	●	●	●	●	·	●	●	·
Hungary	●	●	●	✓	✓	✓	●	●	●	●	●	✓	●	●	✓
Iceland	●	●	●	·	·	·	●	●	●	●	●	·	●	●	·
Ireland	●	●	●	✓	✓	✓	●	●	●	●	●	✓	●	●	✓
Italy	●	●	●	·	·	·	●	●	●	●	●	·	●	●	·
Latvia	●	●	●	✓	✓	✓	●	●	●	●	●	✓	●	●	✓
Liechtenstein	○	○	○	·	·	·	○	○	○	○	○	·	○	○	·
Lithuania	●	●	●	✓	✓	✓	●	●	●	●	●	✓	●	●	✓
Luxembourg	●	●	●	✓	✓	✓	○	○	○	○	○	✓	○	○	✓
Malta	◐	◐	◐	·	·	·	◐	◐	◐	◐	◐	·	◐	◐	·
Monaco	○	○	○	·	·	·	○	○	○	○	○	·	○	○	·
Netherlands	●	●	●	·	·	·	●	●	●	●	●	·	●	●	·
Norway	●	●	●	✓	✓	✓	●	●	●	●	●	·	●	●	✓
Poland	●	●	●	✓	✓	✓	●	●	●	●	●	✓	●	●	✓
Portugal	●	●	●	·	·	·	●	●	●	●	●	·	●	●	·
Republic of Moldova	◐	◐	◐	·	·	·	●	●	●	●	●	·	●	●	·
Romania	●	●	●	✓	✓	✓	●	●	●	●	●	✓	●	●	✓
Russian Federation	●	●	●	·	·	·	●	●	●	●	●	·	●	●	·
San Marino	○	○	○	✓	✓	✓	○	○	○	○	○	·	○	○	·
Serbia and Montenegro [b]	◐	○	○	·	·	·	●	●	○	○	○	·	○	○	·
Slovakia	●	●	●	✓	✓	✓	●	●	●	●	●	✓	●	●	✓
Slovenia	●	●	●	✓	✓	✓	●	●	●	●	●	✓	●	●	✓
Spain	●	●	●	·	·	·	●	●	●	●	●	·	●	●	·
Sweden	●	●	●	✓	✓	✓	●	●	●	●	●	✓	●	●	✓
Switzerland	●	●	●	✓	✓	✓	●	●	●	●	●	✓	●	●	✓
TFYR Macedonia [c]	●	●	◐	✓	·	·	◐	◐	◐	◐	◐	·			·
Ukraine	●	●	●	·	·	·	●	●	●	●	●	·	●	●	·
United Kingdom	●	●	●	·	·	·	●	●	●	●	●	·	●	●	·
Oceania															
Australia	●	●	●	·	·	·	●	●	●	●	●	·	●	●	·
Fiji	○	○	○	✓	✓	✓	○	○	○	○	○	·	○	○	·
French Polynesia	○	○	○	·	·	·	○	○	○	○	○	·	○	○	·

Legend

✓	Yes
·	No
○	Did not report data for any of the nine years considered (1995 - 2003).
◐	Reported data for one to four out of nine years.
●	Reported data for at least five out of nine years.

Table A4 (continued)
National reporting of statistics on selected economic characteristics, 1995 – 2003

Country or area	Economic activity						Unemployment			Occupation			Status in employment		
	Data reported from labour force surveys [a]			Census data reported			Data reported from labour force surveys [a]			Data reported from labour force surveys [a]		Census data reported	Data reported from labour force surveys [a]		Census data reported
	Total	By sex	By sex and age	Total	By sex	By sex and age	Total	By sex	By sex and age	Total	By sex	By sex	Total	By sex	By sex
Oceania (continued)															
Guam	O	O	O	·	·	·	O	O	O	O	O	·	O	O	·
Kiribati	O	O	O	✓	✓	·	O	O	O	O	O	✓	O	O	·
Marshall Islands	O	O	O	✓	✓	·	◑	◑	O	O	O	✓	O	O	✓
Micronesia (Fed. States of)	O	O	O	·	·	·	O	O	O	O	O	·	O	O	·
Nauru	O	O	O	·	·	·	O	O	O	O	O	·	O	O	·
New Caledonia	O	O	O	✓	✓	✓	◑	◑	◑	O	O	·	O	O	✓
New Zealand	●	●	●	✓	✓	✓	●	●	●	●	●	✓	●	●	✓
Palau	O	O	O	·	·	·	O	O	O	O	O	✓	O	O	·
Papua New Guinea	O	O	O	✓	✓	✓	◑	◑	O	O	O	·	O	O	·
Samoa	O	O	O	·	·	·	O	O	O	O	O	·	O	O	·
Solomon Islands	O	O	O	·	·	·	O	O	O	O	O	·	O	O	·
Tonga	O	O	O	✓	✓	✓	O	O	O	O	O	✓	O	O	✓
Tuvalu	O	O	O	·	·	·	O	O	O	O	O	·	O	O	·
Vanuatu	O	O	O	·	·	·	O	O	O	O	O	·	O	O	·

Legend

✓	Yes
·	No
O	Did not report data for any of the nine years considered (1995 - 2003).
◑	Reported data for one to four out of nine years.
●	Reported data for at least five out of nine years.

Sources:

Prepared by the United Nations Statistics Division, Department of Economic and Social Affairs, based on data from the International Labour Office, LABORSTA database (March 2005) and from the United Nations *Demographic Yearbook* system (November 2004).

Notes:

a   Includes a few household surveys (for economic activity and unemployment), censuses (for unemployment) and labour-related establishment surveys (for occupation).

b   As of 4 February 2003, the official name of the "Federal Republic of Yugoslavia" has been changed to "Serbia and Montenegro".

c   The former Yugoslav Republic of Macedonia.

Table A5
Population

Country or area	Population (thousands) 2005 W	Population (thousands) 2005 M	Annual population growth rate (%) 2000-2005	Urban population (%) 2005	Population under age 15 (%) 2005	Population aged 60 or over (%) 2005 W	Population aged 60 or over (%) 2005 M	Women per 100 men 2005 All ages	Women per 100 men 2005 60+	Women per 100 men 2005 80+	International migrants, women per 100 men 2000
Africa											
Algeria	16 277	16 577	1.5	60	30	7	6	98	118	168	82
Angola	8 081	7 861	2.8	37	46	4	4	103	123	158	88
Benin	4 186	4 253	3.2	46	44	5	4	98	133	160	94
Botswana	898	867	0.1	53	38	6	4	104	148	176	55
Burkina Faso	6 578	6 650	3.2	19	47	5	4	99	115	128	109
Burundi	3 863	3 684	3.0	11	45	5	3	105	156	189	112
Cameroon	8 203	8 119	1.9	53	41	6	5	101	118	142	81
Cape Verde	264	243	2.4	58	40	7	4	108	187	182	102
Central African Republic	2 069	1 969	1.3	44	43	7	5	105	134	172	104
Chad	4 925	4 824	3.4	26	47	5	4	102	122	152	86
Comoros	398	400	2.7	36	42	5	4	99	121	159	111
Congo	2 016	1 983	3.0	54	47	5	4	102	126	162	99
Côte d'Ivoire	8 924	9 230	1.6	46	42	5	5	97	91	117	81
Dem. Rep. of the Congo	29 007	28 542	2.8	33	47	5	4	102	128	167	86
Djibouti	397	396	2.1	85	41	5	4	100	119	157	93
Egypt	36 913	37 120	1.9	42	34	8	7	99	118	145	88
Equatorial Guinea	254	249	2.3	50	44	6	5	102	121	149	89
Eritrea	2 241	2 161	4.3	21	45	5	3	104	146	230	93
Ethiopia	38 917	38 514	2.4	16	45	5	4	101	116	141	93
Gabon	695	689	1.7	85	40	7	6	101	116	135	75
Gambia	765	752	2.9	26	40	6	6	102	114	134	89
Ghana	10 921	11 191	2.1	46	39	6	5	98	108	125	89
Guinea	4 584	4 818	2.2	36	44	6	5	95	111	132	112
Guinea-Bissau	803	784	3.0	36	48	5	4	102	120	151	100
Kenya	17 103	17 153	2.2	42	43	4	4	100	115	122	92
Lesotho	960	835	0.1	18	39	8	7	115	138	170	101
Liberia	1 645	1 638	1.4	48	47	4	3	100	120	154	82
Libyan Arab Jamahiriya	2 834	3 020	2.0	87	30	6	7	94	85	144	55
Madagascar	9 351	9 255	2.8	27	44	5	4	101	116	135	62
Malawi	6 487	6 397	2.3	17	47	5	4	101	113	139	106
Mali	6 782	6 737	3.0	34	48	5	4	101	131	145	93
Mauritania	1 551	1 518	3.0	64	43	6	5	102	120	137	72
Mauritius	627	618	1.0	44	25	11	8	101	134	192	104
Morocco	15 833	15 646	1.5	59	31	8	6	101	131	124	103
Mozambique	10 212	9 580	2.0	38	44	6	5	107	133	159	109
Namibia	1 024	1 007	1.4	33	42	6	5	102	123	147	89
Niger	6 821	7 136	3.4	23	49	4	3	96	120	130	109
Nigeria	64 971	66 558	2.2	48	44	5	4	98	117	142	87
Réunion	402	384	1.6	92	27	11	8	105	140	241	93
Rwanda	4 658	4 379	2.4	22	43	4	4	106	128	194	89
Sao Tome and Principe	79	78	2.3	38	39	6	5	101	119	129	88
Senegal	5 924	5 734	2.4	51	43	5	4	103	127	122	115
Seychelles	41[a]	40[a]	0.9	50	28[b]	12[b]	8[b]	103[a]	150[b]	..	68
Sierra Leone	2 801	2 725	4.1	40	43	6	5	103	122	148	73
Somalia	4 147	4 081	3.2	36	44	4	4	102	118	141	93
South Africa	24 141	23 291	0.8	58	33	8	6	104	143	250	73
Sudan	17 998	18 235	1.9	41	39	6	5	99	114	136	85

Notes:

Two dots (..) indicate that data are not available or are not reported separately.

a   Data refer to 2001.
b   Data refer to 1998.
c   Data refer to 1996.
d   Data refer to 2002.
e   Data refer to 2000.
f   For statistical purposes, the data for China do not include Hong Kong and Macao Special Administrative Regions (SAR).
g   Data refer to 2003.
h   Data refer to 1994.
i   Data for population aged 65 years and over.
j   As of 4 February 2003, the official name of the "Federal Republic of Yugoslavia" has been changed to "Serbia and Montenegro".
k   The former Yugoslav Republic of Macedonia.
l   Data refer to 1992.
m   Data refer to 1991.

Technical notes

Estimates and projections of the total population and population by age and sex are prepared by the Population Division, Department of Economic and Social Affairs, (DESA), United Nations, and revised every two years in order to incorporate new data. In general, the population figures are estimates of persons resident in the country or area at mid-year. They are usually based on population census data adjusted to the specified year, taking account of birth, death and international migration rates as determined from population surveys and registers and other national sources as available. Short-term residents and visitors in the country or area for less than one year are usually excluded. Indicators related to age and sex composition of the population have been calculated from estimates and projections of population by age group and sex described above. For small countries or areas, no estimates and projections were prepared; the figures shown are derived directly from official national statistics of population by age and sex.

The population growth rate shown is an estimate of the annual average over the five-year period indicated. The approach used in estimating rates of population growth assumes exponential growth.

The percentage of the population that is urban is based on estimates and projections prepared by the Population Division, DESA, United Nations. The urban-rural classification of population follows the national census definition and varies from one country or area to another. National definitions are usually based on criteria that may include any of the following: size of population in a locality, population density, distance between built-up areas, predominant type of economic activity, legal or administrative boundaries and such urban characteristics as specific services and facilities.

Estimates of the ratio of women to men among international migrants are taken from the database *Trends in Total Migrant Stock*, maintained by the Population Division, DESA, United Nations. Estimates of migrant stock are based on the number of foreign-born or the foreign residents in a country enumerated by national population censuses and sample surveys, and complemented by the number of refugees in a country. Statistics on the foreign-born provide a crude measure of the volume and composition of migration during an indefinite number of years prior to the census. International comparability of that indicator is affected, among other things, by the fact that some countries report data on non-citizens rather than on the foreign-born.

Table A6
Marriage, households and childbearing

Country or area	Population aged 15-19 ever married (%) 1995/2002		Singulate mean age at marriage 1995/2002		Legal age for marriage[a] around 2003		Average household size 1995/2002	Female-headed households (%) 1995/2003	Contraceptive use (%) 1995/2002	Total fertility rate (births per woman) 2000-2005	Births per 1,000 women aged 15-19 2000-2005
	W	M	W	M	W	M					
Africa											
Algeria	4[b]	..	26[b]	..	18	21	..	..	64	2.5	9
Angola	..	..	..	..	..	..	..	..	6	6.8	143
Benin	29	..	20	..	16	18	5.2	21	19	5.9	136
Botswana	5[b]	2[b]	27[b]	31[b]	21	21	4.8[b]	47[b]	40	3.2	79
Burkina Faso	35	1	19	26	18	21	6.5	9	14	6.7	165
Burundi	7[b]	1[b]	22[b]	26[b]	..	..	4.5[b]	25[b]	16	6.8	50
Cameroon	36	4	20	27	..	..	5.5	22	19	4.6	122
Cape Verde	7[b]	1[b]	26[b]	28[b]	18	18	5.0[b]	38[b]	53	3.8	94
Central African Republic	42[b]	8[b]	20[b]	24[b]	..	..	4.9[b]	21[b]	28	5.0	133
Chad	49	6	18	24	..	..	5.3	22	8	6.7	195
Comoros	12	3	24	28	..	..	6.3	32	26	4.9	59
Congo	..	..	..	..	..	..	..	..	..	6.3	146
Côte d'Ivoire	25	2	22	28	18	21	6.2	14[b]	15	5.1	133
Dem. Rep. of the Congo	..	..	..	..	..	..	..	..	31	6.7	230
Djibouti	..	..	..	..	..	..	6.6[b]	18[b]	..	5.1	57
Egypt	15	2	22	28	16	18	5.2	12	56	3.3	46
Equatorial Guinea	..	..	..	..	..	..	..	..	..	5.9	192
Eritrea	38	2	20	25	..	..	4.8	47	8	5.5	94
Ethiopia	30	3	21	26	18	18	4.8	24	8	5.9	96
Gabon	22	4	22	26	15	18	5.0	26	33	4.0	114
Gambia	39[b]	2[b]	20[b]	28[b]	..	..	..	..	10	4.7	127
Ghana	16	3	21	27	18	18	4.0	34	25	4.4	70
Guinea	46	2	19	28	..	..	6.6	13	6	5.9	201
Guinea-Bissau	..	..	..	..	..	..	7.9[b]	..	8	7.1	197
Kenya	17	1	22	26	18	18	4.3	32	39	5.0	97
Lesotho	18	2	21	26	..	..	..	..	30	3.6	39
Liberia	36	..	20	..	..	..	..	..	..	6.8	227
Libyan Arab Jamahiriya	1	< 1	29	32	..	..	..	..	40[c]	3.0	7
Madagascar	34	..	21	..	18	18	4.6	22	27	5.4	129
Malawi	37	4	19	24	18	18	4.4	27	31	6.1	163
Mali	50	5	18	26	18	20	5.3	11	8	6.9	209
Mauritania	28	1	22	29	..	..	5.8	29	8	5.8	104
Mauritius	11[b]	1[b]	24[b]	28[b]	18	18	3.9	17	75	2.0	33
Morocco	13[b]	1[b]	25[b]	30[b]	18	18	6.0[b]	15	50	2.8	25
Mozambique	47	4	18	23	..	..	4.6	27	6	5.5	104
Namibia	8[b]	..	26[b]	..	21	21	5.1	42	29[b]	4.0	58
Niger	62	4	18	24	21	21	5.9	13	14	7.9	271
Nigeria	28	3	21	27	..	..	5.0	17	13	5.8	153
Réunion	2[b]	< 1[b]	28[b]	30[b]	..	..	3.8[b]	..	67[b,e]	2.5	37
Rwanda	7	2	23	26	21	21	4.6	36	13[f]	5.7	49
Sao Tome and Principe	20[b]	2[b]	18[b]	23[b]	..	..	4.3[b]	33[b]	29	4.1	71
Senegal	29	..	22	..	..	..	9.0	18	13	5.0	87
Seychelles	..	..	..	..	..	..	..	..	..	2.0[g]	..
Sierra Leone	47[b]	6[b]	20[b]	28[b]	..	..	..	..	4	6.5	192
Somalia	..	..	..	..	..	..	..	..	..	6.4	71
South Africa	3	1	28	30	18	18	4.2	42	56	2.8	71
Sudan	21[b]	2[b]	23[b]	29[b]	..	..	6.3[b]	..	8[b,c,h]	4.4	55

Table A6 (continued)
Marriage, households and childbearing

Country or area	Population aged 15-19 ever married (%) 1995/2002		Singulate mean age at marriage 1995/2002		Legal age for marriage [a] around 2003		Average household size 1995/2002	Female-headed households (%) 1995/2003	Contraceptive use (%) 1995/2002	Total fertility rate (births per woman) 2000-2005	Births per 1,000 women aged 15-19 2000-2005
	W	M	W	M	W	M					
Africa (continued)											
Swaziland	9[b]	1[b]	26[b]	29[b]	..	..	..	..	28	4.0	39
Togo	20	2	21	27	17	20	5.4	24	26	5.4	104
Tunisia	3[b]	< 1[b]	27[b]	30[b]	20	20	..	..	60[b]	2.0	7
Uganda	32	7	20	23	18	18	4.8	28	23	7.1	211
United Rep. of Tanzania	25	3	21	25	18	18	5.0	23	25[f]	5.0	118
Western Sahara	..	..	..	..	..	..	..	..	..	3.9	61
Zambia	24	2	21	26	21	21	5.2	23	34	5.7	133
Zimbabwe	23	1	21	26	..	..	4.2	34	54[f]	3.6	97
North America											
Antigua and Barbuda	..	..	..	..	..	..	3.1[b]	..	..	..	..
Bahamas	4[b]	1[b]	27[b]	29[b]	18	18	4.1[b]	36[b]	..	2.3	61
Barbados	1[b]	< 1[b]	32[b]	34[b]	18	18	..	..	..	1.5	43
Belize	8[b]	1[b]	26[b]	28[b]	18	18	4.8[b]	22[b]	47[b,e]	3.2	87
Canada	3	1	27	30	18	18	2.6	36	75[f]	1.5	15
Costa Rica	20	..	21	..	18	18	4.3[b]	20[b]	80	2.3	78
Cuba	..	..	..	..	18	18	..	..	..	1.6	50
Dominica	..	..	..	..	16	16	..	..	..	..	..
Dominican Republic	29	4	21	26	18	18	3.9	28	70	2.7	93
El Salvador	16	4	22	25	18	18	4.1[b]	..	67	2.9	87
Grenada	..	..	..	..	..	..	..	..	54[b,e]	..	..
Guadeloupe	1[b]	< 1[b]	30[b]	32[b]	..	..	3.4[b]	..	..	2.1	19
Guatemala	26	..	20	..	18	18	5.3	20	43	4.6	115
Haiti	19	3	22	27	..	..	4.7	43	28[f]	4.0	64
Honduras	31	..	20	..	..	..	..	..	62	3.7	103
Jamaica	1[b]	< 1[b]	33[b]	35[b]	18	18	..	38[b]	66[e]	2.4	82
Martinique	1[b]	< 1[b]	31[b]	33[b]	..	..	3.4[b]	..	..	2.0	31
Mexico	17	6	23	25	18	18	4.3	21	68	2.4	70
Netherlands Antilles	1	< 1	30	33	..	..	3.3[b]	34[b]	..	2.1	29
Nicaragua	32	9	21	24	..	..	5.3	31	69	3.3	125
Panama	22	5	22	26	18	18	4.4[b]	22[b]	..	2.7	89
Puerto Rico	19	..	23	..	..	..	3.9[b]	32[b]	78	1.9	62
Saint Kitts and Nevis	..	..	..	..	..	..	..	..	..	2.6[g]	..
Saint Lucia	1[b]	< 1[b]	34[b]	35[b]	..	..	4.0[b]	43	..	2.2	63
St. Vincent/Grenadines	1[b]	< 1[b]	31[b]	34[b]	..	..	..	..	..	2.3	67
Trinidad and Tobago	9[b]	1[b]	27[b]	30[b]	18	18	4.1[b]	..	38	1.6	37
United States	4	2	26	29	18-19[i]	18-21[i]	2.6	47	76	2.0	51
South America											
Argentina	12[b]	3[b]	23[b]	26[b]	21[i]	21	3.7[b]	22[b]	..	2.4	61
Bolivia	12	5	23	25	..	..	4.2	20	53	4.0	84
Brazil	17	4	23	25	21	21	4.1	25	77	2.3	90
Chile	12[b]	5[b]	23[b]	26[b]	18	18	4.0[b]	25[b]	30[b]	2.0	62
Colombia	18	3	23	27	18	18	4.2	28	77	2.6	80
Ecuador	22	7	22	25	18	18	4.8[b]	..	66	2.8	85
French Guiana	1	< 1	32	34	..	..	3.3	..	..	3.4	93
Guyana	7[b]	1[b]	28[b]	30[b]	..	..	..	..	37	2.3	67

Table A6 (continued)
Marriage, households and childbearing

Country or area	Population aged 15-19 ever married (%) 1995/2002		Singulate mean age at marriage 1995/2002		Legal age for marriage[a] around 2003		Average household size 1995/2002	Female-headed households (%) 1995/2003	Contraceptive use (%) 1995/2002	Total fertility rate (births per woman) 2000-2005	Births per 1,000 women aged 15-19 2000-2005
	W	M	W	M	W	M					
South America (continued)											
Paraguay	17[b]	2[b]	22[b]	26[b]	18	18	4.6	26	57	3.9	68
Peru	13	3	23	27	18	18	4.5	20	69	2.9	55
Suriname	..	..	..	..	20	20	..	..	42	2.6	45
Uruguay	13	3	23	26	18	18	..	..	..	2.3	70
Venezuela (Bolivarian Rep.of)	18[b]	5[b]	22[b]	25[b]	..	..	4.8[b]	21[b]	..	2.7	92
Asia											
Afghanistan	..	..	..	..	..	..	..	..	5	7.5	132
Armenia	9	..	23	..	17	18	4.3	29	61[f]	1.3	31
Azerbaijan	13	2	24	27	17	18	4.7	26	55	1.9	32
Bahrain	7[b]	< 1[b]	26[b]	28[b]	18	18	5.6[b]	..	62[f,k]	2.5	18
Bangladesh	48	..	19	..	18	20	5.2	9	54	3.2	132
Bhutan	27[b]	8[b]	21[b]	24[b]	..	..	..	..	19[b]	4.4	38
Brunei Darussalam	8[b]	1[b]	25[b]	27[b]	..	..	5.8[b]	..	..	2.5	31
Cambodia	12	3	22	24	18	20	5.4	25	24[f]	4.1	51
China[l]	1	1	23	25	20[m]	22[m]	3.5	..	84	1.7	5
Hong Kong SAR	2	1	29	31	..	..	3.2	29	86[b]	0.9	5
Macao SAR	2[b]	1[b]	27[b]	29[b]	..	..	3.6[b]	26	..	0.8	5
Cyprus	8[b]	1[b]	23[b]	27[b]	18	18	3.1	14[b]	..	1.6	8
Dem. People's Rep. of Korea	..	..	..	..	18	18	..	..	62[b]	2.0	2
Georgia	16	..	24	..	..	..	..	..	41	1.5	35
India	30	4	20	25	18	21	5.4	10	48	3.1	80
Indonesia	13	3	23	26	..	..	4.3	12	60	2.4	55
Iran (Islamic Rep. of)	18	3	22	25	..	..	4.8	6[b]	73	2.1	22
Iraq	21	6	22	26	18	18	..	..	..	4.8	42
Israel	4	< 1	25	28	17	17	3.3	..	..	2.9	16
Japan	1	< 1	29	31	20	20	3.0[b]	20	59[b]	1.3	4
Jordan	8[b]	2[b]	25[b]	28[b]	18	18	5.7	12	56	3.5	27
Kazakhstan	7	1	23	26	18	18	3.6	33	66[f]	2.0	31
Kuwait	5	< 1	25	28	15[d]	17	6.4	..	50[f,k]	2.4	25
Kyrgyzstan	11	1	22	25	18	18	4.3	29	29	2.7	34
Lao People's Dem. Rep.	27	..	21	..	..	..	6.5	..	32	4.8	91
Lebanon	..	..	..	..	..	..	..	..	61	2.3	27
Malaysia	5	1	25	29	18	..	4.8[b]	18[b]	55[b]	2.9	18
Maldives	12	1	22	26	..	..	6.6	..	..	4.3	70
Mongolia	6	1	24	26	..	..	4.3	16	67	2.4	54
Myanmar	11[b]	3[b]	25[b]	26[b]	18	..	..	..	33	2.5	21
Nepal	40	11	19	23	20	20	5.4	16	39	3.7	123
Occupied Palestinian Territory	24	2	22	25	..	..	6.4	..	..	5.6	93
Oman	16	1	22	26	18	18	7.0[b]	..	24[f,k]	3.8	50
Pakistan	21	6	21	26	16	18	6.7[b]	7[b]	28	4.3	70
Philippines	10	3	24	27	18	18	4.8	15	49	3.2	39
Qatar	4	< 1	26	29	..	..	5.5	..	43[f,k]	3.0	19
Republic of Korea	1	< 1	26	29	20	20	3.1	17[b]	81	1.2	3
Saudi Arabia	16	1	22	26	..	..	..	..	32[f,k]	4.1	35
Singapore	1	< 1	27	30	..	..	4.2[b]	..	62	1.4	6
Sri Lanka	7[b]	..	25[b]	..	..	..	..	..	66[b]	2.0	20

Table A6 (continued)
Marriage, households and childbearing

Country or area	Population aged 15-19 ever married (%) 1995/2002		Singulate mean age at marriage 1995/2002		Legal age for marriage[a] around 2003		Average household size 1995/2002	Female-headed households (%) 1995/2003	Contraceptive use (%) 1995/2002	Total fertility rate (births per woman) 2000-2005	Births per 1,000 women aged 15-19 2000-2005
	W	M	W	M	W	M					
Asia (continued)											
Syrian Arab Republic	..	..	..	..	..	..	6.3[b]	..	36[c]	3.5	36
Tajikistan	12	1	21	23	..	..	..	..	34	3.8	32
Thailand	15[b]	4[b]	24[b]	26[b]	17	17	4.4[b]	..	72	1.9	49
Timor-Leste	..	..	..	..	..	..	..	..	..	7.8	182
Turkey	16	..	22	..	17	17	4.3	10	64	2.5	45
Turkmenistan	6	..	23	..	..	..	5.1	27	62[f]	2.8	17
United Arab Emirates	19	3	23	26	..	..	..	..	28[k]	2.5	22
Uzbekistan	13	..	21	..	..	..	5.2	22	68	2.7	37
Viet Nam	8	..	22	..	..	..	4.4	27	79	2.3	21
Yemen	27	..	21	..	..	..	7.0	10	21	6.2	98
Europe											
Albania	8	1	23	27	..	..	..	..	75	2.3	16
Andorra	..	..	..	..	..	..	..	..	..	..	..
Austria	3[b]	1[b]	26[b]	29[b]	18	18	2.4	22	47[n]	1.4	14
Belarus	6	1	23	25	18	18	2.6	..	50	1.2	28
Belgium	1	< 1	28	30	18	18	..	..	78[b]	1.7	9
Bosnia and Herzegovina	..	..	..	..	..	..	..	..	48	1.3	24
Bulgaria	16	3	21	25	18	18	..	..	42	1.2	46
Croatia	2	< 1	26	30	18	18	3.1[b]	..	..	1.3	15
Czech Republic	1	< 1	25	28	18	18	2.4	29	72	1.2	12
Denmark	1	< 1	31	33	18	18	2.3[b]	42[b]	..	1.8	7
Estonia	9	3	22	25	18	18	2.3	56	70[b,o]	1.4	24
Finland	1	< 1	30	32	18	18	2.2	42	..	1.7	11
France	< 1	< 1	30	32	18	18	2.6[b]	24[b]	75[b,n]	1.9	14
Germany	..	..	..	..	18	18	..	30[b]	75[b]	1.3	11
Greece	6[b]	1[b]	25[b]	29[b]	18[p]	18[p]	2.8	28	..	1.3	10
Hungary	2	< 1	26	29	18	18	2.6	28	77[b,n]	1.3	22
Iceland	1	< 1	31	33	18	18	..	..	..	2.0	19
Ireland	< 1	< 1	31	32	..	..	3.3[b]	26[b]	..	1.9	15
Italy	1	< 1	28	32	18	18	2.6	..	60	1.3	7
Latvia	1	< 1	27	29	18	18	2.9	59	48[n]	1.3	18
Liechtenstein	..	..	..	..	18	18	..	..	..	1.6[g]	..
Lithuania	2	< 1	25	27	18	18	2.5	50	47	1.3	22
Luxembourg	2[b]	< 1[b]	26[b]	29[b]	..	..	2.5	27	..	1.7	9
Malta	3	< 1	22	26	16	16	..	..	..	1.5	17
Monaco	..	..	..	..	..	..	..	..	..	..	..
Netherlands	1	< 1	30	33	18	18	..	24	79[b,n]	1.7	5
Norway	< 1	< 1	31	34	18	18	2.3	39	..	1.8	10
Poland	2	< 1	25	28	18	18	2.8	40	49[b,n]	1.3	15
Portugal	6[b]	1[b]	24[b]	27[b]	18	18	3.1[b]	20[b]	..	1.5	20
Republic of Moldova	12	2	21	24	..	..	..	..	62	1.2	33
Romania	6	< 1	24	27	..	..	2.9	27	64	1.3	36
Russian Federation	11	3	22	24	18	18	..	..	73[q]	1.3	30
San Marino	..	..	..	..	18	18	2.8[b]	..	..	..	..
Serbia and Montenegro[r]	11[b]	2[b]	23[b]	27[b]	18	18	3.6[b]	22[b]	58	1.7	25
Slovakia	2	< 1	25	28	..	..	3.2	34	74[b]	1.2	21

Table A6 (continued)
Marriage, households and childbearing

Country or area	Population aged 15-19 ever married (%) 1995/2002		Singulate mean age at marriage 1995/2002		Legal age for marriage[a] around 2003		Average household size 1995/2002	Female-headed households (%) 1995/2003	Contraceptive use (%) 1995/2002	Total fertility rate (births per woman) 2000-2005	Births per 1,000 women aged 15-19 2000-2005
	W	M	W	M	W	M					
Europe (continued)											
Slovenia	< 1	< 1	30	32	18	18	2.9	49	74[b]	1.2	6
Spain	2[b]	1[b]	26[b]	28[b]	18	18	..	..	81[n]	1.3	10
Sweden	< 1	< 1	32	35	18	18	2.1[b]	37[b]	..	1.6	7
Switzerland	1	< 1	29	32	18	18	2.4[b]	28[b]	82[b]	1.4	5
TFYR Macedonia[s]	9	1	23[b]	27[b]	..	..	3.6	..	..	1.5	25
Ukraine	10	..	22	..	17	18	..	..	68	1.1	30
United Kingdom	2[b]	1[b]	26[b]	28[b]	18	18	..	..	84	1.7	28
Oceania											
Australia	1	< 1	29	31	..	..	..	..	..	1.7	16
Fiji	10	2	23	26	21	21	..	..	..	2.9	41
French Polynesia	1	< 1	30	32	..	..	..	..	..	2.4	44
Guam	6[b]	2[b]	24[b]	27[b]	..	..	4.0[b]	21[b]	..	2.9	72
Kiribati	..	..	..	..	..	..	6.4[b]	..	..	..	..
Marshall Islands	..	..	..	..	..	..	..	..	..	5.7[g]	..
Micronesia (Fed. States of)	10[b]	4[b]	..	..	..	..	..	..	..	4.4	37
Nauru	..	..	..	..	..	..	..	..	..	..	..
New Caledonia	1	< 1	30	32	..	..	..	..	..	2.4	31
New Zealand	7	3	25	27	20	20	2.8[b]	55	75	2.0	26
Palau	..	..	..	..	..	..	5.0[b]	..	..	..	..
Papua New Guinea	21	..	21	..	21	21	..	8	26	4.1	67
Samoa	8	1	24	27	16	18	..	..	34[b]	4.4	37
Solomon Islands	..	..	..	..	..	..	..	..	..	4.3	51
Tonga	5	2	26	28	..	..	..	..	..	3.5	13
Tuvalu	..	..	..	..	..	..	..	..	..	..	..
Vanuatu	12	2	23	25	..	..	..	..	15[b]	4.2	52

Sources:

For percentage aged 15–19 years ever married and for singulate mean age at marriage: United Nations, *World Fertility Report 2003* (United Nations publication, Sales No. E.04.XIII.10).

For legal age for marriage: Population Division, Department of Economic and Social Affairs, United Nations, "Eighth and ninth United Nations inquiry on population and development", supplemented by periodic country reports to the Committee on the Elimination of All Forms of Discrimination against Women (CEDAW).

For average household size and percentage female-headed households: United Nations *Demographic Yearbook* system (January 2005), supplemented by Demographic and Health Survey national reports, and *Women's Indicators and Statistics Database (Wistat)*, Version 4, CD-ROM (United Nations publication, Sales No. E.00.XVII.4).

For contraceptive use: Demographic and Health Survey national reports; Reproductive Health Survey national reports; Gulf Family Health Survey national reports; United Nations, *World Population Monitoring, 2002* (United Nations publication, Sales No. E.02.XIII.14); and Centers for Disease Control and Prevention and ORC Macro, *Reproductive, Maternal and Child Health in Eastern Europe and Eurasia: A Comparative Report* (Atlanta; and Calverton, Maryland, 2003).

For total fertility rate: United Nations, *World Population Prospects: The 2004 Revision,* Comprehensive CD-ROM edition (United Nations publication, Sales No. E.05.XIII.11), supplemented by United Nations *Demographic Yearbook 2000* (United Nations publication, Sales No. E/F.02.XIII.1) and *Demographic Yearbook 2001* (United Nations publication, Sales No. E/F.03.XIII.1).

For births per 1,000 women aged 15-19: United Nations, *World Population Prospects: The 2004 Revision,* Comprehensive CD-ROM edition (United Nations publication, Sales No. E.05.XIII.11).

Notes:

Two dots (..) indicate that data are not available or are not reported separately.

< 1 Indicates magnitude nil or less than half of the unit employed.

a   In many countries a lower age at marriage is allowed with parental consent.
b   Data refer to a year between 1990 and 1994.
c   Adjusted from source to exclude breastfeeding.
d   With the consent of the woman's guardian and the woman herself or the person acting on behalf of either.
e   Including visiting unions.
f   Including the lactational amenorrhoea method and/or breastfeeding if reported as the current contraceptive method.
g   Data refer to a year between 1997 and 2001.
h   North Sudan only.
i   The legal minimum age at marriage varies by State.
j   Exceptions require legal recourse – acceptable only if the woman is pregnant by the man she wishes to marry.
k   From a health survey covering only households of nationals of the country.
l   For statistical purposes, the data for China do not include Hong Kong and Macao Special Administrative Regions (SAR).
m   Exceptions apply.
n   Respondents whose contraceptive status is unknown are considered non-users of contraception. The percentage of respondents in this category is 45.7 in Austria, 19.5 in Canada, 18.4 in Finland, 6.2 in France, 4.1 in Hungary, 29.3 in Latvia, 0.0 in Netherlands, 1.5 in Norway, 32.1 in Poland and 0.1 in Spain.
o   For all sexually active women of childbearing age.
p   Court may permit marriage of minors if justified.
q   For women aged 15-44, in unions, living in the cities of Ivanovo, Yekaterinburg and Perm.
r   As of 4 February 2003, the official name of the "Federal Republic of Yugoslavia" has been changed to "Serbia and Montenegro".
s   The former Yugoslav Republic of Macedonia.

Technical notes

The indicators "percentage aged 15-19 years ever married" and "singulate mean age at marriage" are derived from population censuses or nationally representative household surveys. All individuals who have ever been married are included in the count of ever-married persons, regardless of their current marital status.

Singulate mean age at marriage is an estimate of the average age at which women or men marry for the first time. It is the average number of years lived prior to first marriage by a hypothetical cohort, if they marry before age 50. Singulate mean age at marriage is calculated on the basis of a single census or survey according to procedures described by Hajnal in "Age at marriage and proportions marrying" (Population Studies, vol. 7, No. 2).

The legal age for marriage shown in the table is the legal minimum age at which marriage can be performed without parental consent. Marriage is defined in terms of the laws of the individual country or area. In most countries or areas, a lower minimum legal age than the one shown is specified for marriage with parental consent.

Average household size and percentage of households headed by women are based mainly on population census results, supplemented by data from nationally representative sample surveys. The average household size is calculated from the total household population and the total number of households. In most censuses, persons not resident in a given household at the date of the census are not considered members of that household. However, a few national population censuses may include some categories of absent household members.

The two most commonly recognized concepts of households are the "housekeeping concept" and the "household-dwelling" concept. The "housekeeping concept" is based on the arrangements made by persons, individually or in groups, for providing themselves with food or other essentials for living. A household may be either (a) a one-person household, in which a person makes provision for his or her own food or other essentials for living without combining with any other person to form part of a multi-person household, or (b) a multi-person household, that is, a group of two or more persons living together who make common provision for food or other essentials for living. The persons in the group may pool their incomes and may, to a greater or lesser extent, have a common budget; they may be related or unrelated persons. The "household-dwelling" concept views all persons living in a housing unit as belonging to the same household. According to this concept, there is one household per occupied housing unit.

The head of the household is defined as that person in the household or the family who is acknowledged as such by the other members. However, it is important to recognize that many countries use the concept of reference person in listing household members and that this person may or may not be the "household head". Where this is the practice, the "household head" identified in tabulations is, in reality, the reference person and should be treated with caution. Even in countries that use the concept of head of household, the procedures followed in applying the concept may distort the true picture, particularly with regard to women heads of households. Nonetheless, for most countries, this is the only practical way of identifying households for which women are responsible.

Contraceptive use pertains to current use of contraceptives by women of reproductive age currently married or in a union, unless otherwise indicated, and includes all contraceptive methods, traditional as well as modern. Data on contraceptive use are taken mainly from representative national sample surveys of women of reproductive age.

The total fertility rate is defined as the number of children that would be born to a woman if she were to live to the end of her childbearing years and bear children in accordance with prevailing age-specific fertility rates.

The indicator "births per 1,000 women aged 15-19 years" refers to the number of children born alive in one year per 1,000 women aged 15-19.

Table A7
Health

Country or area	Life expectancy 2000-2005				Infant mortality rate (per 1,000 live births) 2000-2005		People with HIV/AIDS at the end of 2003		Maternal mortality ratio 2000	Percentage pregnant women receiving prenatal care 1995/2003	Percentage deliveries attended by skilled attendant 1995/2003
	at birth		at age 60				Estimated number[a] (thousands)	Percentage women among adults			
	W	M	W	M	W	M					
Africa											
Algeria	72	70	20	17	36	38	9	16	140[b]	79	92
Angola	42	39	15	14	127	150	240	59	1 700[b]	..	45
Benin	55	53	17	15	101	109	68	56	850	88	66
Botswana	37	36	18	16	46	56	350	58	100[b]	99	94
Burkina Faso	48	47	16	15	116	127	300	56	1 000	72	38
Burundi	44	42	16	15	97	115	250	59	1 000[b]	93	25
Cameroon	47	45	16	15	88	101	560	56	730	77	60
Cape Verde	73	67	19	16	21	38	..	..	150[b]	..	89
Central African Republic	40	38	16	15	87	109	260	54	1 100	75[c]	44
Chad	45	43	16	15	106	126	200	56	1 100	51	16
Comoros	65	61	17	15	50	65	..	..	480[b]	87	62
Congo	53	51	17	15	63	81	90	56	510[b]	..	..
Côte d'Ivoire	47	45	16	15	111	126	570	57	690[b]	84	63
Dem. Rep. of the Congo	44	42	16	15	109	127	1 100	57	990[b]	72	61
Djibouti	54	51	16	15	85	101	9	56	730[b]	..	61
Egypt	72	67	18	16	33	40	12	13	84	54	69
Equatorial Guinea	44	43	16	15	94	109	..	..	880[b]	..	65
Eritrea	55	52	15	12	61	68	60	56	630	..	28
Ethiopia	49	47	16	15	92	107	1 500	55	850	27	6
Gabon	55	54	18	17	54	62	48	58	420	94	86
Gambia	57	54	17	16	71	83	7	57	540[b]	92	55
Ghana	57	56	18	17	60	65	350	56	540[b]	90	47
Guinea	54	53	17	16	104	107	140	55	740	74	35
Guinea-Bissau	46	43	16	15	110	129	..	..	1 100[b]	89	35
Kenya	46	48	18	16	62	74	1 200	65	1 000	88	42
Lesotho	38	35	17	15	61	72	320	57	550[b]	91	60
Liberia	44	41	15	14	132	151	100	56	760[b]	..	51
Libyan Arab Jamahiriya	76	71	21	17	19	20	10	..	97[b]	..	94
Madagascar	57	54	17	16	74	84	140	58	550	91	46
Malawi	40	40	17	15	106	116	900	57	1 800	94	61
Mali	48	47	16	14	128	139	140	59	1 200	53	41
Mauritania	54	51	16	15	89	104	10	57	1 000	63	57
Mauritius	76	69	20	16	12	17	..	..	24	..	99
Morocco	72	67	19	17	33	43	15	..	220	32[d]	40
Mozambique	43	41	16	15	93	108	1 300	56	1 000[b]	71	48
Namibia	49	48	18	16	41	47	210	55	300[b]	85	76
Niger	44	44	15	14	149	156	70	56	1 600[b]	39	16
Nigeria	44	43	16	15	109	120	3 600	58	800[b]	61	35
Réunion	80	71	23	17	7	8	..	..	..	..	..
Rwanda	45	42	16	15	108	123	250	57	1 400	93	31
Sao Tome and Principe	64	62	18	17	81	83	..	..	..	91	79
Senegal	57	54	17	16	79	88	44	56	690[b]	82	58
Seychelles	..	..	..	..	..	..	..	..	..	..	..
Sierra Leone	42	39	14	13	154	176	..	..	2 000[b]	82	42
Somalia	47	45	15	14	119	133	..	..	1 100[b]	..	34
South Africa	51	47	18	14	40	46	5 300	57	230[b]	89	84
Sudan	58	55	17	16	66	78	400	58	590[b]	..	87

Table A7 (continued)
Health

Country or area	Life expectancy 2000-2005				Infant mortality rate (per 1,000 live births) 2000-2005		People with HIV/AIDS at the end of 2003		Maternal mortality ratio 2000	Percentage pregnant women receiving prenatal care 1995/2003	Percentage deliveries attended by skilled attendant 1995/2003
	at birth		at age 60				Estimated number[a] (thousands)	Percentage women among adults			
	W	M	W	M	W	M					
Africa (continued)											
Swaziland	33	32	17	15	66	80	220	55	370[b]	..	70
Togo	56	52	18	16	86	99	110	56	570	78	49
Tunisia	75	71	20	17	20	24	1	..	120	..	90
Uganda	47	46	17	16	76	87	530	60	880	92	39
United Rep. of Tanzania	46	46	17	15	98	111	1 600	56	1 500	96	36
Western Sahara	66	62	17	16	48	59	..	..	..	..	..
Zambia	37	38	16	15	88	102	920	57	750	94	43
Zimbabwe	37	38	18	16	57	68	1 800	58	1 100	82	73
North America											
Antigua and Barbuda	..	..	..	..	..	..	..	..	..	..	100
Bahamas	73	66	23	19	12	16	6	48	60	..	99
Barbados	78	71	22	18	10	12	3	32	95	89	91
Belize	75	69	22	20	29	32	4	37	140	..	83
Canada	82	77	25	21	5	5	56	24	5	..	98
Costa Rica	81	76	24	21	9	12	12	33	25	..	98
Cuba	79	75	23	20	5	7	3	33	33	..	100
Dominica	..	..	..	..	..	..	..	..	..	..	100
Dominican Republic	71	64	20	18	29	40	88	27	150[b]	100	98
El Salvador	74	68	22	19	24	29	29	34	150[b]	..	90
Grenada	..	..	..	..	..	..	..	..	..	..	100
Guadeloupe	82	75	25	20	6	8	..	..	..	..	..
Guatemala	71	63	21	20	33	44	78	42	240	86	41
Haiti	52	51	17	16	58	66	280	58	680	79	24
Honduras	70	66	22	20	27	36	63	56	110	..	56
Jamaica	73	69	22	20	14	16	22	48	87	..	95
Martinique	82	75	25	20	6	8	..	..	..	..	..
Mexico	77	72	22	21	18	23	160	33	83	..	86
Netherlands Antilles	79	73	22	18	10	16	..	..	..	..	..
Nicaragua	72	67	20	19	26	34	6	34	230[b]	85	67
Panama	77	72	23	21	17	24	16	41	160	..	90
Puerto Rico	80	72	24	19	9	11	..	..	..	..	..
Saint Kitts and Nevis	..	..	..	..	..	..	..	..	..	..	100
Saint Lucia	74	71	20	18	13	17	..	..	..	..	100
St. Vincent/Grenadines	74	68	19	17	19	32	..	..	..	..	100[e]
Trinidad and Tobago	73	67	21	18	11	16	29	50	110	96	96
United States	80	75	24	20	7	7	950	26	14	..	99
South America											
Argentina	78	71	23	18	13	17	130	20	70	..	99
Bolivia	66	62	19	17	51	60	5	27	420[b]	84	65
Brazil	74	66	22	19	24	31	660	37	260	84	88
Chile	81	75	24	20	7	9	26	33	30	..	100
Colombia	75	69	22	19	22	29	190	34	130	90	86
Ecuador	77	71	24	22	21	29	21	34	130	56	69
French Guiana	78	73	22	18	11	17	..	..	..	..	..
Guyana	66	60	19	16	41	57	11	55	170	88	86

Table A7 (continued)
Health

Country or area	Life expectancy 2000-2005 at birth W	at birth M	at age 60 W	at age 60 M	Infant mortality rate (per 1,000 live births) 2000-2005 W	2000-2005 M	People with HIV/AIDS at the end of 2003 Estimated number[a] (thousands)	Percentage women among adults	Maternal mortality ratio 2000	Percentage pregnant women receiving prenatal care 1995/2003	Percentage deliveries attended by skilled attendant 1995/2003
South America (continued)											
Paraguay	73	69	20	18	32	42	15	26	170	..	61
Peru	72	67	21	18	30	37	82	34	410	85	59
Suriname	73	66	19	17	20	31	5	34	110	91	85
Uruguay	79	72	23	18	11	15	6	33	20	..	100
Venezuela (Bolivarian Rep. of)	76	70	22	20	16	19	110	32	78	..	94
Asia											
Afghanistan	46	46	15	14	145	152	..	..	1 900[b]	52	14
Armenia	75	68	20	17	28	32	3	36	55[b]	82	97
Azerbaijan	70	63	21	17	73	78	1	..	94	70	84
Bahrain	76	73	20	18	14	14	<1	..	33	63	98
Bangladesh	63	62	17	15	57	61	..	..	380	39	14
Bhutan	64	61	18	17	53	59	..	..	420[b]	..	24
Brunei Darussalam	79	74	22	18	5	7	<1	..	37	..	99
Cambodia	60	52	18	16	90	100	170	30	450	44	32
China[f]	73	70	20	17	42	28	840	23	56	..	97
Hong Kong SAR	85	79	26	22	4	4	3	35	..	..	..
Macao SAR	82	78	24	21	7	8	..	..	..	..	..
Cyprus	81	76	23	20	6	7	..	..	47	..	..
Dem. People's Rep. of Korea	66	60	17	13	43	49	..	..	67[b]	98	97
Georgia	74	67	20	17	36	45	3	33	32[b]	91	96
India	65	62	18	16	68	68	5 100	38	540	65	43
Indonesia	69	65	18	16	37	48	110	14	230[b]	97	66
Iran (Islamic Rep. of)	72	69	18	17	33	34	31	12	76	..	90
Iraq	60	57	16	15	88	100	<1	..	250[b]	..	72
Israel	82	78	24	21	5	5	3	..	13	..	..
Japan	85	78	27	22	3	3	12	24	10	..	100
Jordan	73	70	19	17	22	25	1	..	41	99	100
Kazakhstan	69	58	19	14	50	71	17	34	210[b]	82	99
Kuwait	79	75	22	19	10	10	..	..	12	83	98
Kyrgyzstan	71	63	20	16	50	60	4	..	110[b]	88	98
Lao People's Dem. Rep.	56	53	17	16	83	93	2	..	650[b]	44	19
Lebanon	74	70	19	17	18	27	3	..	150[b]	..	88
Malaysia	75	71	19	17	9	12	52	17	41	..	97
Maldives	66	67	17	16	48	38	..	..	110[b]	98	70
Mongolia	66	62	18	15	55	61	<1	..	110	..	99
Myanmar	63	57	18	17	66	83	330	30	360[b]	..	56
Nepal	62	61	17	15	64	65	61	27	740	49	11
Occupied Palestinian Territory	74	71	19	17	19	23	..	..	..	..	..
Oman	76	73	20	18	14	17	1	..	87[b]	77	95
Pakistan	63	63	17	17	81	76	74	12	500[b]	36	20
Philippines	72	68	19	17	23	33	9	22	200	94	60
Qatar	76	71	20	18	10	13	..	..	7	62	99
Republic of Korea	80	73	23	18	4	4	8	11	20	..	100
Saudi Arabia	74	70	19	17	19	26	..	..	23	77	91
Singapore	81	77	23	20	3	3	4	24	15	..	100
Sri Lanka	77	71	21	17	13	21	4	17	92	..	97

Table A7 (continued)
Health

Country or area	Life expectancy 2000-2005				Infant mortality rate (per 1,000 live births) 2000-2005		People with HIV/AIDS at the end of 2003		Maternal mortality ratio 2000	Percentage pregnant women receiving prenatal care 1995/2003	Percentage deliveries attended by skilled attendant 1995/2003
	at birth		at age 60				Estimated number [a] (thousands)	Percentage women among adults			
	W	M	W	M	W	M					
Asia (continued)											
Syrian Arab Republic	75	71	19	17	15	21	<1	..	160 [b]	..	76g
Tajikistan	66	61	20	17	85	94	<1	..	100 [b]	75	71
Thailand	74	66	20	17	15	24	570	36	44	..	99
Timor-Leste	56	54	16	14	88	99	..	..	660 [b]	..	24
Turkey	71	66	18	16	37	46	..	..	70 [b]	67	83
Turkmenistan	67	58	19	15	70	87	<1	..	31 [b]	87	97
United Arab Emirates	81	76	23	20	9	9	..	..	54 [b]	97	99
Uzbekistan	70	63	20	16	52	64	11	34	24 [b]	95	96
Viet Nam	72	68	20	18	26	34	220	33	130 [b]	70	85
Yemen	62	59	17	15	64	74	12	..	570	34	22
Europe											
Albania	77	71	21	17	22	28	..	..	55 [b]	81	99
Andorra	..	..	..	..	..	..	..	..	..	..	..
Austria	82	76	24	20	4	5	10	22	5	..	100g
Belarus	74	62	19	14	12	18	..	..	36	..	100
Belgium	82	76	25	20	4	5	10	35	10	..	..
Bosnia and Herzegovina	77	71	20	17	12	15	1	..	31	99	100
Bulgaria	76	69	20	16	12	15	<1	..	32	..	..
Croatia	78	71	21	17	7	7	<1	..	10	..	100
Czech Republic	79	72	21	17	5	6	3	32	9	99g	100
Denmark	79	75	22	19	5	5	5	18	7	..	..
Estonia	77	65	21	15	8	12	8	34	38	..	100
Finland	82	75	24	19	4	4	2	..	5	..	100
France	83	76	26	20	4	5	120	27	17	..	99g
Germany	81	76	24	19	4	5	43	22	9	..	..
Greece	81	76	23	20	6	7	9	20	10	..	..
Hungary	77	68	21	16	8	9	3	..	11	..	..
Iceland	83	79	25	22	3	4	<1	..	0	..	..
Ireland	80	75	23	19	5	6	3	31	4	..	100
Italy	83	77	25	21	5	5	140	32	5	..	..
Latvia	77	66	22	15	10	11	8	33	61	..	100
Liechtenstein	..	..	..	..	..	..	..	..	..	..	..
Lithuania	78	66	22	16	7	11	1	..	19	..	..
Luxembourg	81	75	24	19	5	5	<1	..	28	..	100
Malta	81	76	23	19	7	7	<1	..	..	..	98g
Monaco	..	..	..	..	..	..	..	..	..	..	..
Netherlands	81	76	24	19	4	5	19	20	16	..	100
Norway	82	77	24	21	3	4	2	..	10	..	..
Poland	78	70	22	17	8	9	14	..	10	..	100
Portugal	81	74	23	19	5	6	22	20	8	..	100
Republic of Moldova	71	64	18	15	24	28	6	..	36	99	99
Romania	75	68	20	16	16	20	7	..	58	89	98
Russian Federation	72	59	19	14	15	19	860	34	65	96	99
San Marino	..	..	..	..	..	..	..	..	..	..	..
Serbia and Montenegro [h]	76	71	20	17	12	14	10	20	9	..	93
Slovakia	78	70	21	16	7	8	<1	..	10	..	99

Table A7 (continued)
Health

Country or area	Life expectancy 2000-2005				Infant mortality rate (per 1,000 live births) 2000-2005		People with HIV/AIDS at the end of 2003		Maternal mortality ratio 2000	Percentage pregnant women receiving prenatal care 1995/2003	Percentage deliveries attended by skilled attendant 1995/2003
	at birth		at age 60				Estimated number [a] (thousands)	Percentage women among adults			
	W	M	W	M	W	M					
Europe (continued)											
Slovenia	80	73	23	18	5	6	<1	..	17	..	100
Spain	83	76	25	20	4	5	140	21	5	..	..
Sweden	82	78	24	21	3	4	4	26	8	..	..
Switzerland	83	78	26	21	4	5	13	30	7	..	..
TFYR Macedonia [i]	76	71	20	17	15	17	<1	..	13	..	98
Ukraine	72	60	19	14	13	18	360	33	38	90	99
United Kingdom	81	76	23	20	5	6	51	30	11	..	99
Oceania											
Australia	83	78	25	21	5	5	14	7	6	..	100
Fiji	70	66	17	14	20	23	1	..	75 [b]	..	100
French Polynesia	76	71	20	17	8	9	..	..	..	..	..
Guam	77	72	20	18	8	11	..	..	..	..	..
Kiribati	67 [j]	58 [j]	..	..	..	..	..	..	..	..	85
Marshall Islands	69 [k]	66 [k]	..	..	..	..	..	..	..	..	95
Micronesia (Fed. States of)	68	67	18	16	38	38	..	..	..	..	93
Nauru	..	..	..	..	..	..	..	..	..	..	..
New Caledonia	78	73	21	18	7	7	..	..	..	..	..
New Zealand	81	77	24	21	5	6	1	..	7	..	100
Palau	75 [l]	67 [l]	..	..	..	..	..	..	..	..	100
Papua New Guinea	56	55	14	12	72	69	16	30	300 [b]	..	53
Samoa	73	67	20	15	24	27	..	..	..	..	100
Solomon Islands	63	62	14	14	33	36	..	..	130 [b]	..	85
Tonga	73	71	20	17	25	18	..	..	..	..	92
Tuvalu	65 [l]	62 [l]	..	..	..	..	..	..	..	..	99
Vanuatu	70	67	18	16	30	38	..	..	..	..	89

Sources:

For life expectancy and infant mortality rate: United Nations, *World Population Prospects: The 2004 Revision,* Comprehensive CD-ROM edition (United Nations publication, Sales No. E.05.XIII.11), supplemented by United Nations *Demographic Yearbook 2001* (United Nations publication, Sales No. E/F.03.XIII.1); United Nations *Demographic Yearbook* system (June 2004); *Statistical Yearbook for Asia and the Pacific 2002* (United Nations publication, Sales No.E/F.03.II.F.1); Secretariat of the Pacific Community, population on census dates by island, available from http://www.spc.int/prism/social/health.html (accessed 28 January 2005); and for Palau http://www.spc.int/prism/country/pw/stats/PalauStats/Social/Health&Vital/Health.htm (accessed 28 January 2005).

For HIV/AIDS: UNAIDS, *2004 Report on the Global AIDS Epidemic,* fourth global report (UNAIDS/04.16E, June 2004), table 1.

For maternal mortality rate, prenatal care and skilled attendance: World Health Organization, *The World Health Report,* annex table 8, "Selected indicators related to reproductive, maternal and newborn health", available from http://www.who.int/whr/2005/annex/en/index.html (accessed 23 April 2005).

Notes:

Two dots (..) indicate that data are not available or are not reported separately.

< 1 Indicates magnitude nil or less than half of the unit employed.

a   Adults (15-49) and children.
b   Estimates derived by regression and similar estimation methods.
c   Data refer to 1994.
d   Data refer to 1992.
e   Data refer to 1990.
f   For statistical purposes, the data for China do not include Hong Kong and Macao Special Administrative Regions (SAR).
g   Data refer to 1993.
h   As of 4 February 2003, the official name of the "Federal Republic of Yugoslavia" has been changed to "Serbia and Montenegro".
i   The former Yugoslav Republic of Macedonia.
j   Data refer to 2000.
k   Data refer to 1999.
l   Data refer to 2002.

Technical notes

Life expectancy at birth is the expected number of years to be lived by a female or male newborn, if she or he is subject to the age-specific mortality rates prevailing in the year(s) to which the life expectancy refers. Life expectancy at age 60 is the additional number of years expected to be lived by a woman or man who has survived to age 60. The indicators are obtained from the estimates and projections prepared every two years by the Population Division, Department of Economic and Social Affairs, United Nations. For many developing countries that lack complete and reliable statistics on births and deaths based on civil registration, various estimation techniques are used to calculate life expectancy using other sources of data, mainly population censuses and demographic surveys. Life expectancy at birth by sex gives a statistical summary of current differences in male and female mortality across all ages. Trends and differentials in infant and child mortality rates are the predominant influence on trends and differentials in life expectancy at birth in most developing countries.

Infant mortality rate is the total number of deaths in a given year of girls or boys less than one year old divided by the total number of female or male live births in the same year, multiplied by 1,000. It is an approximation of the number of deaths per 1,000 girls or boys born alive who die within one year of birth. That series is obtained from the estimates and projections of the number of survivors at exact age 1 by sex, prepared by the Population Division, based on a review of all available national sources. In countries where civil registration and vital statistics are deficient, the most reliable sources are demographic surveys of households. Where the surveys are not available, other sources and general estimates are made, which are necessarily of limited reliability.

The estimated number of people living with HIV/AIDS and the percentage of women among adults living with HIV/AIDS have been produced and compiled by UNAIDS/WHO. The estimates have been shared with national AIDS programmes for their review and comment, but are not necessarily the official estimates used by national Governments. The estimated number of people living with HIV/AIDS includes all adults aged 15-49 and children under 15 infected with HIV, whether they have developed symptoms of AIDS or not, alive at the end of 2003. The percentage of women among those living with HIV/AIDS is calculated for adults aged 15-49 years.

Maternal mortality ratio is the most commonly used measure of maternal mortality, and it is defined as the number of maternal deaths per 100,000 live births during a given time period. The tenth revision of the International Statistical Classification of Diseases and Related Health Problems (ICD-10) defines a maternal death as the death of a woman while pregnant or within 42 days of termination of pregnancy, irrespective of the duration and site of the pregnancy, from any cause related to or aggravated by the pregnancy or its management but not from accidental or incidental causes. Maternal mortality is difficult to measure, particularly in settings where deaths are not comprehensively reported through the civil registration system and where there is no medical certification of cause of death. Moreover, even where overall levels of maternal mortality are high, maternal deaths are nonetheless relatively rare events and thus prone to measurement error. As a result, all existing estimates of maternal mortality are subject to greater or lesser degrees of uncertainty. Approaches used for estimating levels of maternal mortality in this table vary considerably in terms of methodology, source of data and precision of results. The main approaches are household surveys (including sisterhood surveys), censuses,

Reproductive Age Mortality Studies (RAMOS) and statistical modelling.

The percentage of women receiving prenatal care refers to women who had one or more antenatal care contacts during their last pregnancy. For most countries, the main sources of information on antenatal care use are household surveys. Data sources used by the World Health Organization include the Demographic and Health Surveys (ORC Macro and national statistical offices), Reproductive Health Surveys (Centers for Disease Control and Prevention), Multiple Indicator Cluster Surveys (UNICEF), Pan Arab Project for Child Development (PAPCHILD) maternal and child health surveys, Gulf Family Health Surveys, Fertility and Family Surveys (ECE), national surveys, and the data files of the Population Division and of the World Health Organization.

The percentage of deliveries attended by a skilled attendant is based on all deliveries by a skilled attendant, irrespective of the outcome (live birth or foetal death). A skilled attendant is an accredited health professional – such as a midwife, doctor or nurse – who has been educated and trained to proficiency in the skills needed to manage normal (uncomplicated) pregnancies, childbirth and the immediate postnatal period and in the identification, management and referral of complications in women and newborns. Traditional birth attendants, trained or not, are excluded from the category of skilled attendant at birth. As with prenatal care, information on childbirth care is drawn primarily from household surveys.

Table A8
Education and literacy

Country or area	Primary net enrolment ratio 1999/2003		Secondary net enrolment ratio 1999/2003		Girls' share of second-level enrolment (%) 1999/2003	Percentage illiterate, population aged 15-24 1995/2003		Tertiary gross enrolment ratio 1999/2003		Women's share of third-level enrolment (%) 1999/2003	Women's share of teachers (%) 1999/2003	
	Girls	Boys	W	M		W	M	W	M		2nd level	3rd level
Africa												
Algeria	94	96	69[a]	65[a]	51	14	6	..	..	..	48[a]	46[a]
Angola	57[a,b]	66[a,b]	..	..	44	37	17	1[a]	1[a]	40[a]	33[a]	20[a]
Benin	47[a]	69[a]	13[a]	27[a]	32	68	42	1	6	20	11[a]	9
Botswana	83[a]	79[a]	57[a]	50[a]	51[a]	7[c]	15[c]	4[a]	5[a]	43[a]	47	..
Burkina Faso	31	42	7	11	40	86	75	1[a]	2[a]	25[a]	11	..
Burundi	52	62	8[a]	10[a]	42	31	24	1[a]	3[a]	32[a]	21	9
Cameroon	..	..	..	..	45	..	..	4[a]	7[a]	39[a]	..	14[a]
Cape Verde	98	100	61	55	52	14[c]	8[c]	5	4	53	41	..
Central African Republic	..	..	..	..	..	53	30	1	3	16	..	9
Chad	51[a]	75[a]	4[a]	12[a]	25[a]	77	45	< 1	2	15	4[a]	5
Comoros	50[a]	59[a]	..	..	45	48[c]	34[c]	2	3	43	11	..
Congo	53	55	..	..	42[a]	..	..	1[a]	8[a]	12[a]	9[a]	5
Côte d'Ivoire	54[a]	67[a]	15[a]	27[a]	36[a]	49	31	..	..	26[b]	..	..
Dem. Rep. of the Congo	..	..	..	..	34[a]	39	23	..	..	..	10[a]	..
Djibouti	32	40	17[a]	25[a]	40	..	..	2	2	45	23[a]	19
Egypt	90[a]	93[a]	79[a]	83[a]	47[a]	33	21	..	..	..	41[a]	..
Equatorial Guinea	78	91	19[a]	33[a]	36[a]	6	6	2	4	30	4[a]	16
Eritrea	42	49	18	25	39	..	..	< 1[a]	3[a]	13[a]	11	13
Ethiopia	47	55	13[a]	23[a]	36	48[c]	37[c]	1	4	25	9[a]	7
Gabon	78[a]	79[a]	..	..	46[a]	..	..	..	..	36[b]	..	..
Gambia	78[a]	79[a]	27[a]	39[a]	41[a]	..	..	..	..	23[b]	17[a]	..
Ghana	53	65	33[a]	39[a]	45	..	..	2	4	32	24[a]	14
Guinea	58	73	13[a]	28[a]	31	..	..	..	..	..	..	..
Guinea-Bissau	37[a]	53[a]	6[a]	11[a]	35[a]	..	..	< 1	1	16	7[a]	19
Kenya	66	66	24[a]	25[a]	48[a]	19	20	2[a]	4[a]	35[a]	35[a]	..
Lesotho	89	83	27[a]	18[a]	56	..	..	4	2	61	54	50
Liberia	61	79	13[a]	23[a]	40	45[c]	14[c]	15	19	43	20	16[a]
Libyan Arab Jamahiriya	..	..	..	..	50[a]	6[c]	< 1[c]	61[a]	56[a]	51[a]	..	13[a]
Madagascar	79	78	12[a,b]	11[a,b]	49[a,b]	32	28	2	2	45	..	26
Malawi	..	..	26[a]	32[a]	44[a]	29	18	< 1	1	29	24	44
Mali	39	50	..	..	35	83	68	..	..	..	14[a]	..
Mauritania	67	68	14[a]	18[a]	44	45	32	2[a]	6[a]	21[a]	12	4
Mauritius	98	96	74[a]	74[a]	49	5	6	18	13	58	50	..
Morocco	87	92	33[a]	38[a]	45	39[c]	23[c]	10	12	45	33[a]	23
Mozambique	53	58	10	14	40	62	40	< 1[a]	1[a]	44	19	23[a]
Namibia	81	76	50	39	53	7	9	7	8[a]	47[a]	52[a]	31
Niger	31	45	5	7	39	86	74	1[a]	2[a]	25[a]	19	15[a]
Nigeria	60[a]	74[a]	26	32	44	14[c]	9[c]	7[a]	10[a]	40[a]	38	42
Réunion	..	..	..	..	..	< 1[c]	4[c]	..	..	..	..	..
Rwanda	88	85	..	..	47	24	23	2	4	37	19	13
Sao Tome and Principe	94[a]	100[a]	26[a]	32[a]	45[a]	..	..	1[a]	1[a]	36[a]	..	33[a]
Senegal	54[a]	61[a]	..	..	41	59	42	..	..	..	14[a]	..
Seychelles	99	100	100	100	50	1	1	..	..	..	55	..
Sierra Leone	..	..	..	..	42[a]	70	53	1[a]	3[a]	29[a]	27	15[a]
Somalia	..	..	..	..	..	..	..	< 1	< 1	..	..	..
South Africa	89	89	68[a]	63[a]	52[a]	6	6	16	14	54	51[a]	49
Sudan	42[a]	50[a]	..	..	45	31	18	6[a]	7[a]	47[a]	55[a]	..

Table A8 (continued)
Education and literacy

Country or area	Primary net enrolment ratio 1999/2003		Secondary net enrolment ratio 1999/2003		Girls' share of second-level enrolment (%) 1999/2003	Percentage illiterate, population aged 15-24 1995/2003		Tertiary gross enrolment ratio 1999/2003		Women's share of third-level enrolment (%) 1999/2003	Women's share of teachers (%) 1999/2003	
	Girls	Boys	W	M		W	M	W	M		2nd level	3rd level
Africa (continued)												
Swaziland	75	75	36[a]	29[a]	50	11	13	5[a]	4[a]	54[a]	47[a]	35[a]
Togo	83	99	17[a]	36[a]	31[a]	37	17	1	6	17	11[a]	..
Tunisia	97	97	68	61	51	8[d]	4[d]	30	23	55	46[a]	38
Uganda	..	..	16[a]	17[a]	45[a]	26[c]	14[c]	2[a]	4[a]	34[a]	21[a]	18[a]
United Rep. of Tanzania	81[e]	83[e]	4[a,b]	5[a,b]	45[a]	24	19	1	1	31	..	17
Western Sahara	..	..	..	..	..	..	..	..	..	..	..	..
Zambia	68	69	21[a]	25[a]	45	34	27	2[a]	3[a]	32[a]	27[a]	..
Zimbabwe	80	79	33	35	48	..	..	3[a]	5[a]	39[a]	40	..
North America												
Antigua and Barbuda	..	..	..	..	72	..	..	..	..	..	71	..
Bahamas	88[a]	85[a]	77[a]	74[a]	50	..	..	..	..	..	67[a]	..
Barbados	100	100	90	90	50	< 1[c]	< 1[c]	55	22	71	59[a]	51[a]
Belize	100	98	71[a]	67[a]	51[a]	15	16	3[a]	1[a]	65	65[a]	47
Canada	100[a]	100[a]	98[a]	97[a]	49[a]	..	..	66[a]	50[a]	56[a]	68[a]	41[a]
Costa Rica	91	90	55	50	50	1[c]	2[c]	21	18	52	54	..
Cuba	93	94	86	86	48	< 1[c]	< 1[c]	39	29	56	57	46
Dominica	79	83	98[a]	86[a]	52	..	..	..	..	..	61	..
Dominican Republic	94[a]	99[a]	41[a]	30[a]	54[a]	5	7	43	26	61	72[a]	41
El Salvador	90	90	49[a]	48[a]	50	12[c]	10[c]	19	16	54	..	32
Grenada	80[a]	89[a]	..	..	49	..	..	..	..	..	63[a]	..
Guadeloupe	..	..	..	..	..	..	..	..	..	..	..	..
Guatemala	86	89	29	30	47	22	14	8	10	43	..	..
Haiti	..	..	..	..	..	34[c]	34[c]	..	..	..	..	..
Honduras	88[a]	87[a]	..	..	..	9	13	17[a]	13[a]	56[a]	..	36[a]
Jamaica	95	94	77[a]	74[a]	50	2[c]	9[c]	25[a]	10[a]	70[a]	67	60
Martinique	..	..	..	..	..	< 1[c]	< 1[c]	..	..	..	..	..
Mexico	100	99	64	61	51	3	2	22	23	50	45[a]	..
Netherlands Antilles	91[a]	86[a]	67[a]	60[a]	52[a]	2[c]	2[c]	17	11	60	55[a]	34[a]
Nicaragua	85	86	42	36	53	11	16	19	17	52	56[a]	46
Panama	99	100	66[a]	60[a]	51	4	4	55	32	62	57	52
Puerto Rico	..	..	..	..	..	2[c]	3[c]	..	..	..	..	..
Saint Kitts and Nevis	100	90	100	94	55	..	..	..	..	..	67[a]	..
Saint Lucia	100	99	85[a]	68[a]	56	4	5	..	..	..	63[a]	77
St. Vincent/Grenadines	90	90	61	56	52	..	..	..	..	..	59[a]	..
Trinidad and Tobago	90	91	75[a]	69[a]	51[a]	< 1[c]	< 1[c]	11	7	61	61[a]	33
United States	93	92	89	88	49	..	..	96	71	57	61	42
South America												
Argentina	..	..	84	79	51	1	1	72	48	59	66	50
Bolivia	95	95	71[a]	72[a]	48[a]	4	2	..	..	35[a,b]	51[a]	..
Brazil	91	98	78	72	52	2	4	23	18	56	79	53
Chile	84	85	81	80	49	1	1	44	47	48	63[a]	..
Colombia	87[a]	88[a]	58[a]	53[a]	52	2	3	25	23	51	50	33
Ecuador	100	99	51	50	50	4	4	..	..	..	49[a]	..
French Guiana	..	..	..	..	..	..	..	..	..	..	..	..
Guyana	98[a]	100[a]	81[a]	75[a]	50[a]	..	..	7[a]	5[a]	61[a]	70[a]	..

Table A8 (continued)
Education and literacy

Country or area	Primary net enrolment ratio 1999/2003		Secondary net enrolment ratio 1999/2003		Girls' share of second-level enrolment (%) 1999/2003	Percentage illiterate, population aged 15-24 1995/2003		Tertiary gross enrolment ratio 1999/2003		Women's share of third-level enrolment (%) 1999/2003	Women's share of teachers (%) 1999/2003	
	Girls	Boys	W	M		W	M	W	M		2nd level	3rd level
South America (continued)												
Paraguay	89	89	53	50	50[a]	4	4	31[a]	23[a]	58[a]	61	71
Peru	100	100	68	70	48	4[d]	2[d]	33[a]	31[a]	51[a]	44	..
Suriname	98[a]	96[a]	74[a]	54[a]	56[a]	8	5	15	9	62	61[a]	48[a]
Uruguay	91	90	77	70	52	1	2	50[a]	26[a]	65[a]	72[a]	..
Venezuela (Bolivarian Rep. of)	91	90	64	55	53	2	4	42[a]	39[a]	51	..	38
Asia												
Afghanistan	..	..	..	..	..	..	..	..	..	..	..	..
Armenia	93	95	85	82	50	< 1	< 1	31	24	55	84	46
Azerbaijan	79	81	75	77	48	< 1	< 1	14	19	45	65	46
Bahrain	91	89	90	84	50	3	3	44	24	62	54[a]	36
Bangladesh	86	82	47	42	51	59[c]	42[c]	4	8	32	14	15
Bhutan	..	..	..	..	45[a]	..	..	..	..	34[a]	39[a]	27[a]
Brunei Darussalam	..	..	..	..	49	1	1	17	9	63	53	34
Cambodia	91	96	19[a]	30[a]	38	21[d]	12[d]	2[a]	5[a]	29[a]	30	18
China[f]	..	..	..	..	47	2[d]	1[d]	14	17	44	43	45
Hong Kong SAR	97[a]	98[a]	75[a]	72[a]	49	..	..	31	31	50	55[a]	19[a]
Macao SAR	86	88	78	71	50	< 1	1	56	108	36	57	33
Cyprus	96	96	94	91	49	< 1	< 1	33	32	49	60	41
Dem. People's Rep. of Korea	..	..	..	..	..	..	..	..	..	..	..	..
Georgia	88	89	61	62	49	..	..	38	38	49	82	39
India	85	90	..	..	43	32	16	10	14	38	35	37
Indonesia	92	93	54	54	49	2[c]	2[c]	15	18	44	41	39
Iran (Islamic Rep. of)	85	88	..	..	47	10	5	22	20	51	48[a]	18
Iraq	83[a]	98[a]	26	40	40	..	..	10[a]	18[a]	34[a]	69	30
Israel	99	99	89	89	48	1	< 1	66	49	56	71	..
Japan	100	100	100[a]	99[a]	49	..	..	47	54	46	31[a]	..
Jordan	93	91	81	79	49	1	1	37	33	51	58[a]	20
Kazakhstan	91	92	87	87	49	< 1	< 1	51	39	57	84	59
Kuwait	84	82	79[a]	75[a]	50	6[c]	8[c]	..	..	68[a,b]	56[a]	..
Kyrgyzstan	88	91	..	..	50	< 1	< 1	46	39	54	71	48
Lao People's Dem. Rep.	82	88	32	38	42	25	17	4	7	36	42	35
Lebanon	90	91	..	..	51	..	..	48	40	54	53	29
Malaysia	93	93	74	66	51	3	3	33	26	55	63	44
Maldives	93	92	55[a]	48[a]	53	2	2	..	..	..	33	..
Mongolia	80	78	83	72	53	2	3	47	28	62	70	53
Myanmar	85	84	34	36	48	7	4	15[a]	8[a]	63	78	70[a]
Nepal	66[a]	75[a]	..	..	42	40	19	3	8	24	14	..
Occupied Palestinian Territory	91	91	86	82	50	1	1	35	34	49	46	14
Oman	72	72	70	69	48	3[c]	< 1[c]	10[a]	6[a]	58[a]	50[a]	11
Pakistan	50[a]	68[a]	..	..	40	46[d]	25[d]	2	3	43	..	..
Philippines	95	93	65	54	51	4	6	34	26	55	51	55
Qatar	94	95	85[a]	80[a]	49	4	6	32	12	73	56	31
Republic of Korea	100	100	88	88	47	..	..	64	105	37	49	28
Saudi Arabia	54	55	52[a]	54[a]	46	6	2	30	21	58	49	34[a]
Singapore	..	..	..	..	..	< 1	1	..	..	..	..	..
Sri Lanka	..	..	..	..	51[a]	4	5	..	..	..	63[a]	..

Table A8 (continued)
Education and literacy

Country or area	Primary net enrolment ratio 1999/2003		Secondary net enrolment ratio 1999/2003		Girls' share of second-level enrolment (%) 1999/2003	Percentage illiterate, population aged 15-24 1995/2003		Tertiary gross enrolment ratio 1999/2003		Women's share of third-level enrolment (%) 1999/2003	Women's share of teachers (%) 1999/2003	
	Girls	Boys	W	M		W	M	W	M		2nd level	3rd level
Asia (continued)												
Syrian Arab Republic	96	100	41	44	47	7	3	..	..	..	51ᵃ	..
Tajikistan	91ᵇ	97ᵇ	76ᵃ	90ᵃ	45	< 1	< 1	8	24	25	45	30
Thailand	84	87	..	..	50	2	2	42	36	54	54ᵃ	47
Timor-Leste	..	..	..	..	..	..	..	15ᵃ	10ᵃ	53	..	9
Turkey	84	89	..	..	42ᵃ	5	2	24	32	42	..	37
Turkmenistan	..	..	..	..	..	< 1	< 1	..	..	..	..	..
United Arab Emirates	82	84	72	70	49	5ᶜ	12ᶜ	53ᵃ	21ᵃ	66ᵃ	54	..
Uzbekistan	..	..	..	..	49	< 1ᶜ	< 1ᶜ	14	17	44	..	38ᵃ
Viet Nam	92ᵃ	98ᵃ	..	..	47	6ᵍ	6ᵍ	9ᵃ	11ᵃ	43ᵃ	65	40
Yemen	59	84	21ᵃ	47ᵃ	30	49ᶜ	16ᶜ	5ᵃ	17ᵃ	21ᵃ	19ᵃ	1ᵃ
Europe												
Albania	94	96	78	76	48	1	1	21	12	62	56	..
Andorra	90	88	74	69	50	..	..	8	9	49	56	50
Austria	91	89	89	89	47	..	..	53	45	53	60	29
Belarus	94ᵃ	95ᵃ	86ᵃ	83ᵃ	50	< 1	< 1	72	52	57	79	54
Belgium	100	100	98	97	51	..	..	66	56	53	57	39
Bosnia and Herzegovina	..	..	..	..	..	< 1	< 1	< 1	< 1	..	..	..
Bulgaria	90	91	86	88	48	2	2	42	36	53	77	44
Croatia	89	90	87	86	49	< 1	< 1	43	36	53	67	37
Czech Republic	87	87	92	89	49	..	..	37	34	51	67	39
Denmark	100	100	98	94	50	..	..	79	55	58	48	..
Estonia	94	95	90	87	50	< 1	< 1	83	50	62	82	48ᵃ
Finland	100	100	95	94	51	..	..	96	80	53	..	46ᵃ
France	99	99	95	93	49	..	..	63	49	55	58	34
Germany	84	82	88	88	48	..	..	51	51	49	54ᵃ	32
Greece	99	99	87	85	49	1	1	78	71	51	..	..
Hungary	90	91	94	94	49	< 1	1	59	43	57	74	39
Iceland	99	100	88	84	50	..	..	81	45	64	62ᵃ	48ᵃ
Ireland	97	95	87	80	51	..	..	59	45	56	..	35ᵃ
Italy	99	100	92	91	48ᵃ	..	..	65	49	56	65	33
Latvia	85	86	88	88	49	< 1	< 1	91	55	62	82	55
Liechtenstein	..	..	..	..	45	..	..	..	..	27	..	..
Lithuania	91	91	94	94	49	< 1	< 1	88	56	60	80ᵃ	53ᵃ
Luxembourg	91	90	83	77	50	..	..	13	11	53	43	..
Malta	96	96	88	86	48	2	6	35	25	57	53	22
Monaco	..	..	..	..	48	..	..	..	..	..	61ᵃ	..
Netherlands	99	100	89	88	49	..	..	61	56	51	43	34
Norway	100	100	97	96	49	..	..	99	64	60	58ᵃ	36ᵃ
Poland	98	98	93	90	48	..	..	71	50	58	67ᵃ	..
Portugal	99	100	89	81	51	1	1	64	48	57	69ᵃ	..
Republic of Moldova	79	79	70	68	50	1	2	34	26	56	75	54
Romania	88	89	82	79	49	2	2	39	31	54	66	41
Russian Federation	90ᵃ	89ᵃ	..	..	..	< 1	< 1	80	60	57	..	56
San Marino	..	..	..	..	49	..	..	..	..	58	..	..
Serbia and Montenegroʰ	96	96	..	..	49	1	1	39	33	54	61	38
Slovakia	86	85	88	88	49	< 1	< 1	36	31	53	73	42

Table A8 (continued)
Education and literacy

Country or area	Primary net enrolment ratio 1999/2003		Secondary net enrolment ratio 1999/2003		Girls' share of second-level enrolment (%) 1999/2003	Percentage illiterate, population aged 15-24 1995/2003		Tertiary gross enrolment ratio 1999/2003		Women's share of third-level enrolment (%) 1999/2003	Women's share of teachers (%) 1999/2003	
	Girls	Boys	W	M		W	M	W	M		2nd level	3rd level
Europe (continued)												
Slovenia	93	94	94	93	49	< 1[c]	< 1[c]	79	58	56	70	29[a]
Spain	99	100	98	94	50	..	..	67	57	53	53[a]	37
Sweden	99	100	100	99	53	..	..	102	66	60	56	40
Switzerland	99	99	84	89	47	..	..	44	53	44	40[a]	28
TFYR Macedonia[i]	91	91	80[a]	82[a]	48	2	1	32	24	56	52	43
Ukraine	84[a]	84[a]	85[a]	84[a]	49	< 1	< 1	67[a]	56[a]	54	78	..
United Kingdom	100	100	97	94	54	..	..	72	57	56	60	35
Oceania												
Australia	97	96	89[a]	87[a]	48	..	..	82	67	54	..	..
Fiji	100[a]	100[a]	79[a]	73[a]	50[a]	1	1	..	..	..	49[a]	..
French Polynesia	..	..	..	..	..	..	..	..	..	..	..	..
Guam	..	..	..	..	..	..	..	..	..	..	..	..
Kiribati	..	..	..	..	52	..	..	..	..	..	..	..
Marshall Islands	84	85	66	64	50	..	..	20	16	56	39	52
Micronesia (Fed. States of)	..	..	..	..	..	..	..	..	..	..	..	..
Nauru	82[a,b]	80[a,b]	..	..	51[a,b]	..	..	..	..	..	..	..
New Caledonia	..	..	..	..	..	1[g]	1[g]	..	..	..	..	..
New Zealand	99[a]	100[a]	94	91	50	..	..	90	59	59	59	45
Palau	94[a]	98[a]	..	..	48[a]	..	..	54[a]	26[a]	63[a]	59[a]	46[a]
Papua New Guinea	69[a]	79[a]	21[a]	27[a]	41	36	31	..	..	36[b]	37	..
Samoa	96[a]	99[a]	65[a]	59[a]	50	1[c]	1[c]	6[a]	7[a]	44[a]	59[a]	43[a]
Solomon Islands	..	..	..	..	..	..	..	..	..	..	..	..
Tonga	100	100	77[a]	67[a]	50	1	1	4[a]	3[a]	58[a]	50[a]	22[a]
Tuvalu	..	..	..	..	46	..	..	..	..	..	83	..
Vanuatu	95[a]	93[a]	28	27	50	..	..	..	..	..	49	..

Sources:
For primary, secondary and tertiary enrolment ratios, share of enrolment and women's share of second-level teachers: UNESCO Institute for Statistics (UIS) website, http://www.uis.unesco.org (accessed May 2005), and additional data provided by the UIS on 1 June 2005.

For women's share of third-level teachers: UNESCO, *Global Education Digest 2005* (Montreal, 2005).

For illiteracy: prepared by the United Nations Statistics Division, Department of Economic and Social Affairs, based on data from the United Nations *Demographic Yearbook* system (November 2004) and estimates of youth literacy available from UIS website, http://www.uis.unesco.org (accessed May 2005).

Notes:
Two dots (..) indicate that data are not available or are not reported separately.

< 1 Indicates magnitude nil or less than half of the unit employed.

a   UIS estimate.
b   Data refer to 1998/1999.
c   Estimates prepared by UNESCO Institute for Statistics (July 2002 assessment).
d   Data refer to 2004.
e   Data refer to 2004/2005.
f   For statistical purposes, the data for China do not include Hong Kong and Macao Special Administrative Regions (SAR).
g   For ages 15-29.
h   As of 4 February 2003, the official name of the "Federal Republic of Yugoslavia" has been changed to "Serbia and Montenegro".
i   The former Yugoslav Republic of Macedonia.

Technical notes

Statistics on enrolment and teachers are compiled by the UNESCO Institute for Statistics (UIS) from data provided by national Governments in response to UIS questionnaires.

The 1997 International Standard Classification of Education (ISCED 97) defines primary education as programmes that are normally designed on a unit or project basis to give students a sound basic education in reading, writing and mathematics along with an elementary understanding of other subjects such as history, geography, natural science, social science, art and music. The customary or legal age of entrance to this level of education ranges between ages 5 to 7 years and is the start of compulsory education where it exists. In principle, this level covers six years of full-time schooling.

The primary net enrolment ratio (NER) is the number of boys and girls of primary-school age that are enrolled in primary education, expressed as a percentage of the total population in that age group. It shows the extent of participation in primary education of children belonging to the official age group corresponding to primary education in the given country. A high primary NER denotes a high degree of participation of primary school-age children in primary education. The theoretical maximum value is 100. If the primary NER is below 100, then the complement, that is, the difference between the NER and 100, provides a measure of the proportion of children not enrolled at the specified level of education. However, since some of those children could be enrolled at levels of education other than the primary level, the difference should in no way be considered as indicating the proportion of primary school-age children not enrolled in schools.

While enrolment data offer an easy way of comparing the number of boys and girls enrolled in schools, these statistics do not reflect differences between boys and girls in rates of absenteeism, repetition or dropping out.

The 1997 International Standard Classification of Education defines secondary education as education programmes at ISCED levels 2 and 3. Lower secondary education (ISCED 2) is generally designed to continue the basic programmes of the primary level but is typically more subject-focused, requiring more specialized teachers for each subject area. The end of the level often coincides with the end of compulsory education where it exists. In upper secondary education (ISCED 3), the final stage of secondary education in most countries, instruction is often organized even more along subject lines and teachers typically need higher or more subject-specific qualification than those at ISCED level 2.

The secondary net enrolment ratio is the number of boys and girls in the theoretical second-level age group that are enrolled in that level, expressed as a percentage of the total population in the corresponding age group. It shows the extent of participation in secondary education of children belonging to the official age group corresponding to second-level education in the given country. A high secondary NER denotes a high degree of participation of secondary school-age children or youth in second-level education. The theoretical maximum value is 100. If the secondary NER is below 100, then the complement, that is, the difference between the NER and 100, provides a measure of the proportion of children or youth of secondary school age not enrolled at that level of education. However, since some of those children or youth could be enrolled at levels of education other than at the secondary level, the difference should in no way be considered as indicating the proportion of secondary school-age children not enrolled in schools.

Rates of illiteracy are generally derived from national population censuses or sample surveys.

UNESCO defines a "literate" person as one who can "with understanding both read and write a short simple statement on [her or] his everyday life", and an "illiterate" person as one who cannot "with understanding both read and write a short simple statement on [her or] his everyday life". That definition of literacy is widely used in national population censuses and surveys, but its interpretation and application may vary to some extent among countries, depending on national, social and cultural circumstances. Furthermore, this concept of literacy includes persons who, although familiar with the basics of reading and writing, might still be considered functionally illiterate. Though, a measure of functional illiteracy would thus also be useful, such statistics are collected in only a few countries.

The illiteracy rate refers in general to the proportion of the population above a certain age who are illiterate, expressed as a percentage of the corresponding population. Illiteracy rates are shown for the age group 15-24. For young people in developing regions, literacy may be a better measure of education than enrolment since it usually reflects a minimal level of successfully completed schooling. Data are lacking for a number of countries or areas in the developed regions. For those areas, a question on literacy was not included in the population censuses, since illiteracy has been reduced to minimal levels through several decades of universal primary education.

The ISCED 97 defines tertiary education as education programmes at ISCED levels 5 and 6. Education at ISCED level 5 includes programmes that are theoretically based or research preparatory (history, philosophy, mathematics, etc.) or that give access to professions with high skill requirements (e.g., medicine, dentistry, architecture, etc.), and those programmes that are practical, technical or occupationally specific. Level 6 includes tertiary programmes that lead to the award of an advanced research qualification. The programmes are therefore devoted to advanced study and original research and are not based on course work only.

The tertiary gross enrolment ratio is defined as enrolment at the third level, regardless of age, expressed as a percentage of the population in the theoretical school age group corresponding to that level of education. For the tertiary level, the population is the five-year age group following on from the secondary-school leaving age. The tertiary gross enrolment ratio is used to show the general level of participation in this level of education.

The term "teachers" refers to persons employed full-time or part-time in an official capacity to guide and direct the learning experience of pupils and students, irrespective of their qualifications or the delivery mechanism, i.e. face-to-face and/or at a distance. Excluded from this category are educational personnel who have no active teaching duties (e.g. headmasters, headmistresses or principals who do not teach) and persons who work occasionally or in a voluntary capacity.

Table A9
Economic activity and maternity leave benefits

Country or area	Adult economic activity rate (%) 1997/2003		Women's share of the adult labour force (%) 1997/2003	Unemployment rate (%) 1997/2003		Percentage of adult employment that is part-time 1999/2002		Women's share of part-time employment (%) 1999/2002	Maternity leave benefits, as of 2004		
									Length of maternity leave	Percentage of wages paid in covered period	Provider of coverage
	W	M		W	M	W	M				
Africa											
Algeria	7 [a]	47 [a]	12 [a]	31	27	..	..	..	14 weeks	100	Social security
Angola	..	..	..	..	..	..	..	..	3 months	100	Social security [b]
Benin	69 [c]	67 [c]	52 [c]	..	..	..	..	..	14 weeks	100	50% employer, 50% soc sec
Botswana	49	68	45	24	16	..	..	..	12 weeks	25	Employer
Burkina Faso	..	..	..	..	..	..	..	..	14 weeks	100	Social security [d]
Burundi	..	..	..	13 [e]	15 [e]	..	..	..	12 weeks	100	50% employer, 50% soc sec
Cameroon	..	..	..	..	..	..	..	..	14 weeks	100	Social security
Cape Verde	..	..	..	..	..	..	..	..	..	..	..
Central African Republic	..	..	..	..	..	..	..	..	14 weeks	50	Social security
Chad	..	..	..	..	..	..	..	..	14 weeks	50	Social security
Comoros	..	..	..	..	..	..	..	..	14 weeks	100	Employer
Congo	..	..	..	..	..	..	..	..	15 weeks	100	50% employer, 50% soc sec
Côte d'Ivoire	..	..	..	..	..	..	..	..	14 weeks	100	Social security
Dem. Rep. of the Congo	..	..	..	..	..	..	..	..	14 weeks	67	Employer
Djibouti	..	..	..	..	..	..	..	..	14 weeks	50 (100 for public servants)	Employer
Egypt	20 [f]	69 [f]	22 [f]	23 [f]	6 [f]	..	..	..	90 days	100	Employer
Equatorial Guinea	..	..	..	..	..	..	..	..	12 weeks	75	Social security
Eritrea	..	..	..	..	..	..	..	..	60 days	..	Employer
Ethiopia	72	90	46	..	..	..	..	..	90 days	100	Employer
Gabon	..	..	..	..	..	..	..	..	14 weeks	100	Social security
Gambia	..	..	..	..	..	..	..	..	12 weeks	100	Employer
Ghana	73	77	50	..	..	..	..	..	12 weeks	100	Employer
Guinea	..	..	..	..	..	..	..	..	14 weeks	100	50% employer, 50% soc sec
Guinea-Bissau	..	..	..	..	..	..	..	..	60 days	100	Employer or social security subsidy and employer pays difference
Kenya	..	..	..	..	..	..	..	..	2 months	100	Employer
Lesotho	..	..	..	47	31	..	..	..	12 weeks	0	—
Liberia	..	..	..	..	..	..	..	..	..	..	..
Libyan Arab Jamahiriya	..	..	..	..	..	..	..	..	50 days	50 (100 for self-employed women)	Employer (social security for self-employed women)
Madagascar	79	86	49	6	4	..	..	..	14 weeks	100	50% employer, 50% soc sec
Malawi	76	79	50	..	..	..	..	..	8 weeks (every three years)	100	Employer
Mali	..	..	..	..	..	..	..	..	14 weeks	100	Social security

Table A9 (continued)
Economic activity and maternity leave benefits

Country or area	Adult economic activity rate (%) 1997/2003 W	Adult economic activity rate (%) 1997/2003 M	Women's share of the adult labour force (%) 1997/2003	Unemployment rate (%) 1997/2003 W	Unemployment rate (%) 1997/2003 M	Percentage of adult employment that is part-time 1999/2002 W	Percentage of adult employment that is part-time 1999/2002 M	Women's share of part-time employment (%) 1999/2002	Maternity leave benefits, as of 2004 Length of maternity leave	Maternity leave benefits, as of 2004 Percentage of wages paid in covered period	Maternity leave benefits, as of 2004 Provider of coverage
Africa (continued)											
Mauritania	..	..	..	..	..	..	..	..	14 weeks	100	Social security
Mauritius	41	80	35	13	9	..	..	..	12 weeks	100	Employer
Morocco	27 [g]	77 [g]	27 [g]	26 [g]	17 [g]	..	..	..	14 weeks	100	Social security
Mozambique	87	80	47	..	..	..	..	..	60 days	100	Employer
Namibia	..	..	..	39	28	..	..	..	12 weeks	80	Social security
Niger	..	..	..	..	..	..	..	..	14 weeks	50	Social security
Nigeria	..	..	..	..	..	..	..	..	12 weeks	50	Employer
Réunion	50	66	45	..	..	..	..	..	..	..	..
Rwanda	..	..	..	..	..	..	..	..	12 weeks	67	Employer
Sao Tome and Principe	..	..	..	..	..	..	..	..	70 days	100 for 60 days	Social security [h]
Senegal	..	..	..	..	..	..	..	..	14 weeks	100	Social security
Seychelles	65	74	48	..	..	..	..	..	14 weeks	Flat [i]	Social security
Sierra Leone	..	..	..	..	..	..	..	..	..	..	..
Somalia	..	..	..	..	..	..	..	..	14 weeks	50	Employer
South Africa	48	61	47	33	27	..	..	..	4 months	Up to 60 depending on income level	Unemployment insurance fund
Sudan	..	..	..	..	..	..	..	..	8 weeks	100	Employer
Swaziland	..	..	..	..	..	..	..	..	12 weeks	0	—
Togo	..	..	..	..	..	..	..	..	14 weeks	100	50% employer, 50% soc sec
Tunisia	24	73	24	..	..	..	..	..	30 days	67	Social security
Uganda	..	..	..	4	3	..	..	..	8 weeks	100 for 1 month	Employer
United Rep. of Tanzania	87	90	51	6	4	..	..	..	12 weeks	100	Soc sec/employer
Western Sahara	..	..	..	..	..	..	..	..	..	..	..
Zambia	..	..	..	..	..	..	..	..	12 weeks	100	Employer
Zimbabwe	65	79	48	5	7	..	..	..	90 days	100	Employer
North America											
Antigua and Barbuda	..	..	..	..	..	..	..	..	13 weeks	60	Social security
Bahamas	66	74	49	10	11	15	12	53	13 weeks	60	Soc sec/employer
Barbados	62	76	48	13	10	18	11	63	12 weeks	100	Social security
Belize	..	..	..	15	8	26 [j]	12 [j]	49 [j]	14 weeks	80	Social security
Canada	61	73	46	7	8	28 [j]	11 [j]	69 [j]	17 - 18 weeks	55 (up to a ceiling)	Employment insurance
Costa Rica	42	80	36	8	6	..	..	..	4 months	100	Soc sec/employer
Cuba	..	..	..	..	..	..	..	..	18 weeks	100	Social security
Dominica	60	75	..	27	20	..	..	..	12 weeks	60	Soc sec/employer
Dominican Republic	40	69	38	26	9	15 [k]	8 [k]	50 [k]	12 weeks	100	Soc sec/employer
El Salvador	46	79	41	4	9	..	..	..	12 weeks	75	Social security
Grenada	62	75	..	..	..	..	..	..	3 months	100 for 2 months and 60 for the last month	Soc sec/employer [l]

Table A9 (continued)
Economic activity and maternity leave benefits

Country or area	Adult economic activity rate (%) 1997/2003		Women's share of the adult labour force (%) 1997/2003	Unemployment rate (%) 1997/2003		Percentage of adult employment that is part-time 1999/2002		Women's share of part-time employment (%) 1999/2002	Maternity leave benefits, as of 2004		
									Length of maternity leave	Percentage of wages paid in covered period	Provider of coverage
	W	M		W	M	W	M				
North America (continued)											
Guadeloupe	..	..	..	29	23	..	..	..	..	..	..
Guatemala	..	..	..	2	2	..	..	..	84 days	100	Soc sec/employer
Haiti	..	..	..	..	..	..	..	..	12 weeks	100 for 6 weeks	Employer
Honduras	43	85	36	5	4	..	..	..	84 days	100	Soc sec/employer
Jamaica	53	71	44	22	10	16	10	52	12 weeks	100 for 8 weeks	Employer
Martinique	..	..	..	25	19	..	..	..	..	..	..
Mexico	38	81	34	2	2	26[j]	7[j]	66[j]	12 weeks	100	Social security
Netherlands Antilles	53[m]	67[m]	49[m]	16[m]	12[m]	..	..	..	..	..	..
Nicaragua	36	91	30	15	9	..	..	..	12 weeks	60	Social security
Panama	46	79	37	19	11	13[k]	12[k]	36[k]	14 weeks	100	Social security
Puerto Rico	36	58	43	11	13	..	..	..	..	..	..
Saint Kitts and Nevis	..	..	..	..	..	..	..	..	13 weeks	60	Social security
Saint Lucia	54	76	43	21	13	..	..	..	3 months	65	Social security
St. Vincent/Grenadines	..	..	..	..	..	..	..	..	13 weeks	65	Social security
Trinidad and Tobago	48	75	39	15	8	10	6	48	13 weeks	100 then 50[n]	Employer/soc sec
United States	60	74	47	6	6	17[o,p]	7[o,p]	68[o,p]	12 weeks	0	—
South America											
Argentina	46[q]	72[q]	43[q]	15[q]	16[q]	..	..	..	90 days	100	Social security
Bolivia	60[g]	82[g]	45[g]	9[g]	6[g]	..	..	..	12 weeks	at least 70[r]	Social security
Brazil	54[s]	81[s]	42[s]	12[s]	8[s]	..	..	..	120 days	100	Social security
Chile	36	71	34	8	7	..	..	..	18 weeks	100	Social security
Colombia	51	76	43	19	11	..	..	..	12 weeks	100	Social security
Ecuador	54	81	41	15	9	..	..	..	12 weeks	100	Soc sec/employer
French Guiana	53	68	44	30	21	..	..	..	..	..	..
Guyana	..	..	..	..	..	..	..	..	13 weeks	70	Social security
Paraguay	..	..	..	14	9	..	..	..	12 weeks	50 for 9 weeks	Social security
Peru	56[t]	75[t]	44[t]	12[t]	9[t]	..	..	..	90 days	100	Social security
Suriname	33	61	37	20	10	..	..	..	..	..	..
Uruguay	49[g]	69[g]	45[g]	21[g]	14[g]	..	..	..	12 weeks	100	Social security
Venezuela (Bolivarian Rep.of)	55	84	40	18	14	..	..	..	18 weeks	100	Social security
Asia											
Afghanistan	..	..	..	..	..	..	..	..	90 days	100	Employer
Armenia	58	74	47	14	6	..	..	..	..	..	..
Azerbaijan	57	73	46	2	1	..	..	..	126 days	100	Social security
Bahrain	14	86	22	..	..	..	..	..	45 days	100	Employer
Bangladesh	56	87	37	3	3	..	..	..	12 weeks	100	Employer
Bhutan	..	..	..	..	..	..	..	..	..	..	..
Brunei Darussalam	..	..	..	..	..	..	..	..	..	..	..
Cambodia	74	81	52	2	2	..	..	..	90 days	50	Employer
China	..	..	..	..	..	..	..	..	90 days	100	Employer

Table A9 (continued)
Economic activity and maternity leave benefits

Country or area	Adult economic activity rate (%) 1997/2003 W	M	Women's share of the adult labour force (%) 1997/2003	Unemployment rate (%) 1997/2003 W	M	Percentage of adult employment that is part-time 1999/2002 W	M	Women's share of part-time employment (%) 1999/2002	Length of maternity leave	Percentage of wages paid in covered period	Provider of coverage
Asia (continued)											
Hong Kong SAR	52	72	44	6	9	..	..	..	..	..	..
Macao SAR	56	73	47	5	7	..	..	..	..	..	..
Cyprus	54	74	45	5	4	..	..	..	16 weeks	75	Social security
Dem. People's Rep. of Korea	..	..	..	..	..	..	..	..	..	..	..
Georgia	58	76	47	12	12	..	..	..	..	..	..
India	..	..	..	4	4	..	..	..	12 weeks	100	Social security[h]
Indonesia	52	85	40	..	..	..	..	..	3 months	100	Employer
Iran (Islamic Rep. of)	..	..	..	4	8	..	..	..	90 days	67	Social security
Iraq	9	77	11	..	..	..	..	..	62 days	100	Social security
Israel	49	60	46	11	10	..	..	..	12 weeks	100 (up to a ceiling)	Social security
Japan	48	74	41	5	6	40[o]	14[o]	67[o]	14 weeks	60	Health insurance or social security
Jordan	12	64	15	21	12	..	..	..	10 weeks	100	Employer
Kazakhstan	65	76	49	10	7	..	..	..	126 days	..	Employer
Kuwait	30[a]	53[a]	38[a]	2	1	..	..	..	70 days	100	Employer
Kyrgyzstan	55	74	44	14	11	..	..	..	126 days	100	Social security
Lao People's Dem. Rep.	..	..	..	..	..	..	..	..	3 months	70	Social security
Lebanon	..	..	..	..	..	..	..	..	7 weeks	100	Employer/soc sec
Malaysia	47	83	35	4	4	..	..	..	60 days	100	Employer
Maldives	37	72	34	..	..	..	..	..	..	..	..
Mongolia	56	61	50	4	3	..	..	..	120 days	70	Social security
Myanmar	..	..	..	..	..	..	..	..	12 weeks	67	Social security
Nepal	60	82	43	..	..	..	..	..	52 days	100	Employer
Occupied Palestinian Territory	10	66	14	19	27	..	..	..	..	..	..
Oman	13[u]	62[u]	18[u]	..	..	..	..	..	..	..	..
Pakistan	16	83	16	17	7	..	..	..	12 weeks	100	Employer
Philippines	53	82	39	10	9	..	..	..	60 days	100	Social security
Qatar	33	89	13	13	2	..	..	..	50 days	100	Employer
Republic of Korea	49	75	41	3	4	11[o,v]	5[o,v]	58[o,v]	90 days	100	Employer 60 days, social security 30 days
Saudi Arabia	..	..	..	12	4	..	..	..	10 weeks	50 or 100 (depending on the duration of employment)	Employer
Singapore	56	81	40	5	6	..	..	..	8 weeks	100	Employer for first two children, Government for third
Sri Lanka	36[w]	77[w]	33[w]	15[w]	6[w]	..	..	..	12 weeks	100	Employer
Syrian Arab Republic	24	82	21	24	8	..	..	..	50 days	70	Employer
Tajikistan	..	..	..	3	2	..	..	..	140 days	..	Social security
Thailand	65	81	45	1	2	..	..	..	90 days	100 for first 45 days then 50 for 45 days	Employer for first 45 days then social security

Table A9 (continued)
Economic activity and maternity leave benefits

Country or area	Adult economic activity rate (%) 1997/2003		Women's share of the adult labour force (%) 1997/2003	Unemployment rate (%) 1997/2003		Percentage of adult employment that is part-time 1999/2002		Women's share of part-time employment (%) 1999/2002	Maternity leave benefits, as of 2004		
									Length of maternity leave	Percentage of wages paid in covered period	Provider of coverage
	W	M		W	M	W	M				
Asia (continued)											
Timor-Leste	..	..	..	..	..	..	..	..	..	..	..
Turkey	27	70	28	10	11	13 [o]	4 [o]	58 [o]	16 weeks	67 for 12 weeks	Social security
Turkmenistan	..	..	..	..	..				..	..	..
United Arab Emirates	..	..	..	3	2	..	..	..	3 months	100	Employer
Uzbekistan	..	..	..	..	..	..	..	..	126 days	100	Social security
Viet Nam	..	..	..	3	2	..	..	..	4 to 6 months [x]	100	Social security
Yemen	..	..	..	8	13	..	..	..	60 days	100	Employer
Europe											
Albania	49	71	44	18	13	..	..	..	365 days	80 prior to birth and for 150 days then 50 for rest of period	Social security
Andorra	..	..	..	..	..	..	..	..	..	..	..
Austria	51	68	45	4	4	24 [j]	3 [j]	88 [j]	16 weeks	100	Social security
Belarus	53	66	49	4	2	..	..	..	126 days	100	Social security
Belgium	40	56	43	9	8	32 [j,y]	6 [j,y]	80 [j,y]	15 weeks	82 for first 30 days and 75 for the rest (up to a ceiling)	Social security
Bosnia and Herzegovina	..	..	..	..	..	..	..	..	..	..	..
Bulgaria	44	55	47	13	14	..	..	..	135 days	90	Social security
Croatia	45	61	44	16	13	..	..	..	45 days before delivery and 1 year after	100 from 28 days before to 6 months after birth. The remainder flat rate	Croatian Health Insurance Fund then State budget (flat rate)
Czech Republic	51	69	44	9	6	5 [j]	1 [j]	73 [j]	28 weeks	69	Social security
Denmark	73	82	47	6	5	23 [j,y]	10 [j,y]	66 [j,y]	18 weeks	90 (up to a ceiling)	State
Estonia	58	69	49	10	10	..	..	..	140 days	100	Social security
Finland	64	70	48	9	9	15 [j]	8 [j]	65 [j]	150 working days	70	Social security
France	49	63	46	11	9	24 [j,y]	5 [j,y]	80 [j,y]	16 weeks	100 (up to a ceiling)	Social security
Germany	49	65	44	10	10	35 [j,y]	6 [j,y]	84 [j,y]	14 weeks	100	Social security (up to a ceiling)/ Employer (pays difference)
Greece	38	61	40	15	6	10 [j,y]	3 [j,y]	68 [j,y]	119 days	100	Soc sec / employer
Hungary	47	61	46	6	6	4 [j]	1 [j]	70 [j]	24 weeks	Prenatal (min. 4 weeks):70 then flat rate	Social security

Table A9 (continued)
Economic activity and maternity leave benefits

	Adult economic activity rate (%) 1997/2003		Women's share of the adult labour force (%) 1997/2003	Unemployment rate (%) 1997/2003		Percentage of adult employment that is part-time 1999/2002		Women's share of part-time employment (%) 1999/2002	Maternity leave benefits, as of 2004		
Country or area	W	M		W	M	W	M		Length of maternity leave	Percentage of wages paid in covered period	Provider of coverage
Europe (continued)											
Iceland	79	87	47	3	4	31[o]	10[o]	73[o]	3 months	80	Social security
Ireland	49	70	42	4	5	33[j,y]	7[j,y]	77[j,y]	18 weeks	70	Social security
Italy	37	62	39	12	7	23[j,y]	5[j,y]	74[j,y]	5 months	80	Social security
Latvia	50	65	48	11	11	..	..	..	112 days	100	Social security
Liechtenstein	..	..	..	..	..	..	..	..	..	..	..
Lithuania	52	64	49	12	13	..	..	..	126 days	100	Social security
Luxembourg	43	64	41	..	..	28[j,y]	2[j,y]	89[j,y]	16 weeks	100	Social security
Malta	31	70	31	9	7	..	..	..	14 weeks	100 for 13 weeks	Employer
Monaco	..	..	..	..	..	..	..	..	..	..	..
Netherlands	56	73	44	4	4	60[j,y]	15[j,y]	75[j,y]	16 weeks	100	Unemployment fund
Norway	69	77	47	4	5	33[o]	9[o]	76[o]	42 or 52 weeks[z]	100 or 80[z]	Social security
Poland	48	62	46	20	19	17[o]	8[o]	65[o]	16 weeks	100	Social security
Portugal	55	70	46	7	6	14[j,y]	6[j,y]	68[j,y]	120 days	100	Social security
Republic of Moldova	54	59	51	6	10	..	..	..	126 days	100	Social security
Romania	56	69	46	6	8	..	..	..	126 days	85	Social security
Russian Federation	59	70	49	9	9	..	..	..	140 days	100	Social security
San Marino	57	76	40	6	2	..	..	..	5 months	100	Social security
Serbia and Montenegro [aa]	..	..	..	16	14	..	..	..	365 days	100	Social security
Slovakia	53	68	46	18	17	2[j]	1[j]	66[j]	28 weeks	55	Social security
Slovenia	50	63	46	7	6	..	..	..	105 days	100	Social security
Spain	43	67	41	16	8	16[j,y]	2[j,y]	80[j,y]	16 weeks	100	Social security
Sweden	76	80	48	4	5	20[j]	7[j]	72[j]	14 weeks	80 for 390 days; 90 days at flat rate	Social security
Switzerland	59	77	45	5	4	45[j]	8[j]	83[j]	98 days	80	Social security
TFYR Macedonia [bb]	43	66	40	36	37	..	..	..	..	..	..
Ukraine	58	67	49	9	9	..	..	..	126 days	100	Social security
United Kingdom	55	71	46	4	6	40[j,y]	9[j,y]	79[j,y]	26 weeks	90 for first 6 weeks and flat rate after	Employer (refunded for 92% by public funds)
Oceania											
Australia	56	71	45	6	7	39[o]	16[o]	67[o]	52 weeks	0	—
Fiji	..	..	..	..	..	..	..	..	84 days	Flat rate	Employer
French Polynesia	..	..	..	..	..	..	..	..	..	..	..
Guam	..	..	..	..	..	..	..	..	..	..	..
Kiribati	..	..	..	..	..	..	..	..	12 weeks	25	Employer
Marshall Islands	35	66	34	37	28	..	..	..	..	..	..
Micronesia (Fed. States of)	..	..	..	..	..	..	..	..	..	..	..
Nauru	..	..	..	..	..	..	..	..	..	..	..
New Caledonia	..	..	..	..	..	..	..	..	..	..	..
New Zealand	57	72	46	5	4	36[o]	11[o]	73[o]	14 weeks	100 (up to a ceiling)	State
Palau	..	..	..	..	..	..	..	..	..	..	..

Table A9 (continued)
Economic activity and maternity leave benefits

	Adult economic activity rate (%) 1997/2003		Women's share of the adult labour force (%) 1997/2003	Unemployment rate (%) 1997/2003		Percentage of adult employment that is part-time 1999/2002		Women's share of part-time employment (%) 1999/2002	Maternity leave benefits, as of 2004		
									Length of maternity leave	Percentage of wages paid in covered period	Provider of coverage
Country or area	W	M		W	M	W	M				
Oceania (continued)											
Papua New Guinea	71	74	48	1	4	..	..	..	As necessary before delivery and 6 weeks after	0	—
Samoa	..	..	..	..	..	..	..	..	..	..	..
Solomon Islands	..	..	..	..	..	..	..	..	12 weeks	25	Employer
Tonga	..	..	..	..	..	..	..	..	..	..	..
Tuvalu	..	..	..	..	..	..	..	..	..	..	..
Vanuatu	..	..	..	..	..	..	..	..	3 months	50	..

Sources:

For adult economic activity rate, women's share of the labour force and unemployment rate: International Labour Office, *Yearbook of Labour Statistics 2003* (Geneva, 2003) and LABORSTA database (accessed 26 November 2004); International Labour Organization, Caribbean Office, *Digest of Caribbean Labour Statistics 1998* (Port of Spain, 1999); and national statistical reports.

For part-time employment: International Labour Office, *Key Indicators of the Labour Market* (KILM), updates provided to the United Nations Statistics Division, Department of Economic and Social Affairs, in November 2004; supplemented by International Labour Organization, Caribbean Office, Caribbean labour statistics dataset, available from http://www.ilocarib.org.tt/system_links/link_databases.html (accessed 15 February 2005).

For maternity leave benefits: provided by the International Labour Office in January 2005, based on *Conditions of Work and Employment* database: maternity protection.

Notes:

Two dots (..) indicate that data are not available or are not reported separately.

A dash (—) indicates "not applicable".

a   Refers to persons of all ages: that is, activity rate shown is crude activity rate.

b   If necessary the employer adds coverage, up to the full wage.

c   Cotonou City only.

d   If necessary the employer tops up.

e   Bujumbura only.

f   For the Egyptian population only.

g   For urban areas only.

h   Employer pays for women not covered by social security.

i   Flat monthly allowance for 10 weeks.

j   Based on hours worked on the main job.

k   Based on hours worked on the primary and secondary jobs.

l   Social security (60 for 12 weeks) and employer (40 for two months).

m   Curaçao only.

n   100 for one month, 50 for two months (employer) and a sum depending on earnings (social security).

o   Based on hours worked on all jobs.

p   Wage and salaried workers only.

q   31 urban agglomerations.

r   100 of national minimum wage plus 70 of wages above the minimum.

s   Excluding rural populations of Acre, Amapá, Amazonas, Pará, Rondônia and Roraima.

t   Metropolitan Lima only.

u   For Omanis only.

v   Excluding contributing family workers working less than 18 hours per week.

w   Excluding Northern and Eastern provinces.

x   Depending on the working conditions and nature of the work.

y   Excluding travel time between home and work as well as main meal breaks. Estimates based on the European Labour Force Survey.

z   100 for 42 weeks or 80 for 52 weeks of parental leave (9 weeks reserved for the mother).

aa   As of 4 February 2003, the official name of the "Federal Republic of Yugoslavia" has been changed to "Serbia and Montenegro".

bb   The former Yugoslav Republic of Macedonia.

Technical notes

Indicators concerning the total economically active population aged 15 or over have been compiled by the International Labour Office (ILO). Data shown are for the latest year for which data are available. The adult economic activity rate is defined as the proportion of the population aged 15 years or over who furnish, or are available to furnish, the supply of labour for the production of goods and services in accordance with the System of National Accounts.

The definition of the economically active population provided by the ILO comprises all employed and unemployed persons, including those seeking work for the first time. It covers employers operating unincorporated enterprises, persons working on their own account, employees, contributing family workers, members of producers' cooperatives and members of the armed forces. In principle, a person who performs such work for as little as one hour per week is considered economically active. The definition recommended by the ILO also accounts for production of primary products, such as foodstuffs, fetching and transporting water, and collecting firewood for own consumption. Certain other non-monetary activities – for example construction, major repair and renovation of owner-occupied dwelling – are considered economic activity, and persons engaged in such production are regarded as economically active.

The unemployment rate is the proportion of the labour force that is unemployed. The unemployed are persons who are currently without work, who are seeking or have sought work recently and who are currently available for work. The base for these statistics is the labour force (the economically active portion of the population), not the total population.

The International Conference of Labour Statisticians adopted the following definition of the unemployed as an international recommendation in 1982:

All persons who during the reference period were:

(1) "without work", that is, were not in paid employment or self-employment as specified by the international definition of employment;

(2) "currently available for work", that is, were available for paid employment or self-employment during the reference period; and

(3) "seeking work", that is, had taken specific steps in a specified recent period to seek paid employment or self-employment.

The term "part-time workers" refers to persons with jobs whose working hours total less than "full time" (see definition below). The measures presented are total part-time employment as a percentage of total employment, calculated separately for women and for men, and the proportion of women among all part-time workers. All but two countries derived the information from labour force surveys; the remaining two obtained their information from population censuses.

There is no internationally accepted standard for the minimum number of hours worked per week that would constitute full-time work. The framework is therefore established on a country-by-country basis or in special regional compilations. Many countries have established demarcation points that lie between 30 and 40 hours per week. Other countries classify part-time and full-time workers on the basis of respondents' interpretations of their personal work situations, that is, whether they view themselves as full-time or as part-time jobholders. In an attempt to make statistics on part-time work comparable across countries, the Organization for Economic Cooperation and Development applied a 30-hour cut-off for distinguishing part-time from full-time workers. Thus, in the OECD data set, one of the main sources of the KILM database, persons who work 30 hours or more per week are considered "full-time workers" and those who work less than 30 hours per week are considered "part-time workers".

Data on maternity leave benefits currently available to women in countries surveyed by the ILO include the length of time for which benefits are provided, the extent of compensation and the institution responsible for providing the coverage. The data was compiled by the ILO, based on information provided by countries as of 2004.

Table A10
Employment characteristics and political participation

Country or area	Percentage distribution of the employed population by status in employment, each sex, 1995/2003								Ratio of female to male wages in manufacturing 1995/2003	Percentage women among legislators and managers 1995/2003	Women's share of parliamentary seats (%) 2004
	Employers		Own-account workers		Employees		Contributing family workers				
	W	M	W	M	W	M	W	M			
Africa											
Algeria	..	..	..	..	..	..	..	..	..	..	6
Angola	..	..	..	..	..	..	..	..	..	..	16
Benin	..	..	..	..	..	..	..	..	..	..	7
Botswana	3	4	14	11	82	83	1	1	52[a,b]	31	7
Burkina Faso	..	..	..	..	..	..	..	..	..	..	12
Burundi	..	..	..	..	..	..	..	..	..	..	18
Cameroon	1	2	61	55	9	29	27	9	..	..	9
Cape Verde	..	..	..	..	..	..	..	..	..	..	11
Central African Republic	..	..	..	..	..	..	..	..	..	..	..
Chad	..	..	..	..	..	..	..	..	..	..	6
Comoros	..	..	..	..	..	..	..	..	..	..	3
Congo	..	..	..	..	..	..	..	..	..	..	9
Côte d'Ivoire	..	..	..	..	..	..	..	..	..	..	9
Dem. Rep. of the Congo	..	..	..	..	..	..	..	..	..	..	12
Djibouti	..	..	..	..	..	..	..	..	..	..	11
Egypt	6	20	7	13	68	58	20	8	68	9	2
Equatorial Guinea	..	..	..	..	..	..	..	..	..	..	18
Eritrea	..	..	..	..	..	..	..	..	66	..	22
Ethiopia	..	..	..	..	..	..	..	..	..	..	8
Gabon	..	..	..	..	..	..	..	..	..	..	9
Gambia	..	..	..	..	..	..	..	..	..	..	13
Ghana	5	5	71	61	11	21	10	8	..	34	10
Guinea	..	..	..	..	..	..	..	..	..	..	19
Guinea-Bissau	..	..	..	..	..	..	..	..	..	..	..
Kenya	..	..	..	..	..	..	..	..	..	..	7
Lesotho	1	1	53	65	44	32	..	..	..	..	12
Liberia	..	..	..	..	..	..	..	..	..	..	5
Libyan Arab Jamahiriya	..	..	..	..	..	..	..	..	..	..	..
Madagascar	2	2	34	49	12	18	52	30	..	..	4
Malawi	< 1	< 1	93	76	5	21	2	3	..	15	15
Mali	..	..	..	..	..	..	..	..	..	..	10
Mauritania	..	..	..	..	..	..	..	..	..	..	4
Mauritius	2	5	5	15	91	79	2	< 1	..	22	6
Morocco	< 1	3	12	31	34	40	52	22	..	..	11
Mozambique	..	..	..	..	..	..	..	..	..	..	30
Namibia	6	10	32	17	56	68	4	3	..	30	26
Niger	..	..	..	..	..	..	..	..	..	..	1
Nigeria	1	4	..	..	33	49	..	..	..	..	6
Réunion	..	..	..	..	..	..	..	..	..	..	..
Rwanda	< 1	< 1	65	56	3	9	30	33	..	..	49
Sao Tome and Principe	..	..	..	..	..	..	..	..	..	..	9
Senegal	..	..	..	..	..	..	..	..	..	..	19
Seychelles	1	2	4	20	86	73	..	1	..	..	29
Sierra Leone	..	..	..	..	..	..	..	..	..	..	15
Somalia	..	..	..	..	..	..	..	..	..	..	..
South Africa	15	15	4	3	79	82	1	1	..	27	33[c]

Table A10 (continued)
Employment characteristics and political participation

Country or area	Percentage distribution of the employed population by status in employment, each sex, 1995/2003								Ratio of female to male wages in manufac- turing 1995/2003	Percentage women among legislators and managers 1995/2003	Women's share of parliamentary seats (%) 2004
	Employers		Own-account workers		Employees		Contributing family workers				
	W	M	W	M	W	M	W	M			
Africa (continued)											
Sudan	..	..	..	..	..	..	..	..	..	..	10
Swaziland	..	..	..	..	..	..	..	..	63[d]	24	11
Togo	..	..	..	..	..	..	..	..	..	..	7
Tunisia	..	..	..	..	..	..	..	..	..	..	23
Uganda	..	..	..	..	..	..	..	..	..	..	25
United Rep. of Tanzania	..	..	..	..	..	..	..	..	..	49	21
Western Sahara	..	..	..	..	..	..	..	..	..	..	..
Zambia	..	..	..	..	..	..	..	..	..	..	12
Zimbabwe	..	..	..	..	..	..	..	..	..	..	10
North America											
Antigua and Barbuda	..	..	..	..	..	..	..	..	..	..	11
Bahamas	..	..	..	..	88	83	..	..	..	40	20
Barbados	< 1	1	8	18	91	80	..	..	..	45	13
Belize	..[e]	..[e]	25[e]	34[e]	71	62	4	3	..	31	3
Canada	..[e]	..[e]	11[e]	19[e]	89	81	< 1	< 1	..	35	21
Costa Rica	5	11	20	19	71	69	4	2	83	29	35
Cuba	..	..	..	..	..	..	..	..	..	..	36
Dominica	6	15	19	22	71	61	3	1	..	59	19
Dominican Republic	2	4	28	46	68	48	..	..	..	31	17
El Salvador	3	6	36	22	42	62	9	8	69	32	11
Grenada	..	..	..	..	..	..	..	..	..	..	27
Guadeloupe	..	..	..	..	..	..	..	..	..	..	..
Guatemala	2	7	37	30	26	31	25	21	..	..	8
Haiti	..	..	..	..	..	..	..	..	..	..	4
Honduras	..[e]	..[e]	42[e]	41[e]	48	46	..	..	..	36	6
Jamaica	1	3	27	38	69	58	2	1	..	..	12
Martinique	..	..	..	..	..	..	..	..	..	..	..
Mexico	2	5	24	26	62	62	12	7	70	25	23
Netherlands Antilles	1[f]	5[f]	3[f]	8[f]	92[f]	84[f]	1[f]	< 1[f]	..	30[f]	..
Nicaragua	1	2	35	35	59	60	..	..	..	..	21
Panama	2	4	19	34	75	60	4	3	93	40	17
Puerto Rico	..[e]	..[e]	7[e]	19[e]	92	80	1	< 1	..	41	..
Saint Kitts and Nevis	..	..	..	..	..	..	..	..	..	..	..
Saint Lucia	3	7	24	31	71	59	1	1	85	55	11
St. Vincent/Grenadines	..	..	..	..	..	..	..	..	..	..	23
Trinidad and Tobago	3	6	12	18	82	74	2	< 1	..	38	19
United States	..[e]	..[e]	6[e]	9[e]	94	91	< 1	< 1	..	46	14
South America											
Argentina	2[g]	5[g]	18[g]	27[g]	79[g]	66[g]	2[g]	1[g]	..	25[g]	34
Bolivia	2[h]	4[h]	44[h]	36[h]	43[h]	55[h]	11[h]	5[h]	..	36[h]	19
Brazil	2	3	13	24	59	55	4	3	61	31	9
Chile	2	4	22	29	73	66	3	1	..	24	13
Colombia	3	6	37	41	52	49	9	4	65	38[i]	12
Ecuador	4[h]	8[h]	32[h]	28[h]	55[h]	60[h]	9[h]	3[h]	..	25[h]	16

Table A10 (continued)
Employment characteristics and political participation

	Percentage distribution of the employed population by status in employment, each sex, 1995/2003								Ratio of female to male wages in manufacturing 1995/2003	Percentage women among legislators and managers 1995/2003	Women's share of parliamentary seats (%) 2004
	Employers		Own-account workers		Employees		Contributing family workers				
Country or area	W	M	W	M	W	M	W	M			
South America (continued)											
French Guiana	..	..	..	..	..	..	..	..	..	..	..
Guyana	..	..	..	..	..	..	..	..	..	..	20
Paraguay	3	8	42	34	45	45	..	..	53	..	10
Peru	2[j]	7[j]	35[j]	33[j]	43[j]	57[j]	6[j]	2[j]	55[k]	23[j]	18
Suriname	< 1	1	9	19	87	78	2	1	..	28	18
Uruguay	2[h]	5[h]	20[h]	29[h]	76[h]	66[h]	2[h]	1[h]	..	35[h]	..
Venezuela (Bolivarian Rep. of)	3	9	37	29	57	60	..	..	..	27	10
Asia											
Afghanistan	..	..	..	..	..	..	..	..	..	..	..
Armenia	< 1	3	12	19	87	76	1	1	..	24	5
Azerbaijan	..	..	..	..	..	..	..	..	..	..	11
Bahrain	..	..	..	..	..	..	..	..	44	10[l]	0
Bangladesh	< 1	< 1	11[m]	50[m]	8	15	73	10	..	8	2
Bhutan	..	..	..	..	..	..	..	..	..	..	10
Brunei Darussalam	..	..	..	..	..	..	..	..	..	26[l]	..
Cambodia	< 1	< 1	33	49	14	19	53	32	..	14	10
China	..	..	..	..	..	..	..	..	..	..	20
Hong Kong SAR	2	7	3	10	93	83	1	< 1	64	26	..
Macao SAR	1	5	3	9	93	86	3	< 1	67	22	..
Cyprus	1	9	8	20	84	70	7	1	61	18	11
Dem. People's Rep. of Korea	..	..	..	..	..	..	..	..	..	..	20
Georgia	1	2	26	44	34	34	39	20	62	28	9
India	..	..	..	..	..	..	..	..	..	..	8
Indonesia	1	2	24	30	28	39	40	8	..	..	11
Iran (Islamic Rep. of)	1	4	17	35	47	48	18	3	80	13	3
Iraq	..	..	..	..	..	..	..	..	..	15	..
Israel	2	7	5	9	91	82	1	< 1	..	29	15
Japan	1	4	5	10	84	85	9	2	60	10	7
Jordan	..	..	..	..	..	..	..	..	65	..	6
Kazakhstan	< 1	1	40	33	58	63	1	1	70	34	10
Kuwait	..	..	..	..	..	..	..	..	..	..	0
Kyrgyzstan	1	2	35	46	44	42	16	7	..	28	10
Lao People's Dem. Rep.	..	..	..	..	..	..	..	..	..	6	23
Lebanon	..	..	..	..	..	..	..	..	..	..	2
Malaysia	1	5	12	18	77	76	10	2	63	23	9
Maldives	1	5	35	55	29	21	3	1	..	15	6
Mongolia	1	2	16	44	44	39	39	14	87	30	5
Myanmar	..	..	..	..	..	..	..	..	89	..	..
Nepal	4	4	71	57	13	34	13	6	..	14	6
Occupied Palestinian Territory	1	4	12	31	55	58	33	7	49	12	..
Oman	1[n]	2[n]	9[n]	10[n]	88[n]	88[n]	..	..	..	9[n]	..
Pakistan	< 1	1	16	42	37	40	47	16	..	2	22
Philippines	..	..	..	..	..	..	..	..	80	58	15
Qatar	< 1	1	..	1	100	99	..	< 1	..	5	..
Republic of Korea	..[e]	..[e]	18[e,m]	34[e,m]	66	65	17	1	56	6	13

Table A10 (continued)
Employment characteristics and political participation

Country or area	Percentage distribution of the employed population by status in employment, each sex, 1995/2003								Ratio of female to male wages in manufacturing 1995/2003	Percentage women among legislators and managers 1995/2003	Women's share of parliamentary seats (%) 2004
	Employers		Own-account workers		Employees		Contributing family workers				
	W	M	W	M	W	M	W	M			
Asia (continued)											
Saudi Arabia	..	..	..	..	..	..	..	..	..	31	0
Singapore	2	7	5	11	92	82	1	< 1	61	26	16
Sri Lanka	1	4	19	35	60	59	21	4	81	21°	5
Syrian Arab Republic	..	..	..	..	..	..	..	..	..	..	12
Tajikistan	..	..	..	..	..	..	..	..	..	..	13
Thailand	1	5	23	38	40	41	35	16	72	26	9
Timor-Leste	..	..	..	..	..	..	..	..	..	..	26 p
Turkey	1	7	12	30	38	55	49	8	97	6	4
Turkmenistan	..	..	..	..	..	..	..	..	..	..	26
United Arab Emirates	..	..	..	..	..	..	..	..	..	8	0
Uzbekistan	..	..	..	..	..	..	..	..	..	..	7
Viet Nam	< 1	< 1	31	51	18	26	50	22	..	..	27
Yemen	< 1	3	24	33	14	51	< 1	< 1	..	4	0
Europe											
Albania	..	..	..	..	..	..	..	..	..	..	6
Andorra	..	..	..	..	..	..	..	..	..	..	14
Austria	4	7	5	5	89	86	3	1	60	27	34
Belarus	< 1	1	1	2	99	97	< 1	< 1	..	..	29
Belgium	..	..	..	..	84	81	6	1	81	31	35
Bosnia and Herzegovina	..	..	..	..	..	..	..	..	..	..	17
Bulgaria	2	5	7	12	88	82	3	1	68	30	26
Croatia	3	7	14	17	77	75	6	2	..	26	18
Czech Republic	2	6	7	14	89	79	1	< 1	..	26	17
Denmark	..e	..e	4e	11e	95	88	1	< 1	87	26	38
Estonia	2	4	4	8	94	88	< 1	< 1	..	35	19
Finland	8	16	..	..	91	82	< 1	< 1	83	28	38
France	..e	..e	6e	11e	94	89	..	..	78	..	12
Germany	3	7	4	7	92	86	2	< 1	74	36	32
Greece	3	10	19	28	64	58	14	4	82	26	14
Hungary	3	7	5	9	91	83	1	< 1	74	34	10
Iceland	3	9	6	14	91	76	< 1	< 1	78	29	30
Ireland	2	8	4	16	92	75	1	1	69	29	13
Italy	8	15	7	12	79	69	6	3	..	21	12
Latvia	2	4	5	7	89	85	4	4	82	40	21
Liechtenstein	..	..	..	..	..	..	..	..	..	..	12
Lithuania	..e	..e	13e	21e	83	76	4	3	77	39	21
Luxembourg	7	10	..	..	82	84	3	1	63	31	20
Malta	..	6	6	11	92	83	..	..	92	18	9
Monaco	..	..	..	..	..	..	..	..	..	..	21
Netherlands	..e	..e	8e	13e	91m	87m	1	< 1	78	26	37
Norway	..e	..e	4e	10e	95	90	< 1	< 1	88	30	36
Poland	2	5	15m	21m	76	70	7	4	..	34	20
Portugal	4	9	19	18	75	72	2	1	64	32	19
Republic of Moldova	< 1	1	31	35	65	63	3	1	..	40	13
Romania	1	2	14	27	62	63	23	8	..	31	11

Table A10 (continued)
Employment characteristics and political participation

Country or area	Percentage distribution of the employed population by status in employment, each sex, 1995/2003								Ratio of female to male wages in manufac-turing 1995/2003	Percentage women among legislators and managers 1995/2003	Women's share of parliamentary seats (%) 2004
	Employers		Own-account workers		Employees		Contributing family workers				
	W	M	W	M	W	M	W	M			
Europe (continued)											
Russian Federation	1	2	5	6	93	92	< 1	< 1	..	39	10
San Marino	9	13	..	..	91	87	..	..	..	18	17
Serbia and Montenegro[q]	..	..	..	..	..	..	..	..	..	..	8
Slovakia	2	4	4	9	94[m]	87[m]	< 1	< 1	..	35	19
Slovenia	2	4	3	9	89	83	6	3	..	33	12
Spain	3	7	9	12	85	79	3	1	..	30	36
Sweden	5	14	..	..	95	86	< 1	< 1	91	30	45
Switzerland	4	9	8	9	85	80	3	2	75	28	25
TFYR Macedonia[r]	4	10	4	11	74	72	18	7	..	27	18
Ukraine	..[e]	..[e]	11[e]	11[e]	87	88	2	1	69	39	5
United Kingdom	..[e]	..[e]	7[e]	17[e]	92	83	< 1	< 1	79[s]	33	18
Oceania											
Australia	2	4	7	12	90	84	1	< 1	89	36	25
Fiji	..	..	..	..	..	..	..	..	..	..	6
French Polynesia	..	..	..	..	..	..	..	..	87	..	..
Guam	..	..	..	..	..	..	..	..	..	..	..
Kiribati	..	..	..	..	..	..	..	..	..	..	5
Marshall Islands	1	1	28	25	68	73	1	1	..	19	3
Micronesia (Fed. States of)	..	..	..	..	..	..	..	..	..	..	0
Nauru	..	..	..	..	..	..	..	..	..	..	..
New Caledonia	..[e]	..[e]	10[e]	19[e]	89	80	< 1	< 1	..	..	..
New Zealand	4	9	8	15	87	76	1	< 1	80	36	28
Palau	..	..	..	..	..	..	..	..	..	39	0
Papua New Guinea	..	..	..	..	..	..	..	..	..	..	1
Samoa	..	..	..	..	..	..	..	..	..	..	6
Solomon Islands	..	..	..	..	..	..	..	..	..	..	0
Tonga	< 1	1	25	26	40	43	34	30	..	19	0
Tuvalu	..	..	..	..	..	..	..	..	..	..	0
Vanuatu	..	..	..	..	..	..	..	..	..	..	4

Sources:

For distribution of employed persons by status in employment and percentage of women among legislators and managers: prepared by the United Nations Statistics Division, Department of Economic and Social Affairs, based on data from International Labour Office (ILO), LABORSTA database, tables 2C and 2D (http://laborsta.ilo.org, accessed 30 November 2004); United Nations *Demographic Yearbook* system (November 2004) and ILO, *Key Indicators of the Labour Market*, 3rd edition (Geneva, 2003), table 3.

For women's wages in manufacturing relative to men's: prepared by the United Nations Statistics Division, Department of Economic and Social Affairs, based on data from International Labour Office, *Yearbook of Labour Statistics 2003* (Geneva, 2003) and LABORSTA database, table 5A (accessed 22 February 2005).

For parliamentary seats: Inter-Parliamentary Union, *Women in National Parliaments*, situation as of 30 October 2004 (http://www.ipu.org/wmn-e/classif.htm, accessed 16 November 2004).

Notes:

Two dots (..) indicate that data are not available or are not reported separately.

< 1 Indicates magnitude nil or less than half of the unit employed.

a Citizens only.
b Excluding government sector.
c The figures on the distribution of seats do not include the 36 special rotating delegates appointed on an ad hoc basis, and the percentages given are therefore calculated on the basis of the 54 permanent seats.
d Skilled wage earners.
e Data for own-account workers and employers are combined and shown under own-account workers.
f Curaçao only.
g 31 urban agglomerations.
h Urban areas only.
i Seven main cities of the country.
j Metropolitan Lima only.
k Lima only.
l Private sector.
m Includes members of producers' cooperatives.
n For Omanis only.
o Excluding Northern Province.
p The purpose of elections held on 30 August 2001 was to elect members of the Constituent Assembly of Timor-Leste. This body became the National Parliament on 20 May 2002, the date on which the country became independent, without any new elections.
q As of 4 February 2003, the official name of the "Federal Republic of Yugoslavia" has been changed to "Serbia and Montenegro".
r The former Yugoslav Republic of Macedonia.
s Including overtime payments.

Technical notes

The distribution of workers of each sex by status in employment is shown for employers, own-account workers, employees and contributing family workers only. The groups may not add up to 100 per cent because members of producers' cooperatives and workers not classifiable by status are not shown.

The four groups are as defined in the International Classification of Status in Employment (ICSE-1993), as follows:

- Employers are those workers who, working on their own account or with one or a few partners, hold the type of job defined as a "self-employment job" and, in this capacity, on a continuous basis (including the reference period) have engaged one or more persons to work for them in their business as "employee(s)".

- Own-account workers are those workers who, working on their own account or with one or more partners, hold the type of job defined as a "self-employment job" and have not engaged on a continuous basis any "employees" to work for them during the reference period.

- Employees are all those workers who hold the type of job defined as "paid employment jobs".

- Contributing family workers are those workers who hold a "self-employment" job in a market-oriented establishment operated by a related person living in the same household, who cannot be regarded as a partner, because their degree of commitment to the operation of the establishment, in terms of working time or other factors to be determined by national circumstances, is not at a level comparable to that of the head of the establishment. (Where it is customary for young persons, in particular, to work without pay in an economic enterprise operated by a related person who does not live in the same household, the requirement of "living in the same household" may be eliminated.)

The ratio of female wages to male wages in manufacturing is shown as a percentage. The wage statistics from which the ratio is computed are, in general, average earnings per wage earner (regardless of age) or in some cases wage rates. The data on average earnings are usually derived from payroll data supplied by a sample of establishments, often also furnishing data on hours of work and on employment. In a few cases, average earnings are compiled from social insurance statistics or labour force surveys.

International comparisons of the wage ratios presented here must be made with great caution. The coverage, definitions and methods of compiling wage statistics differ significantly from country to country. Disaggregation of statistics by sex is available for only a few countries and may be based on a narrow segment of the population. Furthermore, earnings are very much dependent on the number of hours worked, and in countries where female workers generally work many fewer hours than male workers, this factor must be kept in mind when interpreting the wage ratio.

The proportion of women among legislators and managers provides an indication of the presence of women in decision-making positions. It is derived from statistics on the distribution of the employed population (in some cases of the economically active population) by occupation, collected mainly through labour force surveys. Some other household surveys and population censuses also provide this information. The category "legislators, senior officials and managers" refers to major group 1 of the 1988 revision of the International Standard Classification of Occupations (ISCO-88) and includes the following sub-groups: (a) legislators and senior officials; (b) corporate managers; and (c) general managers. In the case of countries that used the earlier international classification (ISCO-68), the category refers to major group 2, administrative and managerial workers, which encompasses (a) legislative officials and government administrators and (b) managers.

The proportion of parliamentary seats occupied by women is calculated for only the lower chamber in countries with a bicameral assembly. Data are based on the sex distribution as at 30 October 2004. The numbers shown reflect changes, if any, after the most recent election prior to that date, such as results of by-elections or replacements following the resignation or death of a member of parliament.

Annex 2
List of countries or areas by development group

List of countries or areas[a] by development group

More developed regions (47 countries or areas)

Albania	Finland	Malta	Slovenia
Andorra	France	Monaco	Spain
Australia	Germany	Netherlands	Sweden
Austria	Greece	New Zealand	Switzerland
Belarus	Hungary	Norway	The former Yugoslav
Belgium	Iceland	Poland	Republic of Macedonia
Bosnia and Herzegovina	Ireland	Portugal	Ukraine
Bulgaria	Italy	Republic of Moldova	United Kingdom of
Canada	Japan	Romania	Great Britain and Northern Ireland
Croatia	Latvia	Russian Federation	United States of America
Czech Republic	Liechtenstein	San Marino	
Denmark	Lithuania	Serbia and Montenegro[b]	
Estonia	Luxembourg	Slovakia	

Less developed regions excluding least developed countries (107 countries or areas)

Algeria	Dominican Republic	Libyan Arab Jamahiriya	Saint Kitts and Nevis
Antigua and Barbuda	Ecuador	Malaysia	Saint Lucia
Argentina	Egypt	Marshall Islands	Saint Vincent and the Grenadines
Armenia	El Salvador	Martinique	Saudi Arabia
Azerbaijan	Fiji	Mauritius	Seychelles
Bahamas	French Guiana	Mexico	Singapore
Bahrain	French Polynesia	Micronesia (Federated States of)	South Africa
Barbados	Gabon	Mongolia	Sri Lanka
Belize	Georgia	Morocco	Suriname
Bolivia	Ghana	Namibia	Swaziland
Botswana	Grenada	Nauru	Syrian Arab Republic
Brazil	Guadeloupe	Netherlands Antilles	Tajikistan
Brunei Darussalam	Guam	New Caledonia	Thailand
Cameroon	Guatemala	Nicaragua	Tonga
Chile	Guyana	Nigeria	Trinidad and Tobago
China	Honduras	Occupied Palestinian Territory	Tunisia
Hong Kong Special Administrative Region	India	Oman	Turkey
	Indonesia	Pakistan	Turkmenistan
Macao Special Administrative Region	Iran (Islamic Republic of)	Palau	United Arab Emirates
	Iraq	Panama	Uruguay
Colombia	Israel	Papua New Guinea	Uzbekistan
Congo	Jamaica	Paraguay	Venezuela (Bolivarian Republic of)
Costa Rica	Jordan	Peru	Viet Nam
Côte d'Ivoire	Kazakhstan	Philippines	Western Sahara
Cuba	Kenya	Puerto Rico	Zimbabwe
Cyprus	Kuwait	Qatar	
Democratic People's Republic of Korea	Kyrgyzstan	Republic of Korea	
Dominica	Lebanon	Réunion	

List of countries or areas[a] by development group (continued)

Least developed countries (50 countries or areas)

Afghanistan	Djibouti	Malawi	Solomon Islands
Angola	Equatorial Guinea	Maldives	Somalia
Bangladesh	Eritrea	Mali	Sudan
Benin	Ethiopia	Mauritania	Timor-Leste
Bhutan	Gambia	Mozambique	Togo
Burkina Faso	Guinea	Myanmar	Tuvalu
Burundi	Guinea-Bissau	Nepal	Uganda
Cambodia	Haiti	Niger	United Republic of Tanzania
Cape Verde	Kiribati	Rwanda	Vanuatu
Central African Republic	Lao People's Democratic Republic	Samoa	Yemen
Chad	Lesotho	Sao Tome and Principe	Zambia
Comoros	Liberia	Senegal	
Democratic Republic of the Congo	Madagascar	Sierra Leone	

Notes:

a   Comprising all United Nations Member States and other countries or areas with a population of at least 150,000 in 2000.

b   As of 4 February 2003, the official name of the "Federal Republic of Yugoslavia" has been changed to "Serbia and Montenegro".